Aquaculture and Ecosystems:
An Integrated Coastal and Ocean Management Approach

Edited by

James P. McVey, Cheng-Sheng Lee and Patricia J. O'Bryen

Published by

WORLD
AQUACULTURE
SOCIETY

Sponsored by

Oceanic Institute
An Affiliate of Hawai'i Pacific University

Dr. Craig Browdy
Managing Book Editor
The World Aquaculture Society

ISBN: 1-888807-17-2
How to cite this volume:

McVey, J.P., Lee, C.-S., and O'Bryen, P.J. editors, 2006. Aquaculture and Ecosystems: An Integrated Coastal and Ocean Management Approach. The World Aquaculture Society, Baton Rouge, Louisiana 70803. United States.

Copies of this volume are available at WWW.WAS.ORG
or by contacting the WAS home office:

> The World Aquaculture Society
> 143 J.M. Parker Coliseum
> Baton Rouge, Louisiana, 70803
> United States
> phone: +1-225-578-3137
> FAX: +1-225-578-3493
> e-mail: carolm@aol.com

Cover design: Topography/Bathymetry in Mercato Projection, courtesy of The National Geophysical Data Center, National Oceanic and Atmospheric Administration; inset photos (l. to r.), courtesy of Richard Langan, Alan Friedlander, Richard Langan and Oceanic Institute.

PREFACE

The U.S. National Oceanic and Atmospheric Administration (NOAA) is moving toward ecosystem-based management for environmental, fisheries, and aquaculture issues. This view of a more holistic management system incorporates the use of geographic information systems, social sciences, environmental models based on hydrographic and nutrient profiles, and an interconnected understanding of the roles of the biotic factors in coastal ecosystems. Some additional tools for such ecosystem management should be environmental engineering and the biological functions available to us through living natural and cultured organisms and the possibility of using aquaculture to put those tools into the correct temporal and spatial locations.

The National Sea Grant College Program (NSGCP) and the International Activities Office (IA) of the Office of Oceanic and Atmospheric Research and the National Ocean Service's Office of Coastal and Ocean Resource Management (OCRM) and the International Program Office (IPO) under NOAA of the U.S. Department of Commerce co-hosted the International Workshop on the Role of Aquaculture in Integrated Coastal Management: An Ecosystem Approach, in Honolulu, Hawaii, April 18-21, 2005. The workshop was organized and facilitated by Oceanic Institute in Hawaii under a grant (No. NA17RG2076) from NOAA's Office of Oceanic and Atmospheric Research.

The workshop aimed to identify key factors and parameters needed for ecosystem based management relative to aquaculture and how aquaculture can contribute to ecological function and better water quality in coastal areas. The workshop organizers invited a total of 65 experts from Canada, China, Japan, South Korea, Vietnam, and the United States to form a five- to six-member multidisciplinary team (i.e., aquaculturists, ecologists, biologists, ecosystem modelers, coastal managers, and/or resource management administrators) from each country (see Appendix A). In addition, the organizers invited representatives from Chile, Malaysia, Sweden, and Taiwan to bring their experiences to the group breakout discussions.

This book includes the working documents provided by participating countries and the conclusions drawn from the breakout discussion groups on Guiding Principles, Modeling, and Considerations for Coastal Managers. The opinions expressed herein do not necessarily reflect those of all of the participants at the workshop, the Oceanic Institute, NOAA, or the NSGCP.

We would like to thank Alcian Clegg and Susan Sparaga for their help preparing the manuscripts and figures for publication, and all who participated in the workshop to make it a success.

Contributors: McVey, J.P. and C.-S. Lee
In J.P. McVey, C.-S. Lee, and P.J. O'Bryen, editors. Aquaculture and Ecosystems: An Integrated Coastal and Ocean Management Approach. The World Aquaculture Society, Baton Rouge, Louisiana, United States.

TABLE OF CONTENTS

INTRODUCTION

1

Aquaculture is one of the ways to make up for the decreasing fisheries yields that are inevitable in the future. The U.S. National Marine Fisheries Service (NMFS 2005) estimated that 100 U.S. fisheries stocks are being over fished or are experiencing overfishing, as compared with 336 stocks that are not over fished. This overexploitation can be seen throughout the world's oceans. According to the Food and Agriculture Organization of the United Nations (FAO 1997), sustainable aquaculture development requires that the diversity of aquaculture practices be recognized, as well as the social, economic, and we would add, environmental conditions in which they take place.

Natural aquatic systems have a built in carrying capacity for handling nutrients that is dependent on the biological and chemical processes that occur in those systems. Christiansen et al. (2000) observed that denitrification processes in a Norwegian Fjord could generally remove 50% of the nitrogen loading from the land. Each phylum or species plays a unique role in a productive ecosystem. The utilization of nutrients by microbes, phytoplankton, macroalgae, and sea grasses; the consumption of microbes and phytoplankton by filter feeders; the everyday activities of fish and invertebrates; and the capture of marine species in fisheries, among other processes, all contribute to the processing or removal of nutrients like nitrogen and phosphorus from coastal waters. The balance of species and their function is critical to a well-functioning ecosystem.

Aquaculture is taking place in coastal oceans already heavily impacted by human activities. Walsh (1988) found that human related loadings of nitrogen have increased 10-fold during the past century. Phosphorus eroded from the landscape and carried in human wastewater into the world's rivers has increased global fluxes of phosphorus to the oceans almost threefold from historic levels of about 8 million tons to current loadings of about 22 million tons per year. Kroeze and Seitzinger (1998) estimated that observed levels of dissolved inorganic nitrogen worldwide are due primarily to agricultural fertilizers (58%), human sewage (24%), and atmospheric deposition (18%). These environmental consequences of human activity were not planned and are seldom taken into account when developing management strategies for coastal ecosystems. The impact of aquaculture relative to the scale of impacts that have already occurred is relatively minor at this time, but it is increasing and needs to be factored into the management strategies that are being proposed for environmental quality and sustainability.

The culture of selected organisms in selected locations in the ecosystem can provide a better balance of ecosystem function than what presently exists. Cultivation of seaweeds and animals complement one another. Plants should be integrated with other species to develop

Contributors: McVey, J.P. and C.-S. Lee
In J.P. McVey, C.-S. Lee, and P.J. O'Bryen, editors. Aquaculture and Ecosystems: An Integrated Coastal and Ocean Management Approach. The World Aquaculture Society, Baton Rouge, Louisiana, United States.

a balanced ecosystem approach to responsible aquaculture (Chopin and Yarish 1999). In China, which produces more than 4.8 million tons of brown and red algae annually, seaweeds are considered to be nutrient removers. Production of *Laminaria* sp. alone is estimated at four million tons, which is equivalent to two million tons dry weight or 60,000 to 100,000 tons of nitrogen removed each year (Fei 1998). Individual bivalves have the capacity to filter from 1 to 4 L of water per individual per hour. Communities of bivalves have the capacity to filter considerable volumes of water. Bivalves filter particles including silt and clay particles, phytoplankton, and detritus (Jorgensen 1966). This entrainment of organic material from the water column and deposition on the bottom in the form of feces and pseudofeces from bivalves is an integral and essential part of ecosystem function.

Proper placement of aquaculture facilities is very important in maintaining ecosystem function. Extractive aquaculture, such as bivalve and macro-algae production, should occur in high nutrient areas where aquaculture can serve to reduce nutrient levels. Finfish culture should be placed in areas that have assimilative capacity for nutrients. Appropriate areas for finfish culture should have high current flow rates, be sited in offshore locations that have low nutrient levels, or be located on land where nutrients can be processed or recaptured through filters or recirculating technologies.

To manage coastal systems in an ecologically balanced way, we must understand and utilize the natural functions of both cultured and wild species so that energy flow and distribution of nutrients is managed through biological activity, as well as by engineering solutions. Modeling and managing these relationships in the context of the hydrographic and environmental conditions found in different regional contexts is our challenge and obligation.

This approach to ecosystem modeling and decision-making is already going on in several countries and needs to be better coordinated. At the workshop, teams reviewed and discussed the status of balanced ecosystem approaches to coastal management in their respective countries and the modeling necessary for good decision-making. Key factors and parameters needed for good ecosystem based modeling, and the ways in which aquaculture can contribute to better water quality in coastal areas were identified.

Following the workshop, participants were asked to update the information about the status of aquaculture in their respective countries and revise the specific working scenarios and international perspectives they had presented at the workshop. These constitute Chapters 2 – 8 of this book. The documents that were produced in the discussion sessions and circulated among the participants for additional comments and input were: (a) a set of guiding principles for coastal management specific to marine aquaculture, (b) primary data and parameter components for coastal ecosystem models that include marine aquaculture, and (c) marine aquaculture siting considerations by a coastal manager for decision-making relative to placement of aquaculture in coastal ecosystems. These are presented in Chapters 9 – 11, respectively.

The participants had a common understanding that this workshop was only a first step in an ongoing discussion of ecosystem-based management as it pertains to aquaculture. The teams composed for this workshop will therefore continue to exchange communications and technical information during our evolution to ecosystem based management for coastal ecosystem management. To continue this dialogue and facilitate progress toward our common goal, the Vietnamese delegation agreed to host the next follow up workshop on the role of aquaculture in integrated coastal and ocean management: an ecosystem approach in 2007.

Literature Cited

Chopin, T. and C. Yarish. 1999. Seaweeds must be a significant component of aquaculture for an integrated ecosystem approach. Bulletin of the Aquaculture Association of Canada 99 (1): 35-37.

Christensen, P.B., S. Rysgaard, N.P. Sloth, T. Dalsgaard, and S. Schwaerter. 2000. Sediment mineralization, nutrient fluxes, denitrification and dissimilatory nitrate reduction to ammonium in an estuarine fjord with sea cage trout farms. Aquatic Microbial Ecology 21: 73-84.

FAO (Food and Agriculture Organization of the United Nations). 1997. Aquaculture Development. FAO Technical Guidelines for Responsible Fisheries, No. 5. Fisheries Department, Food and Agriculture Organization of the United Nations, Rome, Italy. http://fao.org/fi/agreem/codecond/gdlines/abs5.asp.

Fei, X. 1998. Seaweed cultivation in large scale--possible solution to the problem of eutrophication by the removal of nutrients. World Aquaculture 29(4): 22-24.

Jorgensen, C.B. 1966. The Biology of Suspension Feeding. Pergamon Press, Oxford, UK. 357 pp.

Kroeze, C. and S.P. Seitzinger. 1998. Nitrogen inputs to rivers, estuaries and continental shelves and related nitrous oxide emissions in 1990 and 2050: A global model. Nutrient Cycling in Agroecosystems 52 (2-3): 195-212.

NMFS (National Marine Fisheries Service). 2005. Annual report to Congress on the status of U.S. Fisheries-2004. National Marine Fisheries Service, National Oceanic and Atmospheric Administration, U.S. Department of Commerce, Silver Spring, Maryland, USA. 20 pp. http://www.nmfs.noaa.govlsfa/reports.html.

Walsh, J.J. 1988. Use of satellite ocean color observations to refine understanding of global geochemical cycles. Pages 287-318 in T. Rosswall, R. Woodmansee, and P. Risser, editors. Scales and Global Change. John Wiley and Sons, Chichester, UK.

COUNTRY SCENARIOS FOR ECOSYSTEM APPROACHES FOR AQUACULTURE

2

CANADA

Executive Summary

In this chapter, the authors examine the application of an Integrated Resource Management (IRM) model to a multi-resource management situation in which aquaculture is a participant. The management of salmonid mariculture in the Bay of Fundy in eastern Canada is used as illustration. Information is provided to describe the scenario in terms of the industry, the environment, socio-economics, and governance. Approaches to resource inventory, allocation, surveillance, and monitoring that are, or could be, applied to this scenario are discussed. Inter-trophic management and differing physical scales of management are also discussed. The chapter presents a series of key principles that should be considered when applying an IRM model as discussed.

Introduction

Integrated Resource Management (IRM) is composed of a number of broad functions that are implemented in a cyclic process. These broad functions include: inventory of resource availability and current uses; the planning process for best sustainable use of the resource; resource allocation; monitoring or surveillance of resource use; and re-valuation of resource use patterns (Fig. 1). Change in the social, economic, or environment context is an immutable fact, and IRM is an iterative process with constantly evolving optimal solutions. The rate of change varies for each of the three broad categories. The more rapid the rate of change, the more frequent should be the iterations of that component of the management cycle. The optimal frequency will reflect the rate of change in social, economic, or environmental factors. Typical governance approaches to finding a solution involve iterating resource allocation on an annual basis for some of the more variable resources (e.g., fish stocks) and less frequently for more stable resources such as land (20 year leases may be issued). Iterations of the whole, or part, of the cycle represent an increase in the cost of resource governance. Thus, generally speaking, the practical solution to what constitutes the best mix of resources is not a fixed optimal solution, but an iterative best approximation of a cost-effective solution.

The licenses for resource uses must be viewed as temporary if society is to optimize the value derived from using the ecosystem. Temporary, however, does not imply that these resources should be viewed as common property resources. Lack of specific property rights may result in the resources being consumed without regard for their sustained use. Thus, some form of property rights (for certain attributes) is a necessary precursor to sustainable resource use. Those rights might be for a lease to use a space, or to extract some component as inherent in individual transferable fishery quotas, or to utilize a portion of the ecosystem process, such as the system's assimilative capacity to absorb organic inputs to the system (implied in most permits for waste release). The duration of these rights and conditions under

Contributors: Black, E., T. Chopin, J. Grant, F. Page, N. Ridler, and J. Smith
In J.P. McVey, C.-S. Lee, and P.J. O'Bryen, editors. Aquaculture and Ecosystems: An Integrated Coastal and Ocean Management Approach. The World Aquaculture Society, Baton Rouge, Louisiana, United States.

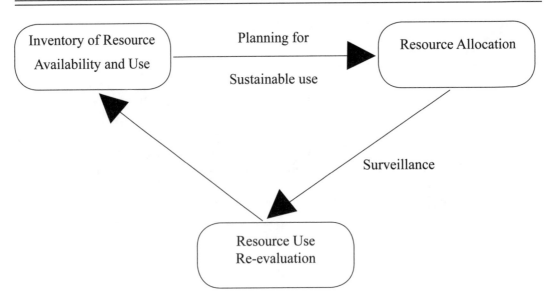

Figure 1. The cyclic Integrated Resource Management process.

which they might be terminated is a delicate socio-political matter. Some societal rights, such as those embodied in treaty rights with first nations, can only be abrogated by mutual consent. Other economic licenses, such as property rights for a physical site, may be of shorter duration and have codicils that allow early termination if certain conditions, such as environmental performance, are not met. In general, the duration of these property rights should be tied to some reasonable expectation that the owner will recover the value of the investment in using the resources and achieve a viable benefit that is at least as good as might be received from other possible uses of that resource.

Aquaculture and Fisheries

Since the 1970s, the expansion of aquaculture in the world has outpaced all other animal food-producing sectors; at an annual compounded rate of 9.2% per year, compared with only 1.4% for capture fisheries and 2.8% for terrestrial farmed meat production (FAO 2002). Table 1 shows this global expansion. Currently, aquaculture accounts for approximately one-third of fish consumed, and forecasts for 2020 suggest a potential increase to 40% or more. Canada's aquaculture growth has been modest compared to the global expansion.

As can be seen in Table 1, Canadian aquaculture accounts for approximately 0.4% of world output. Its high growth rate is attributable to the small base. Ranked twenty-second in world output in 2003, its output actually declined between 2001 and 2003. In terms of value, Canada's share of the world total is slightly higher, at 0.6% in 2003, although total aquaculture value has also been falling since 2001.

A partial explanation for Canada's slow expansion in aquaculture is its reliance on capture fisheries. Canada is among the top five exporters of fishery commodities (by value) in the world. In 2003, it had a net trade surplus of almost $2 billion. Even positioned so, Canada

Table 1. Total aquaculture production of finfish and shellfish worldwide and in Canada (excluding aquatic plants) and production from Atlantic salmon farming only.

| | Finfish and Shellfish | | | | Atlantic Salmon | | |
| | World | | Canada | | World | | Canada |
	Output (MT x 1,000)	Annual growth rate (%)	Output (MT x 1,000)	Annual growth rate (%)	Output (MT x 1,000)	Annual growth rate (%)	Output (MT x 1,000)
1970	2,556	. . .	0.4	. . .	. . .	. . .	. . .
1980	4,765	. . .	0.4	. . .	6	. . .	0.1
1990	13,044	. . .	41	. . .	220	. . .	10
2000	35,612	. . .	131	. . .	75	. . .	75
1970-1980	. . .	6.4	. . .	0.3	. . .	35.6	. . .
1980-1990	. . .	10.6	. . .	27.0	. . .	41.6	. . .
1990-2000	. . .	10.6	. . .	12.4	. . .	15.2	. . .
Average for 1970-2000	. . .	9.2	. . .	12.7	. . .	30.3	. . .
Forecast output	53,600 (by 2020)	. . .	. . .	. . .	2,500 (by 2013)	. . .	. . .

Data are three-year averages centered on 1970, 1980, 1990, and 2000. Growth rates are compounded using three-year averages as end points. Source: Calculated from Fishstat Plus (FAO 2004).

cannot determine the price of aquaculture products in the international market place, and must optimize its benefits in the role of a price taker rather than price giver.

Production Data and Goals

Aquaculture in Canada's Maritime Provinces is dominated by salmonid and shellfish species. There are local areas of development for shellfish and salmonid culture activities in the region, a pattern also seen on Canada's west coast. Shellfish culture, especially mussel (*Mytilus edulis*) culture, dominates in waters around eastern New Brunswick (NB) and Prince Edward Island (Fig. 2). In contrast, salmonid mariculture is concentrated along the southwest corner of NB, and to a lesser degree, the south shores of Nova Scotia and Newfoundland (Fig. 3). This separation is likely a result of where culture activities developed, and that the development was based primarily on the different biophysical requirements of each species. For example, growing some shellfish, like the oyster, for their full life cycle requires environmental conditions that are not favorable for the culture of other species. In the case of oysters, optimal water temperatures for their reproduction are beyond the thermal tolerance of most salmon (*Salmo salar*, *Oncorhynchus* spp.). As, however, culture technologies develop, the requirement to breed and grow an organism in the same location typically becomes less important. For many shellfish species, technologies have developed that allow the seeding of

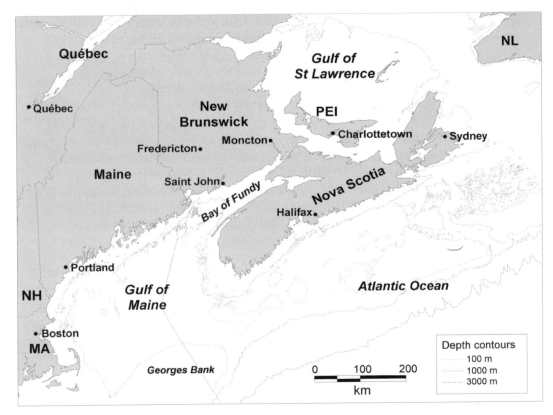

Figure 2. Map of the Maritime Provinces, Canada, and the Gulf of Maine.

artificial substrates that can be moved to locations other than the breeding locations for the on growing of the cultured product. It is not surprising, therefore, that as a culture-based industry matures, both types of culture co-exist in close proximity in some areas. In the development of integrated coastal zone management, it is important to allow for the possibility that just because an organism is not naturally present in an area, governance schemes derived to manage resources should not *a priori* preclude possible future culture activities.

Development of culture technologies allows a constant evolution of the types of habitats utilized. For example, much of Canada's oyster (*Crassostrea virginica, C. gigas*) culture industry initially developed from spreading shellfish in high densities on beach substrates. This evolved to growing the shellfish on artificial substrates or containers anchored to the bottom. Lately, there has been greater use of floating culture substrates. Net cage salmon culture has undergone a similar evolution. Initially, fishes were grown in small cages in sheltered waters. These cages were either anchored to, or close to, the shore (near shore sheltered culture). As production volumes on individual sites increased and access to new sites decreased, the technology evolved from wood based cages to cages made of plastics and metal. This allowed the floating cages to move into more exposed coastal waters (offshore or exposed culture). Recently, there have been attempts to develop commercially viable submersible culture technologies that would allow development of culture under open ocean conditions (oceanic culture).

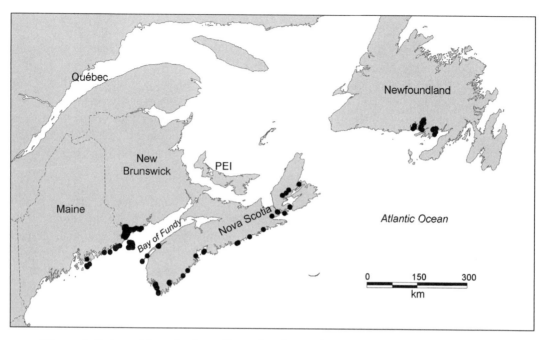

Figure 3. Salmonid mariculture farm sites in northeastern North America (2004).

Markets for aquaculture industry products can be segmented into local and international components. Small firms may specialize in niche marketing to local markets where they attempt to obtain a premium price for their product. As industry production, however, grows in an area, those markets may rapidly saturate and become more difficult to access. Long-term stability and growth is dependent on the international market. The seafood market is a highly competitive market, in which substitute products are available to the consumer. Firms producing for this market typically experience multiple year boom and adjustment cycles. Consequently, firms need the ability to plan for and have the resources to withstand market turndowns that can last several years. This, and because international markets are being served, has resulted in the world fish farming industries gradually evolving towards fewer small players as the industry matures. The same trend has occurred in terrestrial agriculture. The implication for aquaculture in the coastal zone is that farmers need stable production environments in which to create their product and attain the lowest cost of production values. This longer-term stability should be generated, in part, through the length of tenures the resource allocation process provides.

Brand development for the international market may help minimize market pressure described above. Consumers today look for food safety and environmental friendliness (Ridler et al. in press). Internationally, seafood products from Canada are believed to generally have those attributes. This reliance on environmental and product quality in the market process underscores the degree to which industry must ensure that the process of resource allocation maintains a high quality environment in which they can produce their product.

Regulatory System for Aquaculture

Federal and provincial legislation affects aquaculture in Canada. In general, the federal legislation applies to resources or trade that cross provincial or federal borders and fishes or resources that are inter-provincial or international in nature. Leasing of marine real estate for aquaculture production is largely a provincial issue. Prince Edward Island is the exception, where the provincial government requested that the federal government recommend issuance of site leases and licenses. In addition to senior levels of government, regional and urban zoning can also affect aquaculture siting through their ability to zone certain areas for types of use.

The matrix of legislation affecting aquaculture is large and complex (see Appendix 2-1 at the end of this chapter). The length and diversity of legal tools for the regulation of aquaculture illustrates the point that any effort at true integrated coastal zone management must have as a foundation a cooperative regulatory framework that has been agreed upon by regulators and resource managers. The Appendix at the end of this chapter indicates some of the legislation and jurisdictions involved in fisheries and aquaculture management.

Specific Working Scenario: Bay of Fundy

Description of the Area

Marine Atlantic salmon production in the Maritime region of eastern Canada is spread over three provinces (Fig. 2). The smallest portion is in one small area of Newfoundland, followed by production occurring along the shores of Nova Scotia, of which only a very few sites are in waters of the Bay of Fundy. New Brunswick produces the vast majority of salmon in this area. Almost all of it is concentrated in the southwestern corner of the province (Figs. 3 and 4). This area in the lower Bay of Fundy serves as the focus for the development of the scenario for this report.

Presently the lower Bay of Fundy primarily supports finfish culture, although there is also interest in developing multi-trophic culture (salmon [*S. salar*], shellfish, [*M. edulis*] and marine macro-algae [*Laminaria saccharina, Alaria esculenta*]). This area contains some of the densest concentrations of salmon farms anywhere in the world. Because of its socio-economic relevance, recent effort has been placed on developing knowledge of the oceanography in the coastal area (Page and Chang 2002).

The Bay of Fundy is a macro-tidal environment with the tidal amplitude ranging from a few meters (~ 4 m) at the mouth of the Bay to over 10 m at the head of the Bay. This tidal motion generates tidal currents that exceed 1 m sec^{-1} throughout the Bay. Tidal currents can exceed 4 m sec^{-1} in some of the narrow channels in the coastal zone of southwestern New Brunswick (SWNB). Despite the large tides, however, current in much of the coastal zone in SWNB, particularly in the small bays and at the heads of inlets, is often weak (~<0.1 m sec^{-1}). The salmon aquaculture industry in the area began in the relatively sheltered and weak current areas. It has expanded into the stronger current areas, and is considering further expansion into the exposed high current areas (Bridger and Neal 2004).

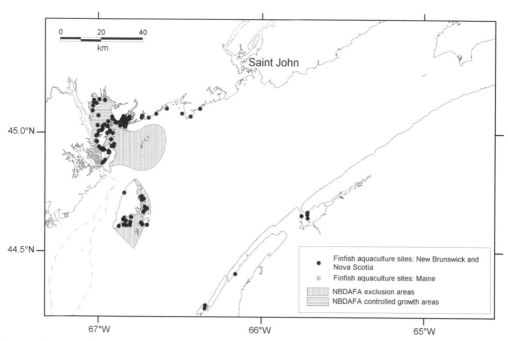

Figure 4. Location of salmon farms in the Bay of Fundy, Canada (2004). Also shown are exclusion zones and controlled growth areas designated by the New Brunswick Department of Agriculture, Fisheries and Aquaculture (NBDAFA).

In addition to the tidal currents, the Bay of Fundy receives freshwater input from nine rivers (Fig. 5). The largest of these is the Saint John River, which accounts for more freshwater input (Fig. 6) than all others combined. The tidal and density driven forces combine to generate a residual circulation that has surface water entering the Bay of Fundy and flowing eastward along the Nova Scotian coast and leaving the Bay of Fundy and flowing westward along the NB coast. The aquaculture activity in the Bay is therefore downstream of the Saint John River plume.

Surface gravity waves in the Bay of Fundy can be as high as 10 m (100 year wave), but more typically are 3-6 m. The wave heights are less in the Bay than in the adjacent Gulf of Maine. Wave heights within the relatively sheltered Passamaquoddy Bay are considerably less than in the open Bay of Fundy (Trites and Garrett 1983).

The long-term (1924-2004) monthly mean (and median) offshore water temperatures in the southwest NB area of the Bay of Fundy range from about 12 C in the summer and early fall to about 2 C in the winter. The inter-annual range in the monthly means is about ± 2 C. The long-term (1924-2004) maximum is about 14 C in the summer and early fall, and the long-term minimum is about -0.5 C in the winter (Fig. 7).

Harmful algal blooms are an annual event in the lower Bay of Fundy. Of particular note is the annual bloom of *Alexandrium fundyense*, a dinoflagellate that causes paralytic shellfish poisoning (PSP). On occasion, *A. fundyense* has caused losses of caged salmon.

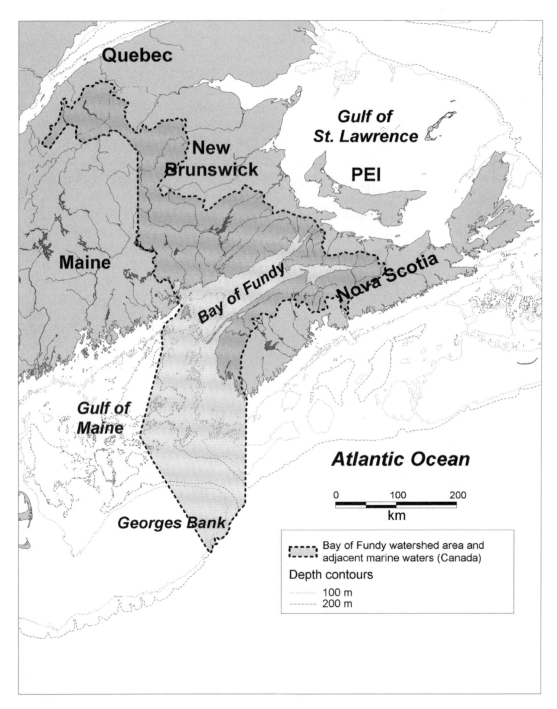

Figure 5. Map of the eastern Gulf of Maine showing the Canadian watershed area that drains into the Bay of Fundy, with adjacent Canadian marine waters.

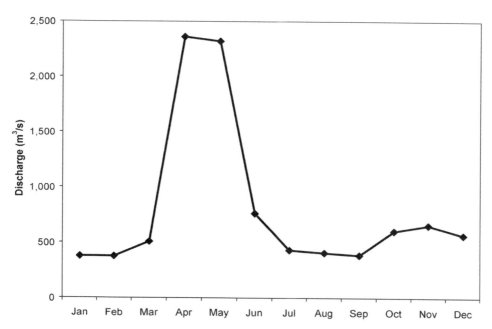

Figure 6. Seasonal cycle in the discharge of freshwater from the Saint John River into the Bay of Fundy. Data are monthly mean discharges, measured at Mactaquac, for 1966-1995. (Data source: Environment Canada, HYDAT database).

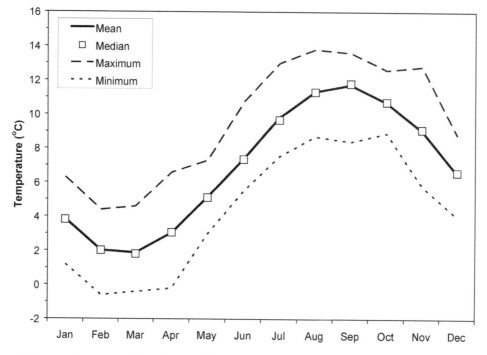

Figure 7. Long-term (1924-2004) monthly mean near surface water temperatures recorded at the Prince 5 oceanographic monitoring station located in the deep offshore area of southwestern New Brunswick.

Historical and Socioeconomic Profile

The main urban center in southern NB is Saint John. In 1996, its population was approximately 124,000. Charlotte County, which contains most of the aquaculture sites, begins approximately 40 km west of Saint John. The economy is dominated by rural activities. One primary road system runs west from Saint John through Charlotte County to the border with the United States at St. Stephen. This is the primary road system for trucking aquaculture products to the large markets of the USA. The other major road system runs north from St. Stephen and St. Andrews to Fredericton, the provincial capital. There are no commercial air hubs in Charlotte County. The nearest is Saint John, though there is another in Fredericton.

Community Historical Background and Context

Charlotte County is primarily made up of seven communities, with Blacks Harbour, Grand Manan, St. Andrews, St. George, and St. Stephen as the main service areas of the region:

- *Blacks Harbour* (pop. 1082) is part company town and part fishing village, hosting both the largest sardine (*Clupea harengus*) canner in the world (Connors Brothers) and headquarters for the largest fresh Atlantic salmon (*S. salar*) supplier in North America (Heritage Salmon).

- *St. George* (pop. 1509) is the major aquacultural center for the province.

- *St. Andrews* (pop. 1869) is one of Canada's oldest towns, characterized by resorts and historic properties. Tourism is an integral part of the local economy.

- *St. Stephen* (pop. 4667) is home to an international chocolate center (Ganong's), and also serves as the main entry point from the USA into the Atlantic Provinces.

- The Fundy Isles consist of *Grand Manan* (pop. 2610), *Deer Island* (pop. 851), and *Campobello* (pop. 1195), situated in the heart of the Bay of Fundy. *Grand Manan* has a long tradition and history, with a tight knit and bonded community of fisherman, writers, and artists.

Population and Demographic Characteristics

Since 1996, the County population has demonstrated no growth. Unlike other more bilingual/francophone regions in the province, 92.7% of Charlotte County speaks only English. Also, compared to the rest of NB, this population has a higher proportion of over 65 year olds. Gender is approximately evenly distributed in the population. Of the working age population, 42.7% had completed high school and continued to some form of post-secondary education, 34.1% completed their post-secondary education, 7.2% work in agricultural related fields, and 17.1% are unemployed, due to the seasonal work in fisheries, farms, and tourism.

Employment and Economic Base

Fisheries and aquaculture are an important part to the Charlotte County lifestyle. With a rich fishing tradition, the area employs approximately 3,500 people in the industry. One area in particular, Blacks Harbour, houses the world's largest sardine industry, employing 1,500 people in all aspects of the catch, process, and distribution of the product. Aquaculture in the County represents over 95% of provincial total aquaculture production (est. 40, 000 metric tons [MT]/annum, a farm gate value of $191 million). The industry has provided over $50 million in wages and benefits per annum, and 2,700 direct and indirect jobs, to the county.

Seaweed harvesting (dulse, *Palmaria palmata*, and rockweed, *Ascophyllum nodosum*) is also a significant activity in the region (Chopin and Ugarte in press). At the present time, most of the dulse (90%) originates from Grand Manan, where 50-100 harvesters (and an additional 15-20 people involved in buying, packaging, and shipping) harvested approximately 100 dry tons (DT) in 1994, between 59 and 68 DT in 1996 (R. Cronk, New Brunswick Department of Agriculture, Fisheries and Aquaculture, personal communication), and approximately 84 DT in 2002 (T. McEachreon, New Brunswick Department of Agriculture, Fisheries and Aquaculture, personal communication). The rockweed industry started in 1995 on the NB side of the Bay of Fundy. The first year landings totalled 703 wet tons (WT); they reached 11,801 WT in 2004. The company employs around 75 harvesters. A drying and processing plant in Pennfield, NB operates with 14 full-time and 15 seasonal employees.

A consequence of the improved economic outlook is potential conflict between resident and non-resident landowners. Charlotte County has a history as a resort and cottage area. The dominant hotel in St. Andrews has its origins as a summer resort for the rich and continues to prosper on the holiday trade. Rural development, particularly along the waterfront, is often at odds with the desire to maintain a holiday/ecotourism-based economy. As a result, the development interests of rural communities are often at risk of being suborned, in the larger provincial political process, to the desire of urban holiday clientele.

Documentation of Uses and Types of Production

On the west coast of Canada, one approach to mapping resource use has attempted to balance social acceptability and biophysical capability. Biophysical capability was evaluated by compiling all known biophysical information on an area (e.g., Ricker 1989a) and documenting it in a set of maps (e.g., Ricker 1989b). Social acceptability was evaluated through the generation of a series of Coastal Resource Interest Study (CRIS) maps (e.g., BCMCL and BCMSVI 1989). In the CRIS coastal resource users, represented by special interest groups, were invited to identify on large-scale maps areas where they felt fish farms might be incompatible with their interests. These were used to evaluate applications for siting new fish farms. In general, areas designated as having uses incompatible with fish farming under the CRIS system were not open to application for fish farm leases. In other areas, the biophysical suitability was used to indicate to applicants what biophysical factors they should consider in siting their new operations and what information was available.

This compilation of suitability and compatibility data was very informative, but it was so costly that it has been undertaken only once in more than 20 years. In addition, there were technical and methodological weaknesses with the approach.

The creation of the biophysical maps suggested that knowledge at the time was adequate to identify appropriate biophysical conditions for fish farming. As shown in an earlier section of this chapter, biophysical conditions suitable for fish farming change over time with the advent of new technologies. In the past 20 years, they have undergone significant changes. An alternate approach to the identification of habitats capable of supporting culture technologies is the use of habitat suitability indices. In British Columbia (BC), this was done for shellfish (Cross and Kingsett 1992). This had the advantage of using a commonly used habitat suitability evaluation technique that built on established relationships between environmental conditions and growth as expressed under conditions in commercial aquaculture. This approach must undergo a constant evolution as industry is driven to search for new and more profitable species to grow and market, and driven by shrinking profit margins as the industry matures, production increases, and prices for products decline.

For the Bay of Fundy region, there has been an effort to map present resource uses. As shown in Fig. 8, the first thing that becomes apparent is that unless some sort of filter is used, essentially all of the water of the Bay is utilized.

Some of the areas mapped are only occasionally used for these fisheries. It becomes evident that there must be differentiation between intensive use and lesser levels of usage. If this is not done, even the most minor activity could preclude new highly beneficial uses of those same resources. One approach is to screen for areas where most of the harvest occurs. As shown in Fig. 9, the most heavily utilized areas are responsible for at least 50% of the production of these fisheries.

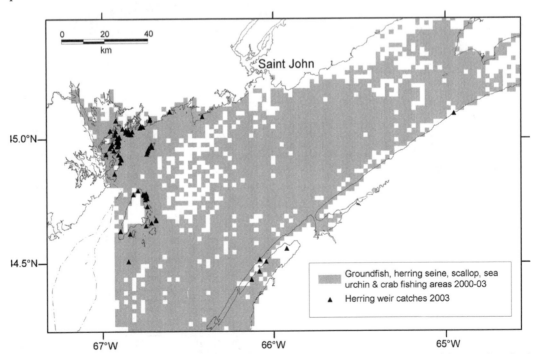

Figure 8. Commercial fishing areas for groundfish, herring, scallops, sea urchins, and crabs in the Bay of Fundy (Data source: Fisheries and Oceans Canada).

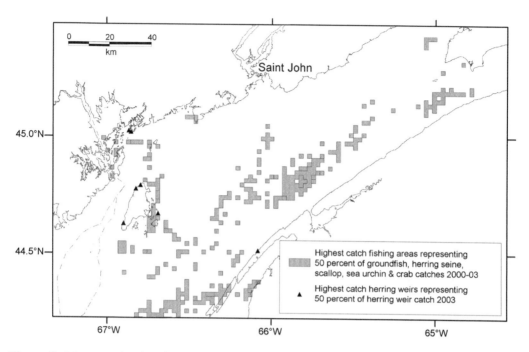

Figure 9. Most productive fishing areas in the Bay of Fundy accounting for 50% of the total catch of groundfish, herring, scallops, sea urchins and crabs (Data source: Fisheries and Oceans Canada).

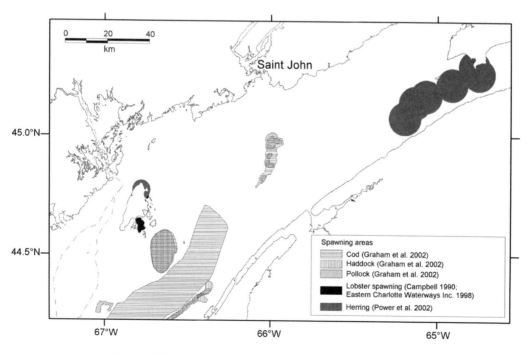

Figure 10. Special fisheries habitats in the Bay of Fundy.

In addition to the extractive uses, there are underlying processes that support these uses. These processes or special habitats are critical to maintaining the function of the ecosystems and its component parts. Some of the spawning areas for fish species, which would constitute special habitats that resource mangers might wish to preserve, are shown in Fig. 10.

Having identified the extractive resource uses and the areas that are critical to the systems' ecological processes, more information on the non-extractive processes should be incorporated in the mapping process, e.g., shipping lanes and underwater cables and pipelines (Fig. 11). Other non-extractive uses can be added to the inventory. These might include areas of special visual value to communities or areas of special historical, cultural, or spiritual value. Even without adding these to the list of inventories captured, it rapidly becomes apparent that there are areas where resource use is particularly intense and others areas where use is less intense (Fig. 12).

Challenges

Socioeconomic, Cultural, and Ecological Factors

Cultivation of Atlantic salmon has expanded rapidly around the world. As Table 1 shows, output of farmed Atlantic salmon more than quadrupled between 1990 and 2000, with an average annual growth of more than 15%. In spite of this massive increase putting pressure on prices, the global value more than doubled over the same period. Falling prices have made salmon more affordable, and rising per capita incomes, urbanization, and population growth have expanded the number of consumers. Dwarfed by Norway and Chile, Canada's share of world tonnage of farmed Atlantic salmon (Canada's principal species by volume and value) is

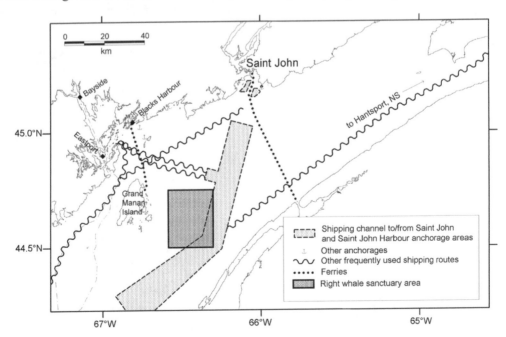

Figure 11. Shipping lanes and related exclusion zones in the Bay of Fundy.

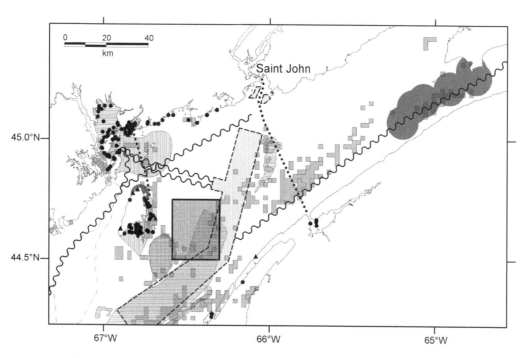

Figure 12. Overlay of information presented in Figs. 4, 9, 10, and 11.

only 8%. In both NB and BC, salmon aquaculture faced the handicap of being a newcomer on the waterways, and an infant compared to the capture fisheries. Constraints have also included limited access to sites, difficulty accessing capital, and negative attitudes by the public.

Benefits of salmon farming are considerable. Farmed salmon is NB's major agri-food commodity, earning about $200 million annually. Most of the output is exported, so it is a significant source of foreign exchange. It directly employs some 1,700 people (most of whom are non-seasonal) in NB, and through linkages, generates an additional 2,900 jobs (Stewart 2001). Employment income, tax revenues, and revitalization of rural communities are therefore major benefits that accrue from the industry.

Salmon farming, however, is an inherently risky business. Risks are economic, social, and environmental. The economic risk comes from dependence on a single species, which is exacerbated by Canada's being a small player in the world market. Reliance on a single species brings an economic risk of falling prices. Norway's Aquaculture Plan has several scenarios, but the most modest projects a doubling of its output by 2020 (Brugère and Ridler 2004). The Chilean government forecasts that world farmed salmon output will double to 2.5 million MT by 2013 (Brugère and Ridler 2004). As a price taker, Canada would suffer if it becomes uncompetitive. It may also not have the ability to sell to countries such as Brazil and China that are experiencing rising incomes and urbanization, and will be the market destination of this increased global supply. Moreover, there is the potential for lost income due to disease, adverse publicity, or weather.

There is a risk of social disruption from alienated communities and fishers, as has occurred elsewhere. In Chile, salmon farming has created more than 30,000 jobs in the remote Xth and XIth Regions, but the poor have been socially dislocated and marginalized and the fish processing work force is transient (Barrett et al. 2002). This has led to resistance to salmon farming and even deliberate destruction of cages. Farmers concerns about further vandalism have caused them to oppose opening the area to salmon fishing. They are worried that the artisanal fishers would deliberately encourage escapees as a potential source of fish for capture. In Canada, there has also been resistance to "enclosing the commons" by salmon farming. Opposition has come from herring (*Clupea harengus*) fishers, cottage owners, and recreational boaters. The task for the future of aquaculture, then, is to develop systems that minimize undesired changes while ensuring community vitality.

Environmental risks are often inadequately described (Auditor General 2004). Salmon farming in the Bay of Fundy is limited to a few inlets, with a potential to change the local ecology. Even with its strong tides, the Bay of Fundy may have insufficient flushing power to avoid accumulation of organic material under the cages and inorganic nutrients in the surroundings. There is also concern over escapees and their interaction with wild Atlantic salmon. Offshore farming has been suggested as an alternative to the Bay, but the economic costs are unknown and may be prohibitive.

User Conflicts

The primary goal of IRM is sustainability. While there are different definitions of the term sustainability, there is a general consensus that the concept includes social and economic variables as well as environmental considerations. For aquaculture to be sustainable, there must be economic viability. The species cultivated must be profitable with minimal risk. Without these two conditions, entrepreneurs have no incentive to invest, or they would need permanent subsidies if they were to remain in the industry. In addition, there must be social acceptance of the industry. The late T.V.R. Pillay, in a keynote address at the Conference on Aquaculture in the Third Millennium, noted, "technological progress in the next millennium has to go hand-in-hand with social and ethical acceptability" (Pillay 2001).

Enough evidence exists of the effect on industry of social discontent as expressed by litigation, theft, and vandalism. On the other hand, if there is community support, the aquaculture industry can be the primary beneficiary (Katrandis et al. 2003). These socio-economic determinants combine with environmental performance to define sustainable resource use.

An approach to resource allocation that often appeals to resource managers, especially when space appears to be plentiful, is to base allocation decisions on techniques whose primary rule for allocation is conflict minimization. That philosophy was part of the basis of the approach that was applied to the allocation of BC's fish farms in the late 1980s and early 1990s utilizing the CRIS mentioned in an earlier section of this chapter.

Experience has shown that problems exist with the use of the CRIS type of approach. Historical uses acquire priority for future use, not because of their value to society, but because the resource was used that way in the past. Thus, more recently devised uses for resources are often directed to areas that are less than optimal. In the case of aquaculture, farms could be sited in areas less well suited for aquaculture due to environmental or economic reasons, but in which they engender no user conflicts. Conceptually, this is analogous to creating a ghetto for aquaculture activities that ignores the full scope of benefits that better-sited aquaculture might offer.

An alternate approach to resource mapping is to identify valued aspects or features of an area, define buffer zones around specific features that may require them, and permit open competition for the remaining areas. This is the philosophy underlying the development of feature-based resource mapping in BC, documented in Black (2001).

Next Steps

Suggested Solutions to Problems

Legislative Response

In 1997, Canada passed its Oceans Act. This marked the beginning of a transition in the approach to the management of Canada's marine and freshwater resources, from one focused on populations and habitats of commercially valuable species (i.e., a Fisheries Act-based approach) to a broader consideration of the impacts of all human activities on the ecosystem within which the activities occur. As part of the transition, efforts are being made to define objectives for the new Ecosystem-Based Management approach. To date, the accepted broad goals for the environmental components are to sustain the human usage of environmental resources and conserve the species and habitats of the ecosystems (Jamieson et al. 2001). The conceptual objectives under the conservation goal are:

- "To conserve enough components (ecosystems, species, populations, etc.) so as to maintain the natural resilience of the ecosystem." This was reiterated as maintenance of communities, species, and populations within the bounds of natural variability.

- "To conserve each component of the ecosystem so that it can play its historic role in the food web (i.e., not cause any component of the ecosystem to be altered to such an extent that it ceases to play its historical role in a higher order component)." This was reiterated as maintenance of primary production and the mean generation times of species within the bounds of natural variability and to maintain trophic structure so that individual species/stages can play their historical role in the food web.

- "To conserve the physical and chemical properties of the ecosystem." This was reiterated as conservation of critical landscape and bottomscape features, water column properties, water quality, and biota quality (Jamieson et al. 2001).

The intent is that under each of the conceptual environmental objectives, more specific objectives, indicators, thresholds, and reference points will be defined that link the conceptual objectives to actions that are suitable for operational management. Although some efforts have been made to pursue this approach for oil and gas, ground fisheries, and aquaculture activities (O'Boyle and Keizer 2003), there is still much discussion and much work that remains to be done.

Integrated Multi-Trophic Aquaculture

The rapid development of intensive fed aquaculture throughout the world is associated with concerns about the environmental effects of mono-specific husbandry practices, especially where activities are highly concentrated geographically or located in suboptimal sites whose assimilative capacity is poorly understood and, consequently, prone to be exceeded.

One emerging consequence of fish aquaculture activities is a significant loading of nutrients (especially dissolved nitrogen [N] and phosphorus [P]), and particulate organic material in coastal waters (Beveridge 1987). Several countries, where intensive aquaculture is already an established industry, are in the process of implementing restrictions on the amount of nutrients allowed to be discharged from fish farms, because excessive fertilization can alter significantly the quality of the benthos and waters generally sought after by multi-users (Håkanson et al. 1988). Nutrient rich waters in the vicinity of fish farms also promote the growth of opportunistic annual filamentous algae, such as *Ulva* spp., *Enteromorpha* spp., *Cladophora* spp., and *Pilayella* spp. Proliferation of these types of algae causes severe biofouling of cages and restricts water and nutrient circulation patterns (Indergaard and Jensen 1983; Rönnberg et al. 1992). At the same time, the decline of economically valuable perennial algae (e.g., *Ascophyllum* spp., *Fucus* spp., and *Laminaria* spp.) has been recorded due to increased competition (for nutrients, light, and substrate), decreased light penetration, and increased sedimentation of organic matter (Wallentinus 1981).

Different methods have been used to try to minimize the effect of nutrient loading, such as reducing nutrients and their leaching from diets and trapping or stabilizing fecal matter (Phillips et al. 1993). About 20%-30% of N and 60%-70% of P, however, may not be consumed or released as feces (Soto 1996). In its search for better management practices, the aquaculture industry looks to develop innovative and responsible practices that optimize its efficiency and create diversification, while ensuring the mitigation of the consequences of its activities to maintain the health of coastal waters. To avoid pronounced shifts in coastal processes, conversion (not dilution) is a common-sense solution used for centuries in Asian countries. By integrated fed aquaculture (finfish) with inorganic and organic extractive aquaculture (seaweed and shellfish) materials as trophic resources, the wastes of one resource user become a resource (fertilizer or food) for the others. Such a balanced ecosystem approach provides nutrient bioremediation capability, mutual benefits to the co-cultured organisms, economic diversification by producing other value-added marine crops, and potentially increased profitability per cultivation unit for the aquaculture industry (Ryther et al. 1975; Indergaard and Jensen 1983; Folke and Kautsky 1989, 1991, 1992; Petrell et al. 1993; Subandar et al. 1993; Folke et al. 1994; Bodvin et al. 1996; Kautsky et al. 1996b; Chopin et al. 2001; Troell et al. 2003; Neori et al. 2004). Moreover, as guidelines and regulations on aquaculture effluents are forthcoming in several countries, using appropriately selected seaweeds and shellfish as renewable biological nutrient/organic matter scrubbers represents a cost-effective means for reaching compliance by reducing the internalization of the total environmental costs of aquaculture operations.

Recently, Kautsky et al. (1996a) have used the concept of "ecological footprint" (the area needed per square meter of aquaculture activity to supply the ecological resources used in culture practices) to describe the environmental effects of salmon and shrimp farming. It was estimated that for 1 m^2 of salmon aquaculture, the N production requires 340 m^2 of pelagic production to be assimilated, and the P production requires 400 m^2 of pelagic production. By integrating the culture of *Gracilaria* sp. to salmon aquaculture in Chile, it was possible to estimate a reduction of these ecological footprints to 150 m^2 for N and 25 m^2 for P (Kautsky et al. 1996a).

At this point, a caution must be made regarding the use of the ecological footprint concept (Black et al. 2001). While visually graphic in its depiction of relative resource utilization, it is difficult to apply with precision and of no value in predicting the environmental change that might result from changes in inputs. For example, it treats the input of N in the form of ammonia as the same as the input of N as nitrate, yet the ecosystem consequences are radically different. In ammonia-dominated marine ecosystems, micrograzer food chains predominate, while in nitrogen-dominated systems, macrograzer food chains predominate (MacIsaac and Dugdale 1969; Dortch 1990; Flynn et al. 1997, 1999; Flynn 1998; Harrison et al. 1996). Similarly, the ecological footprint concept would not allow differentiation between refractory carbon and highly bioavailable carbon. Even so, it is a popular and highly graphic way of depicting consumption of ecosystem resources.

Chopin from the University of New Brunswick in Saint John has been developing, with colleagues in New England, a similar programme of integrated aquaculture in NB and Maine by replacing *Gracilaria* sp. (for the agar market) with *Porphyra* sp. (for direct human consumption and biotechnology markets). The salmon/nori integrated aquaculture project was based on the premise that it should offer several advantages at different levels:

- The seaweed-farming component represents an additional income for the salmon farmer. Moreover, diversifying the sources of income and labor training protects farmers from a dangerously fluctuating salmon market at the national and international level, over which they have very little control. *Porphyra* sp., either as a source of food for direct human consumption or for developing biotechnological applications, is a crop with a very high added value.

- The absence of fertilization costs for seaweed should result in substantial savings, since nutrients produced by the salmon farm could be used at no additional cost. Consequently, a higher nori production can be expected in an integrated system compared to a uniquely nori farm.

- Integrated aquaculture improves the water and habitat quality of coastal waters by increasing nutrient removal by seaweeds naturally and, hence, at a net profit.

- If culture of *Porphyra* sp. turns out to be an efficient biological nutrient removal system, the possibility of increasing the number of salmon cages at a particular site becomes more likely, hence, creating more revenue.

- Integrating economically important marine plants in an aquaculture system allows the management of eutrophication problems associated with present fish mono-aquaculture and coastal agriculture/urban/industrial practices. Nutrients that are utilized by marine harvested crops are unavailable for the growth of toxic phytoplanktonic species or opportunistic and undesirable algae that are responsible for low-value "green tide" biomass, the disposal cost of which becomes rapidly prohibitive (Fletcher 1990).

Frequent harvest of *Porphyra* spp. assures a constantly renewed removal of nutrients from the coastal ecosystem. This is not the case with bloom-forming macro- and microalgae, which recycle their nutrients back to the water column when they die and decay, and consequently, perpetuate conditions favorable for future blooms. Even if the complete replacement of problem species by introducing this competition for nutrients were not achieved, partial replacement might be sufficient to reduce the biomass of problem species below the threshold of hypertrophic events (Merrill 1996).

Preliminary results in Cobscook Bay, northeastern Maine, USA, where a nori company was located, demonstrated that *Porphyra yezoensis* is able to detect high nutrient loading in coastal waters resulting from anthropogenic activities (e.g., fish aquaculture and intense scallop dragging putting back into suspension nutrients trapped in sediments). Tissue N levels were between 6.64% and 7.27% DW in Cobscook Bay on November 1, 1996, compared to findings by Chopin et al. (1996) of 2.68% DW in *A. nodosum* , between 4 and 4.5% DW in *Polysiphonia lanosa* and *Pilayella littoralis*, and 4.38% DW in *Chondrus crispus* (T. Chopin, unpublished data). Tissue P levels were between 7.06 and 8.47 mg P g DW^{-1}. The P content of *Porphyra purpurea* in Dipper Harbour, NB (a location remote from the two above anthropogenic activities) was 3.24 mg P g DW^{-1}. *Chondrus crispus* is known to have tissues saturated at around 4-4.5 mg P g DW^{-1} (Chopin et al. 1995). Consequently, *Porphyra* sp. could be used as a bio-indicator for nutrient loading and as a biological nutrient removal system to sustain and improve the productivity and carrying capacity of coastal waters, especially in regions of intensive fish aquaculture activities, to contribute to the development of a responsible management of near shore coastal waters. *Porphyra* sp. can be considered as an extremely efficient nutrient pump, based on its morphology (a thin blade with one or two layers of cells, all involved in absorption). It could be argued that this morphology, while creating an efficient pump, does not allow storage in reserve tissues, as in the case of the large brown algae (Laminariales, Fucales). The advantage of *Porphyra* sp., however, is its rapid growth, which allows the harvest of a crop every 9-15 days (I. Levine, personal communication). Consequently, frequent harvesting results in significant quantities of nutrients being constantly removed from coastal waters. Thus, *Porphyra* sp. integrated with salmon aquaculture was seen as a potential biological nutrient removal system. Unfortunately, the nori company in Cobscook Bay ceased operations, and the lack of a reliable source of nori-seeded nets stopped further development of this project. Part of it is continuing as a land-based experimental summer flounder (*Paralichthys dentatus*)/nori tank cultivation system in New Hampshire, USA, with another company.

Since 2001, an interdisciplinary research project, with a team of scientists from the University of New Brunswick and the Department of Fisheries and Oceans Biological Station in Saint Andrews, NB, is developing the concept of integrated multi-trophic aquaculture (IMTA). Current marine monoculture production models are premised on the assumption of continual expansion. This fuels the development of commodity-based systems and the eventual erosion of environmental quality, because increased volumes within geographical expansion and carrying capacity constraints are used to compensate for lower profit margins (Chopin and Bastarache 2004). The project focuses on a new paradigm, i.e., how to optimize aquaculture lease space and biomass production through biomitigation to reduce environmental impacts, diversification for sustainable economic viability, and social acceptance of the improved practices (Chopin et al. 1999, 2001; Troell et al. 2003; Neori et al. 2004). Monoculture practices may not offer the best use of cultivation units. When one considers the seawater volume available at a leased site and the volume of water column occupied by a series of salmon cages, it is obvious that a cultivation unit (i.e., a site) is not optimized. Developing IMTA systems provides options for increased profitability per cultivation unit through economic diversification by co-cultivating several value-added marine crops. Improved environmental and social sustainability and acceptability are additional benefits.

Phase I of the project tested the feasibility of the IMTA concept by combining inorganic extractive aquaculture of the kelp, *L. saccharina*, and organic extractive aquaculture of the blue mussel, *M. edulis*, with the fed aquaculture of salmon, *S. salar*, to provide a balanced ecosystem approach to aquaculture practices. Phase II increased the production of kelps and mussels towards an industrial, pilot-scale level. Food safety tracking was a significant component of the second phase. Physical/chemical modeling (especially of the oxygen budget) and the socio-economic component were initiated.

The main results from Phases I and II are:

- Culture techniques for the kelp, *L. saccharina*, have been improved in the laboratory and at three aquaculture sites with different exposure characteristics. The laboratory phase has been reduced from 113 to 35 days, and the biomass production has been increased from 8.0-20.7 kg m^{-1} of rope. Kelps grown in the vicinity of salmon farms increased their growth rates by 46% in comparison to kelps grown at reference sites.

- An *in situ* method (time-lapse underwater video of siphons) to determine the quantitative feeding rate of the blue mussel, *M. edulis*, was developed to show that mussels not only are capable of capturing excess food particles from the fish farm but also increase their feeding rates in response to the presence of these particles. Seston levels at salmon farms are elevated by a factor of 2 to 4 over ambient levels and are of very high quality (up to 90% organic). Enhanced growth rates at farm sites (twice as much as at reference sites) and accelerated production times to commercial size (approximately 18 months from socking) reflect this increase in food energy, as mussels ingest fish food particles with approximately the same efficiency as phytoplankton species.

- None of the therapeutants used in salmon aquaculture have been detected in kelps or mussels collected from the integrated sites (Chopin et al. 2001; Sephton et al. 2003b; Martin et al. 2004).

- Blooms of the phytoplanktonic species, *Alexandrium fundyense*, occur during the summer months and PSP toxins are accumulated by mussels, but the mussels can be safely harvested with proper management (Sephton et al. 2002, 2003a, 2003b, 2003c). Marketing of the product will have to occur outside of the toxic algal season, which will modify the final size of the marketed product. This is a common practice in many shellfish producing countries. Implementation of this management technique for Canada needs to be investigated.

- The logistics of the kelp and mussel culture portion of an integrated operation appear to fit well with the day-to-day operations of a regular salmon farm. Cleaning of the nets provides an abundant source of juvenile mussels.

- A survey of aquaculture attitudes found that the general public has a more negative attitude towards current monoculture practices and, although relatively unfamiliar with the concept, feels significantly more positive that IMTA would be successful and would improve the overall social acceptability of aquaculture in the region.

- A study was conducted on seaweed products and markets. A relatively small volume/ high value-added niche market approach was recommended as the most appropriate strategy at this stage.

- A bio-economic model, depicting the yearly operating costs, financing, and revenue of a standard salmon farm has been built. Two additional ventures, mussel and seaweed farming, were added along with some estimates of the remediation benefits. Net present value calculations were conducted for each venture and the integrated operation. Preliminary findings show that IMTA could enhance the economic sustainability of salmon farming through higher profits.

- Following a successful workshop in March 2004 in Saint John, NB, the network investigators are working with the Canadian Shellfish Sanitation Program (CSSP) partners (i.e., Department of Fisheries and Oceans, Environment Canada, and the Canadian Food Inspection Agency) to define the appropriate food safety and the Hazard Analysis and Critical Control Point (HACCP) -based policies and procedures, on a pilot basis, for an integrated site. Based on further industry/government consultation and development, this should allow for the development of commercial scale integrated operations under an amended/revised CSSP policy framework.

The interdisciplinary team has been able to deliver a varied set of documents (peer reviewed papers, book chapters, proceedings of international conferences, non-refereed technical papers, magazine and newspaper articles, and an English/French bilingual DVD[1]) to disseminate the knowledge it has gained since 2001 to the different targeted audiences: researchers, federal and provincial agencies, industry, professional associations, environmental nongovernmental organizations, and the general and school public.

As current findings support the establishment of IMTA systems in the Bay of Fundy, the team now plans to proceed with Phase III. Objectives include scaling-up the experimental systems to commercial levels, extending application to the West coast of Canada, and increasing trophic components and links by testing and developing the combined aquaculture of other species with similar or complementary functions in an integrated system.

Investment in research and development (R&D) and the implementation of current novel technologies and concepts are pivotal for the success of the aquaculture industry in the future. This is necessary to move aquaculture in new directions that allow it to optimize its efficiency through diversification while maintaining the health of coastal waters. Research and development are only justified if they are followed by commercialization. Frequently, however, a major gap exists after R&D, because the appropriate funding structures and incentives are not in place to make commercialization a reality. To help ensure its sustainability, the aquaculture sector should look at adopting polytrophic practices so that it may become better integrated into a broader coastal management framework.

Recommendations for Ways to Apply Ecosystem-Based Management

Identification of Key Principles

The preceding sections of this chapter describe a general scenario or context developed largely from the experience in eastern Canada. Information presented, discussed, and analyzed highlights a series of key principles that should be applied to the IRM model. These principles, categorized as general, social, economic, and environmental, are presented in the following sections.

General.

- Change happens with or without human participation. It is our job to influence the nature, distribution, and extent of change resulting from human activities.

- Social license, economic viability, and environmental sustainability are required to define viable integrated resource management.

- Clarity is needed in describing the social, economic, and environmental components contributing to the derivation of a decision on resource allocation.

    - Environmental sustainability is a science-based issue and has in it no inherent value judgment.

---

[1] See AquaNet 2005.

- Economic viability is a market value-based issue.

- Non-market-based values are social issues and are defined by political processes.

- Regulatory values are products of political policy processes and as such are based on social values and constructs.

- All combinations and types of resource allocations are valid under some set of socio-economic conditions. The objective is to optimize, into the foreseeable future, the stream of benefits from resource allocations.

- There are no zero risk options. All resource allocations (including the decision to preclude human use of resources) contain an element of risk.

Social.

- Integrated resource management must include all levels of public governance (National, Provincial, First Nations, Regional, and Urban) in resource allocation decisions.

- An explicit statement of shared values and goals must underpin all decisions.

- All participants in resource allocation decisions must respect all users' interests and aspirations.

- Residents in an area of resource use are an equal partner in the decision making process. More remote urban interests should not dominate the decision making process.

- Management units for coastal resources must relate to ecosystem units and be large enough that no one resource user is singled out for unique regulatory control within the management unit.

- Decisions are to be derived in a risk analysis framework and may be supported by tools such as Decision Support Systems and Geographic Information Systems (GIS).

- Failure to participate in consensus formation and the above social principles is valid grounds for exclusion from the decision making process.

Economic.

- Property rights and their duration must be explicitly defined and allow for the evolution of the mix of coastal zone uses over time in response to environmental, social, and economic forces.

- Local, regional, national, and international economic forces and agreements all affect economic optimization.

- Market externalities are important in the evaluation of the utility of resource allocation solutions.

Environmental.

- The smallest ecosystem unit should relate to a water body scale in which ecological processes have some internal integrity.

- Ecosystem modeling for integrated resource management should be based on nested geographic units that build to large ecosystem units.

- Environmental regulation should be based on parameters that are not unique to a single user.

- Evaluation of severity of environmental change should include reference to the duration and geographic extent of the change as well as the level of change in the ecosystem (species to whole ecosystems).

- Environmental management schemes should incorporate adaptive management strategies that compliment research to reduce uncertainty in predictions of environmental change.

- Regulatory schemes should be transparent with clear responsibilities as well as clear performance (data collection and analysis) criteria that include reporting timelines for reporting to the public and participants in resource allocation.

Regional Management

Integrated coastal resource management can be approached from large area planning exercises that define the pattern in which planning for subcomponent areas must fit, or it can be approached as an integration of a series of nested plans for smaller areas which define the overall plan for a larger area. An interesting example of the latter was undertaken on Canada's west coast. The driving force was the need to rationalize the cost of managing five clam species (*Venerupis philippinarium, Protothaca staminea, Saxidomus giganta, Siliqua patula, Nutallia obscurata*) on the West Coast of Vancouver Island. Through canvassing residents and their organizations, it was determined that local people were willing to participate. The breadth of representation included organizations for First Nations, Local Community Government, Regional Government, wild harvesters of shellfish, shellfish aquaculturists, and shellfish processors. The basis for development of the management board was that the board would operate by consensus, that all groups should be treated with mutual respect, and that all groups were equally valid participants. The first exercise in creating the management board was to use a workshop to establish a commonly agreed upon set of values and objectives.

Among the agreed upon principles was that all decision making must be conducted in an open and transparent manner. The provincial and federal resource mangers then participated in the meetings and shared any up-to-date information pertinent to discussions undertaken. They also received advice from the board on areas to be opened or closed to harvesting, the duration of the openings, and the economic effects of increasing or decreasing the number of harvesting licenses. Essentially, the board advised the two levels of government on the management of the local fisheries.

The operation of the board did not impinge on any of the Federal or Provincial government's legal powers and responsibilities, though government agencies did agree to be advised by the board on matters pertaining to the management of the clam species. The area covered was large enough that board recommendations would be robust against potential interference by any individual politicians or managers.

A benefit of the board being dominated by local residents was that board deliberation always exhibited a keen awareness of the balance between the local need for industry development and the need for a sustainable harvest. Involvement of so many locals also meant there was strong local involvement in policing, and social pressure was often enough to curb harvesting outside of the approved harvest plan. A decade later the board is still in operation.

Bay Management

A common level of integration of aquaculture and other resource users in IRM is at the local bay-wide scale. This level of integration has been successfully developed by industry for environmental and fish health management in Canada and elsewhere. In the Bay of Fundy in southwestern NB, there exists a series of 21 Bay Management Areas (BMAs) that primarily serve to coordinate the activities of aquaculturists, but also serve as a means of communication and cooperation among all resource users.

The existing 21 BMAs in NB were established from an original proposed number of six to 10. This proposed number was based for the most part on hydrodynamics and flow of water between aquaculture sites, hence supporting fish health and environment quality. These areas, however, proved to be too large and contained too many farm sites, such that cooperative agreements could not be reached. The resulting larger number reflects key socioeconomic features such as ownership of sites, availability of wharves and other transportation, proximity to process plants, and relationships with other resource users.

Operation of these 21 BMAs has seen a shift in cooperation toward the six to 10 larger areas that were originally proposed. That is, experience has allowed cooperation on a larger scale and emphasis has shifted from small-scale operations to larger scale sustainability.

Environmental Quality Indicators

Marine environmental quality (MEQ) indicators are variables selected to assess environmental changes. In considering changes in the environment associated with aquaculture, there is an orientation toward eutrophication effects. Common MEQ indicators are benthic variables, since sediments integrate environmental influences and are buffered with respect to the temporal changes that characterize variables measured in the water column. For this reason, the benthos is ideal for assessing certain types of environmental change. Water column measures of environmental change are considered further in the ecosystem modeling section below.

Benthic indicators may roughly be divided into geochemical measures and community variables. In the former category, redox potential and sulfide content are the primary variables, because they are comprehensive indicators of eutrophication and a shift toward anaerobic-based sediment communities. Fisheries and Oceans Canada has conducted in-depth studies of procedural and analytical consideration in applying redox and sulfide to aquaculture effects largely in the context of cage culture effects in southwest NB. In general, recent findings suggest that, for soft bottom substrates, sulfides are more reliable measures of benthic conditions than redox potential. Both of the latter variables are proxies for the oxic state of sediments. Sediment oxygen is an obviously more direct measure of the extent of normoxia, but it is usually conducted with microelectrode techniques that are less suited to rapid assessment approaches that have been applied to redox and sulfide.

Sediment indicators based on community structure are popular in light of recent emphases on biodiversity. The costs of enumeration and identification are severe, and the results though internally quantitative, are not necessarily in a format that contributes to ecosystem models that focus on trophodynamics and rate processes. Recent studies have considered modeling of these variables (Duplisea 1998), but models of entire benthic communities are somewhat daunting. It is worth noting that community analysis is an integral part of traditional measures of ecosystem health.

Due to the recent emphasis on GIS and mapping, variables used for Environmental Assessments should be amenable to spatial analysis. The sampling effort required for sufficient spatial coverage is significant, and there are few cases where sufficient data exist for spatial analysis such as contouring. Ecosystems with long-term research attention (e.g., Chesapeake Bay, USA) are more likely to involve mapping of measured indicators. Among Canadian aquaculture sites, Tracadie Bay in Prince Edward Island has received much attention (Dowd 2001; Grant et al. 2005; Waite et al. 2005). Its small size, shallow depth, and extensive suspended mussel culture create a manageable research location for detailed spatial study. Model results such as current speed, seston depletion, and nutrient concentration are also ideal as GIS layers.

Although standing stock types of variables are most commonly used for assessments of environmental change, measurements of rate processes are also desirable. Due to the difficulty in conducting spatial measurements of rate-oriented variables, they are less likely candidates for spatial analysis. Variables such as sulfide or sediment organic content are proxies for organic loading that can be measured directly as a rate with sediment traps, i.e., simple tube traps that can be applied over wide spatial scales, and deployed and recovered over a few days. This approach has been applied at shellfish and finfish culture sites (C. McKindsey, DFO, unpublished). Rate of sediment oxygen demand is classically applied as an assessment variable, but requires effort and specialization that are less suited to rapid assessment. An interesting development in this realm is determination of oxygen demand from near bottom oxygen profiles and estimation of eddy diffusivity. This approach may shift benthic metabolism to the category of a survey variable.

Habitat mapping and subsequent GIS analysis is one of the most important recent developments in coastal zone management. Unfortunately, there are few choices for survey variables that can practically be measured. Echosounding, multibeam sonar, underwater video recordings, and other techniques are growing rapidly as useful survey tools, with hardware for single beam instruments readily available in terms of cost and vessel requirements (Morrison et al. 2001). Delineation of habitats with these tools is being conducted at several Canadian finfish and shellfish culture sites. In eastern Canada, an analogous tool for the water column via a towed body has been used to map variables such as chlorophyll, turbidity, and oxygen.

Remote sensing with satellite imagery or airborne sensors (CASI) is a promising approach for culture sites, and has been applied at eastern Canadian culture sites. There is considerable expertise for CASI on the West Coast as well. Culture sites have many complicating factors in isolating variables like chlorophyll, such as shallow bottoms, epiphytes, and macrophyte beds.

A further comment relates to the relationship between benthic monitoring variables and ecosystem modeling. Ideally, variables designated for field measurement should be amenable to modeling. Unfortunately, redox and sulfide are not often fully resolved in ecosystem models as applied to environmental effects of culture activities. Anaerobiosis has been explored in detail in some diagenetic models of coastal ecosystems (e.g., Chapelle et al. 2000). Beyond the problems with measuring sediment oxygen content, it is subject to the same difficulties as a modeling designate, namely complex vertical and horizontal spatial distribution that is hard to capture without a detailed diagenetic model. Ground-truthing of these indicators is subject to the same impediments caused by spatial variation.

In addition to the above MEQ indicators, there are environmental quality indicators associated with chemicals that may occur because of farming activities. These include a group of compounds associated with maintenance of animal health and others that may enter the ecosystem as a by product of feed formulations or leachates from farm structures. The former are often managed through licensing and reporting requirements for veterinary drugs. The latter, however, constitute a group of chemicals for which environmental quality standards are under development. Typically, these would include copper that may derive from antifouling preparations and zinc that may come from corrosion-resistant metal structures. Some work has been done with these chemicals, but their significance is usually evaluated in relation to human health requirements rather than to environmental effects.

In evaluating environmental quality for coastal zone management the visual environment is often a key consideration. Quantification of the effect of aquaculture on the visual environment is difficult to undertake. In North America, owners of recreational property often consider aquaculture unsightly, causing a reduction in property values. In Europe, with its longer tradition of foreshore development in recreational areas, the valuation of it is less negative. In Japan, it has been used to benefit tourism. That latter approach is beginning to be exploited in BC, where culture operations are offering bread and breakfast services associated with farm tours.

Ecosystem Models

Ecosystem models have been successfully applied to aquaculture sites worldwide, and constitute some of the most powerful management tools (Stigebrandt et al. 2004). Canadian oceanographers have been particularly active in this research area (Page et al. 2002; Duarte et al. 2003; Dowd 2005; Grant et al. 2005; Guyondet et al. in press), although ecosystem models have not been devised for the intensive fish production in Passamaquoddy Bay. Despite the effort involved in these models, they are making the transition from research to management. A critical aspect of an ecosystem model is that of spatial resolution, with increasing effort required for greater spatial reality. Single or multiple box models are the most accessible format for aquaculture application since the coupling between boxes uses only a summary form of the physics involved. Box models often contain sufficient spatial detail to fulfill management purposes.

Fully coupled biophysical models require considerably more effort, but are attainable over time scales useful to managers for designated sites. These models produce maps of desired variables including culture species growth, or dispersion of waste products, and their output is compatible with GIS. They are somewhat difficult to ground-truth, because spatial field data are rare. The scope for "what if" scenarios and management options is greatest with fully coupled models, but their creation and validation is neither routine nor rapid. Model scales are often mixed, e.g., output from a circulation model is used to parameterize the averaged exchange information used in a box model (Lee et al. 2003). Despite the appeal of fully coupled models, it should be emphasized that simpler or screening models are a necessary step in the chain of management, since their output is applicable to advice, and they focus direction for further efforts.

In terms of structure, the most common models are trophodynamic, with compartments for the culture species, phytoplankton, zooplankton, benthos, etc. Model currency is carbon, nitrogen, or other nutrients. In shellfish models, there is an emphasis on seston depletion since shellfish receive their food from the water. Modeling of particle dynamics including biodeposits is thus essential. Finfish models are more concerned with the fate of particulate waste from food, and subsequent nutrient fluxes from fish and benthic regeneration. Due to the participation of the culture species in nutrient and particle flux, bioenergetic submodels are a central feature of the ecosystem structure. There is extensive ecophysiological data on most culture species that can be used for these submodels.

Benthic submodels are often simplified depending on the model intent, and the sediments are treated as a sink for waste materials. Processes such as resuspension and benthic metabolism are neglected for practical reasons, but in shallow waters systems, this is a significant compromise. In attempting to model nutrient fluxes, however, diagenetic detail is mandatory.

Models used for screening environmental changes may be simplified in their spatial structure. The basic approach is to compare some process associated with aquaculture (ammonia excretion, oxygen depletion, seston depletion) to the ability of tides to mitigate the changes (Strain et al. 1995; Gillibrand and Turrell 1997; Grant et al. 2005). Although various degrees of physical modeling have been applied to the tidal component, resolution of flushing is generally rough. The results of these models can be expressed as an index that can be compared among multiple bays or estuaries. The spatial detail of these models is often limited to one box, and they are difficult to apply where there are strong flushing gradients that obviate a tidal prism approach.

There is an emphasis on environmental changes in the near field around culture sites due to the apparent effects. Spatially explicit models which can predict environmental changes in the far-field context are critical in assessing ecosystem-level effects, but have received much less attention due to the difficulty in selecting appropriate variables that include culture influences. Local models have been used to predict near-field effects such as the footprint of culture sites. The DEPOMOD commercial product is most notable in this regard (Cromey et al. 2002).

The basis for all marine ecosystem models is a circulation model. Two or three-dimensional numerical models are the norm for this application. Numerical tracer experiments or time series of vector flows for each grid node can be used to calculate the spatial distribution of residence time or flushing rate. This information can be averaged or contoured in GIS to delineate flushing regions for use in less explicit models. A coarser approach to exchange can be obtained by a tidal prism method, but this has limited potential for management uses beyond initial screening, e.g., consideration of multiple sites simultaneously (Grant et al. 2005). Development of finite element models can be enhanced via various software, but model development cannot be shortcut. Digital boundaries and bathymetry are required, and grid construction and detail is critical in running the model. Tidal time series must be collected or generated as input. Model results must subsequently be ground-truthed by data from tide gauges and/or current meters.

Using ecosystem models, carrying capacity (CC) is estimated with respect to yield of cultured organisms (economic), and/or ecological change (environmental). Economic CC relies on market demand, and husbandry dictates acceptable culture density and profitable yield. On this basis, the management advice that can be provided consists of recommendations for the extent, density, and location of culture. The utility of a fully coupled model is obvious in this case. Estimates of economic CC should be made in the context of environmental CC, but standards and criteria are less well established for the latter. For example, limits for nutrients in marine waters may exist, but it is awkward to apply a single value to a system with poorly known spatial and temporal heterogeneity. Water column oxygen is a good candidate for MEQ since maintaining oxic habitats is recognized as a general MEQ goal, but similar problems of natural variation occur (Page et al. 2002).

Due to the significance of nitrogen and phosphorous in coastal eutrophication, nutrients are an important component of these models. Cultured species participate fully in nutrient cycling via ammonia excretion and through nutrient regeneration of wasted food and biodeposits (Hatcher et al. 1994; Chapelle et al. 2000). Spatially explicit models used to predict far-field concentrations are essential in assessing nutrient distributions that are otherwise difficult to document through field measurements. Modeling of nutrients has several potential problems including lack of time series used for boundary conditions, the complexity of redox reactions for most elements, neglect of likely important components including macrophytes and benthic microalgae, and lack of data for ground-truthing. Furthermore, due to the coupling of land runoff to estuarine nutrient cycling, catchment models arising from GIS topography data are necessary. Local hydrology constitutes a whole other modeling specialty that must be incorporated into the marine ecosystem models.

Ground-truthing of economic CC is fairly direct with shellfish, since growth of cultured animals predicted via the model can be measured directly. Spatial studies of shellfish growth, however, are rare (Waite et al. 2005). Some of the variables used for MEQ, i.e., redox, are less suitable for ground-truthing because their forcing is poorly understood and they are less likely modeled. Ground-truthing using water column variables is difficult due to their temporal variation and lack of spatial data. Time series data using moorings at more than one location is important as a means of capturing temporal change and at least some of the spatial aspect. There are generally fewer options for verifying the output of fully coupled models since spatial data is uncommon.

Risk Analysis Based Management

The previous section discusses some of the models that might be used to predict environmental changes that could result from uses of marine resources. These models, however, are generally very rough predictors. They approximate the degree of change that might be expected. With that prediction, there is usually considerable uncertainty as to whether that specific outcome will be realized. Uncertainty in accurately predicting that the outcome has been addressed in other bio-economic systems, such as the human food supply and the protection of animal health, with risk analysis.

The uncertainty discussed above has broader implications as well. With the development of international markets has come a desire to limit the use of non-tariff trade barriers. One type of trade barrier that has come under particular scrutiny is environmental protection and other biological concerns such as the spread of aquatic diseases and alien invasive species. An approach to justify constrained access to markets (just another type of resource) is the use of risk assessments (as differentiated from risk analysis).

A description of the process can be found in Corvello and Merkofer (1993). There are concerns with this approach. The process, as generally applied, fails to incorporate adequate transparency as a key feature of the derivation of the analysis. Further, once the analysis is completed, the process is not designed to be reinitiated and incorporate new information in the analysis.

As was mentioned earlier, another approach to evaluating likely change and the uncertainty associated with those predictions is risk analysis. This technique is widely used in evaluating the effect of diseases on animal (including aquatic animals) populations. It is explicit in its incorporation of transparency in that it places considerable emphasis on communication. It is also designed to work as part of a larger system that includes zoning areas for particular use and monitoring the status of those areas in relation to future use. The World Animal Health Organization has codified the process for its application to aquatic animal health (OIE 2003). That codification is now utilized by the World Trade Organization in adjudicating the restrictions in access to markets based on disease issues. The International Council for the Exploration of the Seas (ICES) is also examining the application of the technique for application to the evaluation of the environmental effects of mariculture (see ICES 2005).

Decision Support Systems

Man can consider the development of aquaculture in the coastal zone as part of the overall use of the coastal zone. Before man's intervention, a typical coastal bay consisted of various habitat types (different substrates) and biological communities superimposed on these habitats. As humans began to see value in some of the components of the bay's ecosystem, specific resources (fish, gravel) were utilized by various activities (fisheries, mining, recreation). Some of these activities generate plumes that geographically and temporally spread the influence of the activity over an area larger than the specific geo-temporal location of the core activity. As the level of activity or use increased, the number of overlaps between activities and plumes increased and hence, the interactions between activities, resources, and habitat/ecosystem components increased. Decision support is a term used to refer to the development of structured advice to stakeholders and decision makers concerned with the management of the resources.

Salmon aquaculture is one of the activities occurring in the bay. As the salmon aquaculture industry in the southwestern area of NB grew, the conflicts between the traditional users of the coastal marine areas, mainly the fishing industry, and the salmon aquaculture industry grew. In the late 1990s, this resulted in the NB Department of Agriculture, Fisheries and Aquaculture declaring some geographic areas as exclusion zones. In these areas, new aquaculture sites were not permitted. The NB Exclusion Zone Committee reviewed the boundaries and philosophy behind these exclusion areas. This committee consisted of representatives of the major commercial fisheries, the aquaculture industry, and ex-officio representatives of the provincial and federal governments. In 2001, the Bay of Fundy Stakeholders Forum was established to help improve information sharing and dialogue among the various interest groups with a stake in the southwestern NB area of the Bay of Fundy.

It was generally recognized that there was a need to go beyond information sharing and to begin a proactive planning process regarding the use of the SWNB portion of the Bay of Fundy. The Bay of Fundy Marine Resources Planning Process Initiative (BoFMRPP) therefore began in the spring of 2004. The geographic area being considered is the coastal area between Saint John on the east and the Canada-United States border on the west. The Initiative consists of two phases. Phase I is for stakeholders to develop a vision statement, develop a set of guiding principles, better define the geographic area to be considered, and define a planning process (or the steps to be taken) for the stakeholders to follow in working toward the development of the plan. Participants in Phase I include representatives of key resource stakeholders with knowledge of the area (fishing industry, eco-tourism industry, first nations, environmental non-governmental organizations), governments (federal, provincial) and a facilitator. Phase I is scheduled to be completed in the spring of 2005. If senior federal and provincial government officials accept the results of Phase I, then in Phase II, proposed planning process will be implemented and development of the plan will commence.

One process that is being developed to help support the Marine Resource Planning Process is that of a GIS based Decision Support System (Page et al. 2004). In essence, the system consists of a series of GIS maps or layers that contain information in the location of habitats, resources, activities, and infrastructure (Fig. 13). The overlaps between various maps are indicative of the interaction mechanisms between the various components. The degree and intensity of overlap are therefore calculated along with estimates of the biological, social, and economic consequences or significance, and these are used as input into decision support systems that evaluate the merits of different resource or habitat utilization scenarios.

Surveillance and Monitoring

To achieve sustainable resource use, specific parameters that reflect changes in the environmental conditions are tracked as part of the operation of an integrated resource management plan. Determining how, when, and what to measure is a complex task. Most governments are caught between achieving administrative fairness (often a legal requirement) and achieving the most cost effective management of society's resources. Administrative fairness in environmental regulation would have every user pay for the cost of using a managed resource in proportion to the user's level of use. In this context, the concept of "user pays" was developed and the shifting of the onus of proof for sustainable development to those using the resources (a component of the precautionary approach). In the real world, however, it is often difficult if not impossible to identify all ecosystem services and to account for how much each individual, firm, industry, or urban development uses those services.

In the end, some form of risk management approach is usually derived. For example, an unspoken but very common real operational assumption for controlling the risks associated with pollution is that if the environment in the immediate vicinity of discharge is not noticeably affected, then risks to the larger ecosystem are minimal. In aquaculture, this has been translated to controlling near-field effects of aquaculture as a way of controlling effects on the larger ecosystem (far-field effects). A growing body of evidence is amassing that suggests this may not be a good model. It, however, may be a pragmatic necessity, because when larger ecosystem effects are detectable, it often is difficult, if not impossible, to attribute the cause or even a quantifiable portion of the cause to individuals or firms.

Another approach to cost-effective regulation is to try to regulate only those activities that are large contributors to potential serious environmental change. Sometimes, this is referred to as smart regulation. This approach assumes that large contributors are the major drivers in causing environmental changes, but if not all contributors are known, or if there are a great number of small contributors, this logic may be faulty.

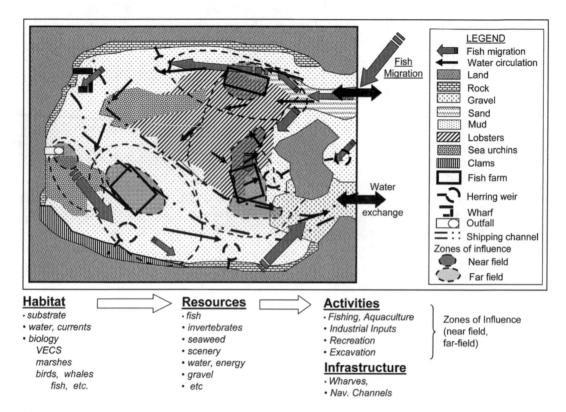

Habitat ⟹ **Resources** ⟹ **Activities**
- substrate
- water, currents
- biology
  VECS
  marshes
  birds, whales
    fish, etc.

- fish
- invertebrates
- seaweed
- scenery
- water, energy
- gravel
- etc

- Fishing, Aquaculture
- Industrial Inputs
- Recreation
- Excavation

Infrastructure
- Wharves,
- Nav. Channels

⎫
⎬ Zones of Influence
⎭ (near field,
      far-field)

Figure 13. Schematic showing a map of natural (habitat and resources) components of a typical coastal bay, superimposed by a range of human activities (activities and infrastructure).

Regulation should try to control environmental effects. Often, however, specific parameters are chosen for regulatory action without any proof or monitoring to demonstrate that those are parameters that represent the driving forces causing the changes you wish to avoid. A good example of this is trying to control the occurrence of harmful algal blooms by controlling human driven nitrogen fluxes. In some instances, nitrogen does control algal abundance, but sometimes in marine waters, algal abundance is light limited. Further, production of the toxins associated with the harmful effects is often the result of low abundance rather than an excess of a particular nutrient. In the end, good regulation should be linked to monitoring for the occurrence of an effect rather than a surrogate parameter.

Some regulators have prescribed the remediation technologies used to control effluent quality. This approach gives the illusion of good management practices. If, however, the effluent quality parameter chosen is in error, the whole approach is invalid. Further, even if the parameter chosen is appropriate, a prescriptive choice of mitigation technology precludes industry being able to find and use more cost-effective methods that they may find or invent.

Performance Based Standards

Performance Based Standards (PBS) is an alternate approach to environmental management. The PBS approach focuses on maintaining environmental quality while recognizing that commercial and environmental sustainability of aquaculture are closely related.

Performance based standards sets out discharge limit or environmental quality objectives for a site without dictating to industry how they conduct their business or how they should operate their industry to achieve the PBS. The current sediment quality definitions in the Environmental Management Guidelines (EMG) for salmon aquaculture that have been established by the NB Department of Environment and Local Government are performance-based standards. Performance based standards are a common component of many environmental management approaches. Other examples include the discharge limits specified for pulp mill effluents or the wastewater from base metal mines. Site-specific water quality objectives for a body of water are performance-based standards, as are sulphur dioxide emission limits from big industries like thermal power plants. The applicability of a PBS approach to salmon aquaculture has been questioned, because salmon farms are not clearly a defined point source discharge and cannot stop production immediately if limits are exceeded.

The goals for the PBS approach are:

- Maintenance of environmental quality with operational flexibility

- Application of a risk-based and science-supported environmental management and regulatory process

- Inter-government and government-industry cooperation

- Public Accountability

Literature Cited

AquaNet. 2005. Integrated aquaculture - an old recycling concept for renewed sustainability [in French]. AquaNet Administrative Centre, Memorial University of Newfoundland, St. John's, Newfoundland and Office of the Executive Scientific Director, AquaNet, University of British Columbia, West Vancouver, British Columbia, Canada. http://www.aquanet.ca/English/media/video/int_aqua_e.wmv and http://www.aquanet.ca/French/media/video/int_aqua_f.wmv.

Auditor General. 2004. New Brunswick Salmon Aquaculture. 2004 Report, Volume 1. Auditor General, Fredericton, New Brunswick, Canada. 68 pp.

Barret, G., M. Caniggia, and L Read. 2002. There are more vets than doctors in Chile; social and community impact of globalization of aquaculture in Chile. World Development 30(11): 1951-2002.

BCMCL (British Columbia Ministry of Crown Lands) and BCMSVI (British Columbia Ministry of State for Vancouver Island). 1989. Coastal resource interest study, finfish aquaculture opportunities: Nootka Sound-Tofino. 1989 pamphlet map. BC Ministry of Crown Lands and BC Ministry of State for Vancouver Island, Victoria, British Columbia, Canada. 2 pp.

Beveridge, M.C.L. 1987. Cage Aquaculture, 2nd edition. Fishing News Books, Farnham, UK. 352 pp.

Black, E. 2001. Aquaculture and integrated resource use. Bulletin of the Aquaculture Association of Canada 101(1): 29-35.

Bodvin, T., M. Indergaard, E. Norgaard, A. Jensen, and A. Skaar. 1996. Clean technology in aquaculture - a production without waste products? Hydrobiologia 326/327: 83-86.

Bridger, C.J. and B. Neal. 2004. Technical and economic considerations of exposed aquaculture site development in the Bay of Fundy. A report compiled and written for the New Brunswick Salmon Growers Association. New Brunswick Salmon Growers Association, L'Etang, New Brunswick, Canada.

Brugère, C. and N. Ridler. 2004. Global aquaculture outlook in the next decades: An analysis of national aquaculture production forecasts to 2030. FAO Fisheries Circular C1001. Food and Agriculture Organization of the United Nations, Rome, Italy. 55 pp.

Chapelle, A., A. Menesguen, J.M. Deslous Paoli, P. Souchu, N. Mazouni, N. Vaquer, and B. Millet. 2000. Modeling nitrogen, primary production and oxygen in a Mediterranean lagoon. Impact of oysters farming and inputs from the watershed. Ecological Modelling 127: 161-81.

Chopin, T. and S. Bastarache. 2004. Mariculture in Canada: Finfish, shellfish and seaweed. Journal of the World Aquaculture Society 35: 37-41.

Chopin, T. and R. Ugarte. In press. The seaweed resources of Eastern Canada. In A.T. Critchley and M. Ohno, editors. Seaweed Resources of the World, 2nd edition.

Chopin, T., A.H. Buschmann, C. Halling, M. Troell, N. Kautsky, A. Neori, G.P. Kraemer, J.A. Zertuche-Gonzalez, C. Yarish, and C. Neefus. 2001. Integrating seaweeds into marine aquaculture systems: A key toward sustainability. Journal of Phycology 37: 975-986.

Chopin, T., T. Gallant, and I. Davidson. 1995. Phosphorus and nitrogen nutrition in *Chondrus crispus* (Rhodophyta): Effects on total phosphorus and nitrogen content, carrageenan production, and photosynthetic pigments and metabolism. Journal of Phycology 31: 283-293.

Chopin, T., P.A. Marquis, and E.P. Belyea. 1996. Seasonal dynamics of phosphorus and nitrogen contents in the brown alga *Ascophyllum nodosum* (L.) Le Jolis, and its associated species *Polysiphonia lanosa* (L.) Tandy and *Pilayella littoralis* (L.) Kjellman, from the Bay of Fundy, Canada. Botanica Marina 39: 543-552.

Chopin, T., C. Yarish, R. Wilkes, E. Belyea, S. Lu, and A. Mathieson. 1999. Developing *Porphyra*/salmon integrated aquaculture for bioremediation and diversification of the aquaculture industry. Journal of Applied Phycology 11: 463-472.

Cross, S.F. and B.C. Kingsett. 1992. Biophysical criteria for shellfish culture in British Columbia: A site capability evaluation system. British Columbia Ministry of Agriculture Fisheries and Food, Victoria, British Columbia, Canada. 56 pp.

Corvello, V.T. and M.W. Merkhofer. 1993. Risk Assessment Methods: Approaches for Assessing Health and Environmental Risks. Plenum Press, New York, New York, USA. 318 pp.

Cromey, C.J., T. Nickell, and K.D. Black. 2002. DEPAMOD—modelling the deposition and biological effects of waste solids from marine cage farms. Aquaculture 214: 211-239.

Dortch, Q. 1990. The interaction between ammonium and nitrate uptake in phytoplankton. Marine Ecology Progress Series 61: 183-201.

Dowd, M. 2005. A bio-physical coastal ecosystem model for assessing environmental effects of marine bivalve aquaculture. Ecological Modelling 183: 323-346.

Dowd, M., F. Page, R. Losier, P. McCurdy, and G. Bugden. 2001. Physical oceanography of Tracadie Bay, PEI: Analysis of sea level, current, wind and drifter data. Canadian Technical Report of Fisheries and Aquatic Sciences/Rapport Technique Canadien des Sciences Halientiques et Aquatiques 2347: 80 pp.

Duarte, P., R. Meneses, A.J.S. Hawkins, M. Zhu, J. Fang, and J. Grant. 2003. Mathematical modelling to assess the carrying capacity for multi-species culture within coastal waters, Sorrento. I. Model development and implementation. Ecological Modelling 168: 109-143.

Duplisea, D.E. 1998. Feedbacks between benthic carbon mineralisation and community structure: A simulation-model analysis. Ecological Modelling 110: 19-43.

Environment Canada. 2003. National HYDAT CD-ROM (version 2003-2.04). National Water Data Archive. Environment Canada's Water Survey of Canada. http://www.wsc.ec.gc.ca/products/hydat/mani_e.cfm?ename=hydat_e.cfm.

FAO (Food and Agriculture Organization of the United Nations). 2002. Aquaculture production statistics 1988-2001. Food and Agriculture Organization of the United Nations, Rome, Italy. http://www.fao.org/fi/statist/FISOFT/FISHPLUS.asp.

Fletcher, R.L., V. Cuomo, and I. Palomba. 1990. The "green tide" problem, with particular reference to the Venice Lagoon. British Phycological Journal 25: 87.

Folke, C. and N. Kautsky. 1992. Aquaculture with its environment: Prospects for sustainability. Ocean and Coastal Management 17: 5-24.

Folke, C., P.A. Gillibrand, and N. Kautsky. 1989. The role of ecosystems for a sustainable development of aquaculture. Ambio 18: 234-243.

Folke, C., J. Grant, P. Cranford, B. Hargrave, M. Carreau, B. Schofield, S. Armsworthy, V. Burdett-Coutts, and N. Kautsky. 1991. Ecological economic principles for aquaculture development. Pages 207-222 in C.B. Cowey and C.Y. Cho, editors. Nutritional Strategies and Aquaculture Waste. University of Guelph Press, Guelph, Ontario, Canada.

Folke, C., N. Kautsky, M. Troell, A. Hatcher, J. Grant, and B. Schofield. 1994. The costs of eutrophication from salmon farming: Implications for policy. Journal of Environmental Management 40: 173-182.

Flynn, K.J. 1998. Estimation of kinetic parameters for the transport of nitrate and ammonium into marine phytoplankton. Marine Ecology Progress Series 169: 13-28.

Flynn, K.J., M.J.R. Fasham, and C.R. Hipkin. 1997. Modelling the interactions between ammonium and nitrate uptake in marine phytoplankton. Philosophical Transactions of Royal Society of London 352B: 1625-1645.

Flynn, K.J., S. Page, G. Wood, and C.R. Hipkin. 1999. Variations in the maximum transport rates for ammonium and nitrate in the prymnesiophyte *Emiliania huxleyi* and the rapidophyte *Hererosigma carterae*. Journal of Plankton Research 21: 355-371.

Gillibrand, P.A. and W.R. Turrell. 1997. The use of simple models in the regulation of the impacts of fish farms on water quality in Scottish sea lochs. Aquaculture 159: 33-46.

Grant J., P. Cranford, B. Hargrave, M. Carreau, B. Schofield, S. Armsworthy, V. Burdett-Coutts, D. Ibarra. 2005. A model of aquaculture biodeposition for multiple estuaries and field validation at blue mussel (*Mytilus edulis*) culture sites in eastern Canada. Canadian Journal of Fisheries and Aquatic Sciences/Journal Canadien des Sciences Halientiques et Aquatiques 62: 1271-85.

Guyondet, T., V.G. Koutitonsky, and S. Roy. 2005. Effects of water renewal estimates on the oyster aquaculture potential of an inshore area. Journal of Marine Systems 58: 35-51.

Harrison, W.G., L.R. Harris, and B.D. Irwin. 1996. The kinetics of nitrogen utilization in oceanic mixed layer: Nitrate and ammonium interactions at nanomolar concentrations. Limnology and Oceanography 41: 16-32.

Hatcher, A., J. Grant, and B. Schofield. 1994. Effects of suspended mussel culture *(Mytilus* spp.) on sedimentation, benthic respiration and sediment nutrient dynamics in a coastal bay. Marine Ecology Progress Series 115: 219-235.

ICES (International Council for the Exploration of the Seas). 2005. Report of the working group on environmental interactions of mariculture (WGEIM), 11-15 April 2005, Ottawa, Canada. Mariculture Committee, International Council for the Exploration of the Seas, Copenhagen, Denmark. http://www.ices.dk/reports/MCC/2005/WGEIM05.pdf.

Indergaard, M. and A. Jensen. 1983. Seaweed biomass production and fish farming. Pages 313-318 *in* A. Strub, P. Chartier, and G. Schleser, editors. Energy from Biomass. Proceedings of the Second European Commission Conference on Biomass. Berlin, Germany, 20-23 September 1982. Applied Science Publishers, London, UK.

Jamieson, G., R.O. O'Boyle, J. Arbour, D. Cobb, S. Courtenay, R. Gregory, C. Levings, J. Munro, I. Perry, and H. Vandermeulen. 2001. Proceedings of the National Workshop on Objectives and Indicators for Ecosystem-Based Management. Sidney, British Columbia, Canada, 21 February-2 March 2001. Canadian Science Advisory Secretariat Proceedings Series 2001/009. Fisheries and Oceans, Ottawa, Canada. 140 pp.

Katrandis, S., E.Nitsi, and A Vakrou. 2003. Social acceptability of aquaculture development in coastal areas; the case of two Greek islands. Coastal Management 31: 37-53.

Kautsky, N., H. Berg, A. Buschmann, C. Folke, and M. Troell. 1996a. Ecological footprint, resource use and limitations to aquaculture development (abstract). Page 193 *in* IX Congreso Latinoamericano de Acuicultura Book of Abstracts. Coquimbo, Chile, 15-18 October 1996. Asociación Latinoamericana de Acuicultura, Coquimbo, Chile.

Kautsky, N., M. Troell, and C. Folke. 1996b. Ecological engineering for increased production and environmental improvement in open sea aquaculture. Pages 387-394 *in* C. Etnier and B. Guterstam, editors. Ecological Engineering for Wastewater Treatment, 2nd edition. CRC Press, Boca Raton, Florida, USA.

Lee, J.H.W., F. Choi, and F. Arega. 2003. Environmental management of marine fish culture in Hong Kong. Marine Pollution Bulletin 47: 202-210.

Martin, W., K. Haya, K. MacKeigan, Nilsson, H.C., and T. Chopin. 2004. Is oxytetracycline used during the culture of salmon, *Salmo salar*, accumulated by mussels, *Mytilus edulis*, in a multi-trophic aquaculture system? In: Proceedings of AquaNet IV Meeting, Québec: 52.

MacIsaac, J.J. and R.C. Dugdale. 1969. The kinetics of nitrate and ammonia uptake by natural populations of marine phytoplankton. Deep-Sea Research 16: 47-57.

Merrill, J.E. 1996. Aquaculture methods for use in managing eutrophicated waters. Pages 115-128 *in* M. Schramm and P.H. Nienhuis, editors. Marine Benthic Vegetation-Recent Changes and the Effects of Eutrophication. Ecological studies 123. Springer Verlag, Berlin, Germany.

Morrison, M.A., S.F. Thrush, and R. Budd. 2001. Detection of acoustic class boundaries in soft sediment systems using the seafloor acoustic discrimination system QTC VIEW. Journal of Sea Research 46: 233-243.

Neori, A., T. Chopin, M. Troell, A.H. Buschmann, G.P. Kraemer, C. Halling, M. Shpigel, and C. Yarish. 2004. Integrated aquaculture: Rationale, evolution and state of the art emphasizing seaweed biofiltration in modern mariculture. Aquaculture 231: 361-391.

O'Boyle, R. and P. Keizer. 2003. Proceedings of three workshops to investigate the unpacking process in support of ecosystem – based management. Canadian Science Advisory Secretariat Proceedings Series 2003/004. Fisheries and Oceans, Ottawa, Canada. 31 pp.

OCAD (Office of the Commissioner for Aquaculture Development). 2001. Legislative and Regulatory Review of Aquaculture in Canada. Aqua KE Government Documents 2003: 10250110. Fisheries and Oceans Canada, Ottawa, Ontario, Canada. 77 pp. http://govdocs.aquake.org/cgi/reprint/2003/1025/10250110.pdf.

OIE (World Organisation for Animal Health). 2003. Aquatic Animal Health Code, 6th edition. World Organisation for Animal Health, Paris, France. 165 pp.

Page, F.H. and B.D. Chang, editors. 2002. Fish health and oceanography project of the aquaculture collaborative research and development program: Report of the initial meeting, 18 December 2001. Canadian Technical Report of Fisheries and Aquatic Sciences/Rapport Technique Canadien des Sciences Halientiques et Aquatiques 2409: vii, 47.

Page, F.H., R. Peterson, and D. Greenberg. 2002. Salmon aquaculture, dissolved oxygen and the coastal habitat: scaling arguments and simple models. Canadian Technical Report of Fisheries and Aquatic Sciences/Rapport Technique Canadien des Sciences Halientiques et Aquatiques 2411: 16-21.

Page, F.H., R.L. Stephenson, and B.D. Chang. 2004. A framework for addressing aquaculture-environment-fisheries interactions in the southwestern New Brunswick portion of the Bay of Fundy. Aquaculture Association of Canada Special Publication 8: 69-72.

Petrell, R.J., K. Mazahari Tabrizi, P.J. Harrison, and L.D. Druehl. 1993. Mathematical model of *Laminaria* production near a British Columbian salmon sea cage farm. Journal of Applied Phycology 5: 1-14.

Phillips, M.J., R. Clarke, and A. Mowat. 1993. Phosphorus leaching from Atlantic salmon diets. Aquacultural Engineering 12: 47-54.

Pillay, T.V.R. 2001. Aquaculture development: From Kyoto 1976 to Bangkok 2000. Keynote Address I. Pages 3-7 *in* R.P. Subasinge, P. Bueno, M.J. Phillips, C. Hough, S.E. McGladdery, and J. E. Arthur, editors. Aquaculture in the Third Millennium. Technical Proceedings of the Conference of Aquaculture in the Third Millennium. Bangkok, Thailand, 20-25 February 2000. Network of Aquaculture Centres in Asia-Pacific (NACA), Bangkok, Thailand and Food and Agriculture Organization of the United Nations (FAO), Rome, Italy.

Ricker, K.E. 1989a. Biophysical suitability of the Sunshine Coast and Johnson Strait/Desolation Sound areas for salmonid farming in net cages. British Columbia Ministry of Agriculture and Fisheries, Victoria, British Columbia, Canada. 98 pp.

Ricker, K.E. 1989b. Biophysical suitability of the Sunshine Coast and Johnson Strait/Desolation Sound areas for salmonid farming in net cages. Map Atlas (Appendix to the Main Report) British Columbia Ministry of Agriculture and Fisheries, Victoria, British Columbia, Canada. 65 pp.

Ridler, N., B. Robinson, T. Chopin, S. Robinson, and F. Page. In press. Development of integrated multitropic aquaculture in the Bay of Fundy, Canada: A socioeconomic case study. World Aquaculture.

Rönnberg, O., K. Ådjers, C. Ruokolahti, P. Strain, D.J. Wildish, and M. Bondestam. 1992. Effects of fish farming on growth, epiphytes, and nutrient content of *Fucus vesiculosus* L. in the Åland Archipelago, northern Baltic Sea. Aquatic Botany 42: 109-120.

Ryther, J.H., J.C. Goldman, J.E. Gifford, J.E. Huguenin, A.S. Wing, J.P. Clarner, L.D. Williams, and B.E. Lapointe. 1975. Physical models of integrated waste recycling-marine polyculture systems. Aquaculture 5: 163-177.

Sephton, D.H., K. Haya, J.L. Martin, M. Ringuette, T. Chopin, and I. Stewart. 2002. Seasonal dynamics of *Alexandrium fundyense* and *Pseudonitzschia pseudodelicatissima* and phycotoxin content in *Mytilus edulis* in an integrated aquaculture system (abstract). Page 80 *in* Proceedings of the AquaNet II Meeting. Moncton, New Brunswick, Canada, 14-17 September 2002. AquaNet, St. John's. Newfoundland, Canada.

Sephton, D.H., K. Haya, J.L. Martin, G.L. Boyer, and T. Chopin. 2003a. Monitoring of therapeutants and phycotoxins in kelp (*Laminaria saccharina*) and mussels (*Mytilus edulis*) cultured in proximity to salmon (*Salmo salar*) in an integrated system (abstract). Page 138 *in* K. Hedley, S. Roe, and A. J. Niimi, editors. Proceedings of the 30th Annual Aquatic Toxicity Workshop. Ottawa, Ontario, Canada. Canadian Technical Report of Fisheries and Aquatic Sciences/Rapport Technique Canadien des Sciences Halieutiques et Aquatiques 2510.

Sephton, D.H., K. Haya, J.L. Martin, G.L. Boyer, and T. Chopin. 2003b. Seasonal dynamics of *Alexandrium fundyense* and PSP toxins content in *Mytilus edulis* in an integrated aquaculture system (abstract). Page 53 *in* S.S. Bates, editor. Proceedings of the Eighth Canadian Workshop on Harmful Marine Algae. Moncton, Canada. Canadian Technical Report of Fisheries and Aquatic Sciences/Rapport Technique Canadien des Sciences Halieutiques et Aquatiques 2498.

Sephton, D., K. Haya, J.L. Martin, T. Chopin, I. Stewart, and G.L. Boyer. 2003c. Dynamics of PSP toxins content in *Mytilus edulis* in an integrated aquaculture system (abstract). Page 57 *in* Proceedings of AquaNet III Meeting. Vancouver, British Columbia, Canada, 25-28 October 2003. AquaNet, St. John's, Newfoundland, Canada.

Soto, D. 1996. Environmental impact and mitigation of the salmon culture activity in southern Chile (abstract). Page 194 *in* IX Congreso Latinoamericano de Acuicultura Book of Abstracts. Coquimbo, Chile, 15-18 October 1996. Asociación Latinoamericana de Acuicultura, Coquimbo, Chile.

Stigebrandt, A., J. Aure, A. Ervik, and P.K. Hansen. 2004. Regulating the local environmental impact of intensive marine fish farming. III. A model for estimation of the holding capacity in the Modelling-Ongrowing fish farm-Monitoring system. Aquaculture 234: 239-261.

Strain, P., D.J. Wildish, and P.A. Yeats. 1995. The application of simple models of nutrient loading and oxygen demand to the management of a marine tidal inlet. Marine Pollution Bulletin 30: 253-261.

Stewart, L. 2001. Salmon Aquaculture in New Brunswick: Natural development of our marine heritage. Prepared for the New Brunswick Salmon Growers' Association. Aquaculture Strategies, Inc., Rothesay, New Brunswick, Canada. 28 pp. http://www.salmonoftheamericas.com/new_brunswick.pdf.

Subandar, A., R.J. Petrell, and P.J. Harrison. 1993. *Laminaria* culture for reduction of dissolved inorganic nitrogen in salmon farm effluent. Journal of Applied Phycology 5: 455-463.

Trites, R.W. and C.J.R. Garrett. 1983. Physical Oceanography of the Quoddy Region. Pages 9-34 *in* M.L.H. Thomas, editor. Marine and Coastal Systems of the Quoddy Region, New Brunswick. Canadian Special Publication of Fisheries and Aquatic Sciences 64. Department of Fisheries and Oceans, Ottawa, Ontario, Canada. 306 pp.

Troell, M., C. Halling, A. Neori, T. Chopin, A.H. Buschmann, N. Kautsky, and C. Yarish. 2003. Integrated mariculture: Asking the right questions. Aquaculture 226: 69-90.

Waite L., J. Grant, and J. Davidson. 2005. Bay-scale spatial growth variation of mussels *Mytilus edulis* in suspended culture, Prince Edward Island, Canada. Marine Ecology Progress Series 297: 157-67.

Wallentinus, I. 1981. Phytobenthos. Pages 322-342 *in* T. Melvasalo, J. Pawlak, K. Grasshoff, L. Thorell, and A. Tsiban, editors. Assessment of the Effects of Pollution on the Natural Resources of the Baltic Sea, 1980. Baltic Sea Environment Proceedings No. 5B. Baltic Marine Environment Protection Commission-Helsinki Commission, Helsinki, Finland.

Appendix 2-1: Canadian Legislation Related to Aquaculture

For more details on the application of the legislation listed below, see "Legislative and Regulatory Review of Aquaculture in Canada" (Office of the Commissioner for Aquaculture Development 2001).

Federal Legislation

- Appropriation Acts
  - o   Atlantic Enterprise Loan Insurance Regulations Northern Ontario Loan Insurance Regulations
- Atlantic Canada Opportunities Agency Act
  - o   ACOA Loan Insurance Regulations
  - o   Action Loan Regulations
- Atlantic Fisheries Restructuring Act
- Canada Shipping Act
  - o   Boating Restriction Regulations
- Canadian Environmental Assessment Act
- Canadian Environmental Protection Act
- Canada Wildlife Act
  - o   Wildlife Area Regulations
- Coastal Fisheries Protection Act
  - o   Coastal Fisheries Protection Regulations
- Employment Equity Act
  - o   Employment Equity Regulations
- Excise Tax Act
  - o   Agriculture and Fishing Property (GSTIHST) Regulations
- Feeds Act
  - o   Feeds Regulations 0 Financial Administration Act 0 Fisheries Act
  - o   Aboriginal Communal Fishing Licenses Regulations Atlantic Fishery Regulations
- Financial Administration Act
- Fisheries Act
  - o   Aboriginal Fisheries Communal Fishing Regulations
  - o   Atlantic Fisheries Regulation
  - o   Fishery (General) Regulations
  - o   Fish Health Protection Regulations
  - o   Fish Toxicant Regulations
  - o   Management of Contaminated Fisheries Regulations
  - o   Marine Mammal Regulations
  - o   Maritime Provinces Fishery Regulations
  - o   Ontario Fishery Regulations
  - o   Pacific Fishery Regulations
  - o   Quebec Fishery Regulations

- Fisheries Development Act
- Fish Inspection Act
    o   Fish Inspection Regulations
- Food and Drugs Act
    o   Food and Drug Regulations
- Freshwater Fish Marketing Act
- Health of Animals Act
    o   Health of Animals Regulations
- Migratory Birds Convention Act
- Navigable Waters Protection Act
- Pest Control Products Act
    o   Pest Control Products Regulations
- Oceans Act

Provincial and Territorial Legislation and Regulations

British Columbia

- Aquaculture Regulation
- Aquaculture Waste Control Regulations
- Corporation Capital Tax Act
- Environmental Assessment Act
- Farm Practices Protection Act
- Fisheries Act
- Freedom of Information and Protection of Privacy Act
- Industrial Development Incentive Act
- Lands Act
- Municipal Act
- Small Business Venture Capital Act
- Social Service Tax Act
- Waste Management Act
- Wildlife Act
- Fish Inspection Act
- Water Act

Quebec

- Loi sur les pecheries et l' aquaculture commerciales (An Act Respecting Commercial Fisheries and Aquaculture)
- Loi sur la conservation et la mise en valeur de la faune
- Loi sur la qualite de l'environnement
- Loi sur les produits alimentaires
- Loi sur le regime des eaux
- Loi sur la transformation des produits marins

New Brunswick

- Aquaculture Act
  - o Aquaculture Regulations
- Fish and Wildlife Act
- Fish Inspection Act
- Fish Processing Act
- Fisheries Development Act
- Inshore Fisheries Representation Act 0 Clean Environment Act
- Pesticide Control Act

Prince Edward Island

- Environmental Protection Act
- Fish and Game Protection Act
- Fisheries Act
- Institute of Man and Resources Act
- Pesticides Control Act
- Fish Inspection Act

Nova Scotia

- Environment Act
- Executive Council Act
- Fisheries and Coastal Resources Act
  - o Aquaculture License and Lease Regulations
- Public Service Act
- Remembrance Day Act
- Pesticide Control Act
- Crown Lands Act
- Wildlife Act

Newfoundland

- Aquaculture Act
  - o Aquaculture Regulations
- Environment Act
- Lands Act
- Pesticides Control Act
- Historic Resources Act

3

CHINA

Executive Summary

As a major producer of aquatic products, the People's Republic of China (China) contributes more than 70% of world mariculture yields, which includes diverse species of finfish, bivalves, crustaceans, and macroalgae. Consumers' preference for mariculture products and the decreasing capture fisheries yield has driven more investment into the cultivation sector. It is a government policy to increase the production of aquaculture to increase both the amount and the diversity of food in the marketplace. Following the fast development of aquaculture in the 1980s, the uncontrolled expansion of the scale of cultivation, along with management of coastal zones by discrete competitive authorities, resulted in damage to marine resources and degradation of environmental quality in some areas, such as Yueqing Bay in Zhejiang Province. With the development of China's economy, however, and improved public awareness of the importance of protecting the environment, considerable progress has been made in management of its coastal zones. The establishment of integrated coastal zone management regimes and the execution of relevant governmental policies will guarantee the sustainable development of aquaculture in the future.

Introduction

Aquaculture and Fishery Sectors

Aquaculture in China has always been a way of fighting food shortages. China, a highly populated country whose economy used to rely largely on agricultural outputs, has a 2,000-year history of aquaculture. The earliest cultivated species were freshwater fish. Mariculture was initiated in the 1950s. Kelp (*Laminaria japonica*) and laver (*Porphyra* yezoensis) were the first marine species studied scientifically, and breakthroughs in cultivation techniques boosted their production in the 1950s and 1960s. In the 1970s, spat collection and long-line farming techniques enhanced the production of mussels. Shrimp farming in ponds prevailed in the 1980s. In the early 1990s, the spread of shrimp viral diseases, which resulted in a sharp decline in shrimp production, was accompanied by an increase in the number of land-based fish farms in Shandong Province, northern China, and unprecedented development of net-cage finfish culture in southern China.

The majority of mariculture activity occurs in the provinces of Liaoning, Hebei, Shandong, Jiangsu, Zhejiang, Fujian, Guangdong, and Hainan. Scallop, sea cucumber, and kelp farms are primarily located in northern China, but most fish, laver, and all *Gracilaria* sp. farms are located in southern China. The cultivation of shrimps and bivalves is well developed all along the 18,000 km coastline of China, where mariculture activities are vigorously carried out, from the tidal zone up to 48.5 km (30 miles) offshore.

Contributors: Wang, Q., H. Liu, Z. Zhang, and J. Fang
In J.P. McVey, C.-S. Lee, and P.J. O'Bryen, editors. Aquaculture and Ecosystems: An Integrated Coastal and Ocean Management Approach. The World Aquaculture Society, Baton Rouge, Louisiana, United States.

In addition to introduced species such as bay scallop (*Argopecten irradians* Lamarck) and turbot (*Scophthalmus maximus*), most of the local marine species under cultivation are those suffering from declining or depleted stocks within China. Some cultivated species are now rarely found in their natural habitats. Cultivated species encompass nearly 100 major economically valuable marine animals and seaweeds, such as raft-culture of *L. japonica*, *Undaria pinnatifida*, *Porphyra* spp., scallops, oysters, and mussels; cage-culture of marine fish species; pond-culture of shrimp, fish, crabs, and molluscs; on-bottom culture of clams and oysters; and land-based intensive fish-farming of olive flounder (*Paralichthys olivaceus*) and turbot (Table 1). Production methods are either mono-species cultivation or polyculture.

Table 1. Major mariculture species and their production in China in 2003.

Species	Production (MT)
Finfish	
Japanese sea bass (*Lateolabrax japonicus* [Cuvier et Valenciennes])	78,346
Yellow croaker (*Pseudosciaena crocea* and *P. polyactis*)	58,684
Red drum (*Sciaenops ocellatus*)	44,925
Sea bream (*Pagrosomus major* and *Sparus macrocephalus*)	42,276
Flatfish (mainly turbot *Scophthalmus maximus* and olive flounder *Paralichthys olivaceus*)	36,227
Crustaceans	
Pacific white shrimp (*Litopenaeus vannamei*)	308,947
Chinese shrimp (*Fenneropenaeus chinensis*)	61,685
Black tiger shrimp (*Penaeus monodon*)	51,086
Kuruma prawn (*Marsupenaeus japonicus*)	42,400
Mud crab (*Scylla serrata*)	100,870
Swimming crab (*Portunus trituberculatus* [Miers])	56,222
Molluscs	
Oysters (mainly *Crassostrea gigas* and *C. ariakensis*; small production of *C. plicatula* [Gmelin])	3,668,237
Clams (incl. Manila clam *Ruditapes phillipinarum*, Chinese clam *Mactra chinensis*, *Meretrix meretrix* Linnaeus, *Cyclina sinensis* [Gmelin])	2,546,133
Scallops (Bay scallop *Argopecten irradians* Lamarck, *Chlamys farrei*, Japanese scallop *Patinopecten yessoensis*, and *C.* [Mimachlamys] *nobilis* [Reeve])	897,956
Mussels (Blue mussel *Mytilus edulis*, Green mussel *Perna viridis*, Thick shell mussel *M. coruscus*)	683,237
Razor clam (mainly *Sinonovacula constricta* Lamarck and *Solen canaliculatus*)	672,402
Macroalgae	
Kelp (*Laminaria japonica*)	818,768
Undaria (*Undaria pinnatifida*)	172,613
Laver (*Porphyra yezoensis* and *P. haitanensis*)	72,753
Gracilaria (*Gracilaria gigas* Harvey)	50,536

In the past 50 years, aquaculture has made tremendous progress as science and technology have improved in China. The rapid development of aquaculture in the 1990s was an achievement made possible by the restructuring of the fishery industry, following the national policy of economic reform and opening up trade to the outside world. The development of aquaculture has brought about a flourishing of related industries, including artificial feed, processing, transportation, and trade. It is estimated that several million people are involved in aquaculture and its related industries in the coastal provinces, and aquaculture has contributed tremendously to the local economic and social development. To some extent, mariculture provides not only high-value food for people but also more employment opportunities for rural laborers, as well as benefits to the country as a whole, both economically and ecologically. The dream of "ranching the sea and farming of fish" is becoming a reality.

Production and Goals

As marine fishery resources in China's seas have been declining sharply during the past two to three decades, the domestic demand for mariculture products has been increasing. The rapid development of a mariculture industry, which increased about 8%-10% annually, has become a trend that is likely to continue into the future. Wave-resistant net-cages and intensive indoor mariculture are developing rapidly, and cultivation of high value species is a fast-growing sector of China's aquaculture industry. Recreational fisheries and ornamental fisheries have also attracted increased attention.

In 1990, total mariculture production in China was 1.62 million metric tons (MT). By 2003, the contribution of mariculture production to the total 47.1 million MT of fishery production was 12.5 million MT (Table 2). While most of the fishery products were consumed domestically, the total export volume of aquatic products in 2003 was about 2.1 million MT, with a value of $5.49 billion. With a favorable trade balance of around $3 billion, the export of aquatic products is greater than all other major agricultural products of China.

Table 2. Marine fisheries production in China in 2003.

Sector	Production (MT)
Marine fishery products	26,856,182
Marine catch	14,323,121
Mariculture	12,533,061
Finfish	519, 157
Crustaceans	661,174
Molluscs	9,853,207
Macroalgae	1,383,790
Others	115,733

According to a 2004 report by the Food and Agriculture Organization of the United Nations (FAO 2004), world aquaculture production is expected to increase to 69.5 million MT by 2020. If the growth of Chinese aquaculture continues at its present rate (about 3.5% per year), this increase will largely be met by production in China. Other developing countries, such as India, Chile, and Thailand, have also seen rapidly increasing domestic aquaculture production. Competition for world fish markets is expected to be keen. The future expansion of the aquaculture industry in China will rely on its economic viability, which results largely from technological improvements and sensible management strategies.

Regulatory System

Legislation

Considerable progress has been made in recent years in Chinese fisheries legislation and resource protection. In 2003, the Chinese State Council enacted the "Fishing Boat Inspection Ordinance," and the Ministry of Agriculture (MOA) enacted the "Ocean Fishery Management Provision" and the "Aquaculture Quality and Safety Management Provision." The People's Congress or local government at the provincial level enacted more than 10 fishery statutes. These statutes deal with the establishment of permit procedures for aquaculture and fishing, fishing boat management, and food safety. This legislation will enhance the enforcement of relevant laws and consistent management of the industry. Conservation of resources has been strengthened, and restricted fishing during the summer has been implemented. Regional resources have been improved through projects such as the Jellyfish Management Project in Bohai Sea and the construction of artificial reefs in southern provinces.

Additional details about environmental, fishery, and aquaculture legislation and regulations impacting coastal management in China are given in the Appendix at the end of this chapter.

Management

Before the concept of integrated coastal zone management (ICZM) was introduced into China, the coastal zone and the seas were under the management of different ministries or administrators with greatly varied interests, including agriculture, transportation, the petroleum industry, salt mining, and tourism. These authorities concentrated on managing and exploiting single marine resources, and usually benefited from the products. In 1988, the Chinese central government granted full rights of ICZM to the State Ocean Administration (SOA), which henceforth became the coordinator among these authorities. Since that time, ICZM has become widely recognized, and local ICZM branches have been set up as subordinates of SOA.

The Fishery Bureau of the Ministry of Agriculture (MOA) is responsible for the management of the fishery industry and mariculture sector in China at the national level. Its major task is to draft and carry out regulations and plans for the proper development of fishery resources and the aquatic environment and management of aquatic wildlife. It is authorized by the State Council to oversee fisheries administration and to inspect fishing harbors and fishing boats, to manage fishing boats, seamen, fishery licenses and telecommunications, and to coordinate the resolution of major foreign-related fishery crises.

At the province level or below, however, the Ocean Administration and Fishery Bureau are usually combined as one agency with the authority to issue aquaculture permits. Both state and local statutes should be applied appropriately for the issuance of the permit. These statutes include the Chinese Fishery Law (Item 11, Chapter 2), the Number (2002) 5 document enacted by MOA, as well as provincial and municipal regulations. Fishery Bureaus also issue aquaculture permits for larval rearing, but by applying a different set of statutes. Thus, it becomes complicated when different local regulations apply in different areas.

Sites for aquaculture are selected on the basis of water quality at a given location. According to fishery statutes, all aquaculture activities should be carried out in waters that meet at least second level Water Quality Standards. In addition, Regulations for Harvesting Area Classification have been drafted.

Supporting system

In the past two decades, China has invested large sums to establish the infrastructure for its fisheries industry. In 2003, national investment in the fisheries industry was at a record high of more than 1.2 billion China Yuan Renminbi (CNY)[1]. This included the projects underwritten by the National Debt Program, proposed capital construction, special financial outlays, and integrated agricultural development. A number of state invested key infrastructures and law-enforcing organizations are now in operation. Local governments have also increased their fisheries investments, which have been used to restructure fisheries industries, construct central fishing harbors, create eugenic breeding systems, manage fisheries environmental conservation projects, launch aquatic epidemic prevention systems, renovate equipment, and modernize law-enforcement equipment of the fisheries administration. All these have contributed to the improvement and modernization of the fisheries industry in China.

Major Challenges of the Fisheries Industry

The Chinese fisheries industry is faced with a number of major challenges. First, serious contradictions persist at different levels of the industry. For instance, fishing effort remains too high, while pollution of waters and exploitation of natural resources has not been kept within limits. Illegal building of fishing boats continues in some places, although the state has enacted fishing-boat reduction and vocation alteration policies. Second, the concept, "quantity is more important than quality," is common, and the safety of fishery products is a major problem. Production, processing, and management need to be further improved so as to meet domestic and international standards for safe, high-quality seafood. Third, the outlook for the development of bilateral fishery agreements and increased operational security is not

---

[1] Approximately $149,950,000 at rates effective in May 2006.

optimistic. In 2003, there were more than 200 disputes involving bilateral fisheries, and more than 400 fishery shipwrecks that resulted in huge losses. Fourth, excessive taxes are imposed on fishermen in some locations, and their legal rights and interests are not protected.

Specific Working Scenario: Yueqing Bay

Description

Yueqing Bay is an important bay in Zhejiang Province of eastern China, known for its four major resources: fisheries species, coastal areas, harbors, and tidal energy. The area is renowned as a base for the large-scale cultivation of three dredged mollusc species (razor clam, oyster, and mud clam). Currently, there is fierce conflict over the future development of Yueqing Bay, including proposed construction of harbors, reclaiming of land in the inter-tidal zone, and mariculture development of the inshore area (Zhang 2000).

Yueqing Bay is a semi-enclosed gourd-shaped bay, situated geologically between lat 27°59'09" - 28°4'16" N and long 120°57'55" - 121°17'09" E, at the mouth of the Oujiang River. The bay has a maximum length of 42 km and an average width of 10 km, with a total surface area of 463.6 km². Yueqing Bay has a 184.4 km coastline. Fine sand and clay constitute more than 95% of the bottom substrate throughout the bay. Generally, the bay is sheltered, with less than optimim water exchange, and an anoxic or weakly anoxic bottom environment.

According to the general partition of Chinese natural geographic districts (1985), Yueqing Bay is in the sub-tropical zone, with a mild and rainy oceanic climate. The annual temperature averages 17.7 C and fluctuates between 7.4 and 27.9 C. The average annual humidity is 81%, with an annual precipitation of 1,557.3 mm. The average wind speed is 2.5 m sec⁻¹, with northwest winds prevailing in the winter, and southeast winds prevailing in the summer. Typhoon season is from July to September; typically, two to three typhoons severely affect this area per year. Tidal energy plays a major role in the sedimentation process of Yueqing Bay. The maximum current velocity driven by tide is 1.25 - 1.43 m sec⁻¹. Because there are no remarkable riverine inputs into the bay, the salinity and temperature of the water are largely influenced by the oceanic water.

Biodiversity

According to marine resource investigations by local authorities, Yueqing Bay was rich in biodiveristy in the late 1990s.

Vegetation specific to the coastal areas and which constitutes the pioneer vegetation species of barren coastal lands is found in the saline soil system of the bay. Plants in this category include *Scirpus marigueter*, *Suaeda australis*, *Suaeda salsa*, and *Saliconia herbacea*. Major plant species in the marshland system of the bay, encompassing the intertidal and upper-tidal lowland areas, include *Phragmites australis*, *Spartina anglica*, *Spartina altermflora*, *Carex scabrifolia*, and *Sporobolus virginicus*. *Phragmites australis* is the most widely spreading species. Although *S. anglica* and *S. altermflora* are planted colonies, they are also major species. *Potamogeton crispu* and *Ruppia rostellta* are the major floral species of the simple aquatic systems found in channels and ponds of Yueqing Bay.

The benthic animal community consists of more than 200 species. Dominant species include polychaete worms, conches, snails, razor clams, shrimp, swimming crabs, and demersal fish. The average annual biomass production of benthic animals is 3.92 g m^{-3}, and the average density is 34.1 individuals m^{-3}. There are 58 mollusc species in the bay. Twenty species are of economic importance, such as razor clams, oysters, mud clams, and the black clam *Cyclina sinensis* (Gmelin). About 40,000 kg of razor clam seeds are produced in the bay, constituting 80% of the total production in Zhejiang Province.

More than 100 species of zooplankton have been found in Yueqing Bay; 55 are feed species. The total biomass of zooplankton is 285 mg m^{-3}. Copepods and *Chaetognatha* spp. are the dominant species; planktonic larvae of finfish and shellfish are also major components of the community. *Calanus* sp. is the major species in the zooplankton community of the bay.

Larger aquatic animals include 190 identified finfish species that belong to 15 Orders, 74 Families, and 131 Genera. These fish may be categorized as migratory fish (diadromous and anadromous species), island and reef fish, inshore fish, and estuary fish. Among them are 106 economically important fish species, such as Japanese sea bass *Lateolabrax japonicus*, and mullet *Mugil cephalus*. There are also 60 Crustacean species, such as *Palaemon carincauda*, Kuruma prawn *Penaeus japonicus* Bate, and the mud crab *Scylla serrata*.

Status of Development and Ecological Problems

Natural resources developed in the bay include various types of agriculture, salt mines, fisheries, harbors, and energy. The area has become established as the production center for oranges, marine finfish, razor clams, oysters, mud clams, mud snails, and laver. In 1997, it produced 1,151,000 MT of mariculture products, 192,000 MT of agriculture crops, and 69,000 MT of fruit. Three of the eight tidal power stations in China are situated in Yueqing Bay, including the largest one in China, which was put into operation in 1980. There are 31 docks in the bay, some of which are national level freight and passenger transport docks. Obviously, the development of these resources plays an important part in the economic growth of the region.

Resource development and utilization have brought about a number of serious ecological problems in Yueqing Bay:

- Stone quarries on the islands and the construction of dams, ponds, and harbors on the coast have changed the coastline, which has resulted in the loss of components of ecological structure, and the deterioration of ecological/environmental function.

- Changes of ecological structure components can impose long-term negative impacts on the bay. Over-fishing severely devastated natural fish resources; terrestrial pollutant runoffs and aquaculture pollutants added to the nutrient enrichment and degraded the water quality; and large-scale terrestrial transformation of the tidal-zone resulted in a decrease of the volume of water in the bay and reduced its capacity for receiving tidal water. In addition, altering the hydraulic factors also affected the rate of water exchange, which reduced pollutant dispersion and the assimilative capacity of the bay.

- The disruption of ecological functions resulted in low efficiency of resource deployment. In the future, this may also result in disastrous environmental destruction, which is not yet predictable. Driven by the attractive benefits of mariculture operations in recent years, a large portion of the tidal zone was converted to shallow ponds, and indigenous biota was extirpated. Overexploitation of the tidal zone for mariculture thus destroyed the habitat of indigenous organisms and reduced biodiversity. It may eventually result in the extinction of some species. Furthermore, there was no holistic management regime set up for the development of the coast and inshore waters. This factor, coupled with the limitations of technology, could likely result in unbalanced development of these areas.

Challenges

Ecological Impacts

Impacts of aquaculture on the ecological environment have drawn increasing attention from researchers and the government. China has already implemented a number of national research projects to study patterns of aquaculture and their ecological consequences, and standard methods have been applied in the analysis of dissolved nutrients, chlorophyll concentration, dissolved oxygen in the water column, nutrient accumulation in the sediments, species diversity, and density and biomass of epifaunal and infaunal benthos. Physical parameters, such as current velocity and water temperature, have also been measured in these studies. Long-term observation is extremely important for revealing interactions between aquaculture and the environment. This area of research needs to be highlighted in future studies.

It is generally agreed that fed aquaculture is an important source of water pollution. Water quality differs greatly in areas where fed aquaculture is practiced. There is evidence that algal blooms occur more often near aquaculture facilities. In some southern China waters (e.g., Dapeng Bay) where large numbers of aquaculture facilities are located, concentrations of inorganic phosphorus and inorganic nitrogen were two and three times greater, respectively, than that of natural seawater.

Currently, feed conversion rates for finfish cultivated and shrimp in China are normally 1: 1.5-3, indicating that about 33%-66% of feed is dissolved in the waters as waste. In recent years, the annual mariculture production of finfish and crustaceans in China has been more than 1 million MT, which demands about 3 million MT of feed. Presumably about half of this feed dissolves in the water or settles to the bottom. This alone would have had a huge impact on the coastal environment. Improved formulations for artificial feed is one way to decrease the feed conversion rate, yet the rising price of the major ingredients (i.e., fish meal and fish oil) is an obstacle to any foreseeable improvement.

Intensive aquaculture is another important source of marine pollution and recirculation systems are a might be an effective solution to this problem. Before seaweeds were used to control dissolved nutrients such as nitrate, however, recirculation systems were hardly ever self-sustaining, and most intensive operations still relied on continuous water exchange. Several researchers have proposed expanding the cultivation of edible seaweeds as a feasible bioremediation method for polluted seawaters. Additionally, suspension-feeding bivalves are another group of environmentally friendly animals that can control the growth of phytoplankton, thereby reducing the impact of algal blooms.

Nevertheless, "Efforts in excess are no better than in deficiency," as it was said by an old Chinese philosopher. Large-scale cultivation of seaweeds and bivalves could also pose environmental threats if not properly controlled at a level below the carrying capacity of the waters. For example, in Sanggou Bay, in northeastern China, raft culture of seaweeds and bivalves has added to the water confinement of the area, reduced current speed, increased organic sedimentation, and exacerbated the deterioration of water quality (Liu et al. 2004). Thus, the major problem for aquaculture in China is that the rationale for issuing an aquaculture permit does not include a risk assessment of possible ecological impacts.

User Conflicts

In China, the coastal zone extends 10 km terrestrially from the coastline, and 15 km from the coastline into the sea. Besides this geological definition, the coastal zone also contains particular social and economic characteristics. The natural physiognomy of the coastal zone includes beaches, wetlands, estuaries, lagoons, coral reefs, rocky seashores, and sand dunes, while the manmade elements include harbors, fishery and aquaculture facilities, factories, mines, recreational sites, historic sites, and residential areas. The coastal zone in China, as in most countries, is also the most populated area. There are more than 40 cities or towns situated on the coastline, and the highest density of cities in China is near large cosmopolitan areas such as Shanghai and Tianjin, with about 1.5 towns per km^2. The coastal zone in China is actually the center of industry and business enterprises, and the total revenue of agriculture and industry in this area contributes 60% of China's gross national product (Yao 2003).

Obviously, the coastal zone plays a most important role in economic and social development. Due to the rapid development of industry and population expansion in the coastal zone, however, a number of serious problems also have a negative impact on this region. For example, overexploitation of natural resources and abuse of ecological function greatly reduced the ability of the environment to self-remediate, and reduced or limited resources often led to more fierce competition between different interest groups. Fishery resources and vegetation are usually exploited unsustainably, and degeneration of the ecosystem is often driven to an irreversible situation. Meanwhile, marine biodiversity decreases comsiderably during this process.

ICZM and Obstacles to its Implementation

Integrated coastal zone management is a positive approach to solving environmental problems, and aquaculture management is an integral part of ICZM in China. The allocation of coastal areas for aquaculture is a key function of local town and village administration. When conflicts arise, either within the industry or with other industries, mediation and reconciliation are the responsibility of local administrators. For example, there have been reports of mass mortality of aquaculture animals as a consequence of severe industrial pollution. Environmental protection authorities, fisheries authorities, and people at different levels of the local government usually participate in settling these types of issues. The judiciary is also involved if a lawsuit is filed. This, however, is an illustration of reversed ICZM. Integrated coastal zone management should be practiced in such a way that coastal resources are rationed reasonably to avoid major potential conflicts.

Integrated coastal zone management should be comprehensive as well as effective. To meet this demand, all of the information input and supervision components must be quantified, and be consistent with each other. In aquaculture, for example, the amount of data needed on environmental monitoring, production-related parameters, expense and profit balances, etc., makes it nearly impossible to draw an overall evaluation without quantifying and modeling. This is particularly evident when trying to compare the results of one management approach with another.

Integrating aquaculture into a system of ICZM also involves managing the industry under a more general framework. It is of utmost importance to evaluate the role of aquaculture, its positive and negative influences upon all other components, and on the ecosystem as a whole. In one sense, the aquaculture sector should be self-sustaining, by operating within the carrying capacity of respective regions, and be harmonized with other businesses.

If properly managed, aquaculture may contribute to environmental protection. For example, suspension feeding bivalves and seaweeds, in addition to extracting dissolved nitrogen and phosphorous from seawater, can utilize large amounts of oceanic carbon. Based on annual production data and on the carbon content of both bivalves and seaweeds and their energy budget, it was estimated that about 1.2 million MT of carbon were removed from the China seas through the harvesting of bivalves and seaweeds in 2002 (Zhang et al. 2005).

Integrated coastal zone management is difficult to implement in China, where most of the coastal zone is already exploited, or overexploited, and there is no clear division of authority over inshore and offshore waters between the various government agencies and interest groups. User conflicts among these groups have proved obstructive to ICZM. All user groups (aquaculture being a major user) tend to cling to their gained benefits, and hinder the implementation of any new management regime, even though it could bring them future recompense. To accept the concept of ICZM is to acknowledge that marine resources are not limitless. Integrated coastal zone management is, to some extent, a way of guaranteeing the rational sharing of resources by all parties and providing maximum benefits to the community. It is consistent with sustainable economic development, and is an effective way of realizing sustainability. Coordination and cooperation among these coastal zone-related authorities and interest groups should be promoted. Government support and the redistribution of administrative power are indispensable to successful ICZM (Cai 1999). There is always a chance for a bright future if we strive for improvement.

Next Steps

Suggested Problem-Solving Ideas

Increasingly intensive production may give rise to an ever-increasing number of problems for China's aquaculture industry. Issues including the availability of seeds, environmental pollution, diseases, and low productivity are acknowledged impediments to the sustainable development of aquaculture. Shortage of seeds seems to be a natural outcome of enhanced production, and indicates for the need of improved technology. On the other hand, environmental pollution, frequent disease outbreaks, and poor efficiency jointly drive a vicious cycle. Environmental protection and remediation are the most effective, if not the only, ways to resolve these problems.

Environmental monitoring plays a key role in aquaculture management. Both long-term and short-term monitoring are helpful in identifying the impact of aquaculture on the environment and forming the basis for decision-making.

Policymaking and enforcement are also important to guarantee the sustainable development of the industry. The uncontrolled development of aquaculture is sometimes the result of a lack of guidelines, but more often, it is due to ineffective law enforcement. China has taken steps to improve aquaculture legislation, by drafting Standards for Harvesting Area Classifications and introducing European Union or United States management regimes. With the continued hard work and diligence of researchers and lawmakers, it is predictable that aquaculture management in China will reach a high standard in the near future.

Improved technology is vital for pollution control and for sustainable development of aquaculture. Studies on carrying capacity, environmental remediation, and polyculture (or integrated aquaculture) techniques have all contributed to enhanced productivity, as well as an improved environment. Seaweeds that extract excessive inorganic nitrogen and phosphorous from the open ocean could be planted to effectively alleviate pollution of intensive fish farms. The inoculation of environmentally friendly microorganisms into shrimp-farming systems may reduce chemical oxygen demand in the water, while posing no harm to the cultivated animals (Li et al. 2001). Other factors that support sustainable aquaculture include the establishment of easily accessible information systems and public awareness of the importance of a harmonized development of the economy, taking the social, cultural, and environmental aspects into consideration.

Application of Ecosystem-Based Management

Ecosystem-based management is a way to generally administer a given region. It encompasses the reasonable utilization of all natural resources while minimizing and preventing damage to the ecological environment caused by natural environmental changes or human activities. This may help illustrate the complexity of ecosystem-based management, because management regimes may differ for different locations. It is recommended that the following approaches be taken to effectively implement ecosystem-based management in China:

- Fortify law enforcement for coastal zone management. China has drafted and issued a series of fishery laws and/or regulations in recent years that cover all aspects of aquaculture activity, from cultivation and harvesting area classification, through processing, to the end products. The Chinese government has increased its efforts regarding the management of aquatic food safety. With complete implementation of these laws and regulations, it is foreseeable that coastal zone management in China will become increasingly integrated and successful.

- Educate and train law enforcement teams and the work force of various industries. If the people who interact directly with the marine environment do not fully understand the importance of protecting its environment, it will be difficult to put the theory of ICZM into practice. Everyone should realize that a polluted and damaged environment would eventually fail to support profitable production, and that protecting the environment equals protecting the industry.

- Divide marine areas, especially the coastal zone, according to their functions. Functional division is the foundation of ICZM, because it is the rational use of land and water resources, sensible development of marine resources, and sustainable protection of the marine environment. The most recent functional division of marine areas in China was done in 1989-1991. In the near future, the government is expected to increase both funding and manpower for fundamental research and division of its marine areas according to their natural functions. International cooperation in this area is also necessary to ensure its success.

- Develop aquaculture technology and optimize aquaculture practices. Advocate an ethic of Healthy Aquaculture, which includes the deployment of rational, scientific, and advanced cultivation facilities, seed production techniques, methods for waste treatment, feed quality assurance, the controlled use of medicine, and management of cultivation. Healthy aquaculture is the way to produce large quantities of high quality and safe aquatic products without polluting the environment. It is also the way to produce such integrated benefits as a strong economy and a healthy society and environment, so that a steady and sustainable development of the industry can be realized.

Literature Cited

Cai, C.Y. 1999. Aquaculture and integrated coastal zone management [in Chinese]. Marine Development and Management 16(2): 21-24.

FAO (Food and Agriculture Organization of the United Nations). 2004. The State of World Fisheries and Aquaculture. Part 3. Highlights of Special FAO Studies. Fisheries Department, FAO, Rome, Italy. http://www.fao.org/documents/.

Li, Q., K. Qu, F. Xin, and Y. Yuan. 2001. Isolation and selection of functional bacteria for bioremediation of shrimp culture environment. Chinese Journal of Applied and Environmental Biology 7(3): 281-285.

Liu, H., J. Fang, J. Zhu, S. Dong, F. Wang, X. Liang, J. Zhang, Y. Lian, L. Wang, and W. Jiang. 2004. Study on limiting nutrients and phytoplankton at long-line-culture areas in Laizhou Bay and Sanggou Bay, northeastern China. Aquatic Conservation: Marine and Freshwater Ecosystems 14(6): 551-574.

Yao, L.N. 2003. Coastal zone management and sustainable development in China. Journal of Harbin Institute of Technology: Social Science 3: 98-101.

You, J.S. 1996. Preliminary discussions on the construction of administration regime for integrated marine and coastal zone management in China. Marine Information 7: 1-2.

Zhang, J.H., J.G. Fang, and Q.S. Tang. 2005. The contribution of shellfish and macroalgae mariculture in China to the carbon cycle of coastal ecosystem [in Chinese, with English abstract]. Advances in Earth Science 20(3): 359-365.

Zhang, L.J. 2000. The resource environmental characteristics and neighbouring coastal zone management of Yueqing Bay, Zhejiang, China. Resource Science 22(6): 57-61.

Appendix 3-1: Environmental, Fishery and Aquaculture Laws and Regulations Impacting Coastal Management in China

The umbrella regulation for coastal management in China is the Chinese Sea Area Employment Supervision Act, which was authorized by the National People's Congress, and was put into effect on January 1, 2002. Under this statute, the coastal areas of China seas belong to the State, and any individual or organization must obtain in advance a legal lease to employ the area. The Act also stipulates the functional division regime for the coastal areas as well as the establishment of a monitoring scheme and an information system. Related legislation, Measures on the Supervision of Marine Area Employment License, was also put into effect in 2002.

The State Oceanic Administration (SOA) is the competent state authority for marine affairs, and manages the employment of national marine areas. Under the China Regulations for Environmental Protection Management of Marine Oil Exploration (1983), for instance, the SOA and its local agencies, as the competent authority, have the right to lease sites for oil exploration and development. The lease application requires that an environmental impact report be prepared together with the overall development plan for the project. Marine administrative branches at the county-level and local marine and fisheries bureaus are authorized to manage the neighboring marine areas.

In accordance with the Chinese Fisheries Act (revised in 2000), the competent state authority for fisheries management supervises the marine fishery industry. Under the Chinese Act for Traffic Safety on the Sea of 1983, the Maritime Affairs Administration supervises traffic safety at sea. The General Administration of Quality Supervision, Inspection and Quarantine of the People's Republic of China, together with its local branches, enforces regulations, including the Chinese Quarantine Act for Import and Export of Animals and Plants, issued in 1991, to prevent the spread of aquatic animal or plant diseases from foreign countries. Other marine regulations issued before 2001 that are relevant to coastal management and aquaculture in China include the China Directives on Prevention of Negative Impact on Marine Environment of Coastal Constructions, issued in 1990, and the China Marine Environmental Protection Act, issued in 1982 and revised in 1999.

Since 2002, the Chinese government has increased the pace at which marine environmental protection legislation is passed. A wide range of factors affecting coastal areas are addressed by statutes that set out Technical Regulations for Monitoring:

- Mariculture Areas

- Marine Environmental Tracing of Constructions

- Bathing Beaches (i.e., for swimming and recreation)

- Riverine Pollutant Inputs and Estuarine Environmental Quality

- Marine Biology Quality

- The Marine Ecological Environment

- Marine Dumping Areas

- Neighboring Marine Areas of Point Source Pollution Discharge

- Marine Atmosphere

Other important legislation includes the Provisions on Information Management of Marine Red Tides. The regulations endow full rights of environmental inspection and enforcement to the competent authorities. Implementation of these acts, however, still depends on an overall action rule, which should specify the administrative procedures, frequency of inspection, penalties for violation, etc.

The Technical Regulations for Monitoring usually embody several national standards for measuring parameters. For example, Technical Regulations for the Monitoring of Mariculture Areas stipulates the subjects, the technical requirements, and the methods for environmental monitoring in aquaculture areas. National standards that are applied when monitoring mariculture areas include the following:

- GB3097   Sea Water Quality Standard

- GB11607 – 91   Fishery Water Quality Standard

- GB17378.1   Marine Monitoring and Survey Criterion—1: General Principles

- GB17378.3   Marine Monitoring and Survey Criterion—3: Sample Collection, Storage, and Transport

- GB17378.4   Marine Monitoring and Survey Criterion—4: Seawater Analysis

- GB17378.5   Marine Monitoring and Survey Criterion—5: Sediment Analysis

- GB17378.7   Marine Monitoring and Survey Criterion—7: Inshore Sea Area Pollution Ecology Investigation and Biological Monitoring

- GB18668-2002   Marine Sediment Quality

Under the Marine Environmental Protection Act, the Chinese Environmental Protection Agency, as the competent state authority for environmental protection, is in charge of general supervision, coordination, and management of national environmental protection actions. The competent state authority for marine affairs is responsible for supervising the marine environment and organizing marine environmental investigations, monitoring, evaluation, and research. The competent state authority for maritime affairs supervises any pollution by non-military vessels and foreign vessels in the China seas. The competent authority for fisheries management also participates in the investigation and in decision-making if pollution from a vessel should damage the fishery. The military environmental protection authority is responsible for supervision, investigation, and management in cases where pollution is caused by military vessels.

According to the Regulations of the People's Republic of China on the Management of Foreign-Related Marine Scientific Research (1996), if marine scientific research activities are to be conducted in China seas and the work is to be done jointly by Chinese and foreign researchers, then the Chinese researchers should apply in writing for approval to the competent authority for marine affairs. For marine scientific research activities in China seas to be conducted solely by foreign researchers, they should apply in writing, through diplomatic channels, for approval to the competent authority for marine affairs. The competent state authority for marine affairs examines the application together with the Ministry of Foreign Affairs, the competent military authorities, and other relevant departments under the State Council, and makes a decision, or submits the case with its comments to the State Council for a final decision.

JAPAN

4

Executive Summary

Aquaculture has become a well-established industry in Japan. The output from aquaculture in 2004 was 1,261,000 metric tons, with a value of 486 billion yen, of which 96% and 89%, respectively, were contributed by mariculture. Intensive culture of finfish and shellfish generates large amounts of organic wastes and nutrients, resulting in environmental deterioration in and around aquaculture facilities. Negative effects such as these have become conspicuous since the substantial commencement of fish farming in the mid 1960s and its subsequent rapid development during the 1970s and 1980s. Numerous countermeasures have been proposed, but only a few have been put to effective use on mariculture farms. The most practical ways to implement environmental management of fish farms are to: (a) reduce the organic matter load by selecting "low-pollution" feed pellets and improving feeding methods, and (b) evaluate farm environments objectively and conduct aquaculture within the range of the assimilative capacity of the surrounding waters. With this goal in mind, fish feed has changed from trash fish and moist pellets to dry (extruded) pellets, and several indicators of benthic organic enrichment and environmental quality standards (EQS) have been proposed in the past 30 years. In this review, these EQS and methods for assessing the assimilative capacity and appropriate siting of fish farms are described.

The studies on aquacultural environments show that locating culture facilities in deep, offshore areas without depressed basins is better for sustaining high production. This would indicate that the facilities should withstand strong wind and waves. At the farm level, however, most mariculture in Japan is conducted on small-scale family-type operations staffed by aged workers. Incomes tend to be low and subsequently, management funds are often in short supply. The Fisheries Cooperative Associations play a key role in the future direction of mariculture development in Japan. Offshore mariculture requires large amounts of investment for building facilities and farm mechanization based on sufficient funds. It is necessary to integrate small-scale farming into a large-scale, intensive industry for environmentally responsible, sustainable mariculture in Japan.

Introduction

Background Information on Fishery and Aquaculture Sectors

Japan has the fourth-highest consumption rate of fishery products worldwide, annually consuming approximately 8.0 million metric tons (MT), or an annual per capita rate of 63 kg in 2004. In recent years, the preferences of Japanese consumers have shifted toward American- and European-style diets, which include more livestock products than the traditional Japanese diet. Consumption of fishery products, which had gradually increased until 1990, has since remained at a fairly constant level. Current estimates suggest that the Japanese obtain 39% of their total animal protein from fishery products.

Contributors: Yokoyama, H., K. Abo, K. Ikuta, T. Kamiyama, J. Higano, and S. Toda
In J.P. McVey, C.-S. Lee, and P.J. O'Bryen, editors. Aquaculture and Ecosystems: An Integrated Coastal and Ocean Management Approach. The World Aquaculture Society, Baton Rouge, Louisiana, United States

The self-sufficiency rate (domestic production volume/domestic intake volume) for food fish and shellfish in Japan is relatively low (55% in 2004), as the volume of imports has increased and domestic production has decreased. Most of the main food fish, excluding Pacific saury (*Cololabis saira*) are imported. In particular, the self-sufficiency rates for crustaceans such as prawns and crabs are remarkably low, at 6% and 24%, respectively.

Japan is one of the world's leading fishing countries. Total production, however, has decreased from a peak of 12.8 million MT in 1988 to 6.18 million MT in 2003. Both distant-water and offshore fisheries have markedly declined due to the tightening of international fishing regulations and depleting stocks in the waters surrounding Japan, whereas production from coastal fisheries and marine aquaculture have remained stable. Thus, to ensure the future of Japan's fisheries, it is essential to create a framework for appropriate conservation and management of resources in coastal areas and to further develop technology for sea farming and aquaculture.

Production Data

In Japan, aquaculture is an essential industry that compensates for the decreasing yield from capture fisheries. Moreover, natural resources can be conserved more effectively if all of the seedlings are supplied by artificial production. Japan's aquaculture production in 2004 was 1.26 million MT (Table 1), the fifth largest in the world, accounting for 2.1% of the total world volume (FAO 2006a). Aquaculture production in Japan has been stable. It represented 22% in weight and 30% in monetary value of the country's total fisheries and aquaculture production in 2004. In Japan, mariculture production exceeded freshwater aquaculture production, accounting for 96% and 89% of the total volume and total value, respectively, of aquaculture production in 2004. The major mariculture products are yellowtail (*Seriola quinqueradiata*), red sea bream (*Pagrus major*), oysters (*Crassostrea gigas*), scallops (*Patinopecten yessoensis*), pearls (*Pinctada fucata*), and nori (laver, *Porphyra yezoensis*) (Table 1). Eels (*Anguilla japonicus*) and trout (*Oncorhynchus mykiss*) are the main products of freshwater aquaculture.

Yellowtail

Yellowtail culture farms are widely distributed from central to southern Japan. Culture of yellowtail started in the 1930s in Kagawa Prefecture (Fig. 1), which faces the Seto Inland Sea on the island of Shikoku. Culture of the fish then rapidly spread to the neighboring prefectures surrounding the Seto Inland Sea. With the development of the floating net-cage culture method around 1965, the production of yellowtail culture rose rapidly. The highest production on record was in Kagoshima Prefecture, on the island of Kyushu, in 2004. Total production in 2004 was 150,000 MT, which was 2.3 times the catch of wild yellowtail for that year.

Table 1. Aquaculture production in Japan (2004).

Mariculture species	Weight (MT x 1,000)	Value (billions of yen)	Major production region
Finfish	262	196	
Yellowtail (*Seriola quinqueradiata*)	150	109	Kagoshima, Ehime, Ooita
Red sea bream (*Pagrus major*)	81	51	Ehime, Kumamoto, Mie
Puffer (*Takifugu rubripes*)	4	11	Nagasaki, Kumamoto
Flounder (*Paralichthys olivaceus*)	5	8	Ooita, Ehime
Coho salmon (*Oncorhynchus kisutch*)	10	4	Miyagi
Shellfish (molluscs)[a]	451[b]	72	
Oyster (*Crassostrea gigas*)	234[b]	37	Hiroshima, Miyagi, Okayama
Scallop (*Patinopecten yessoensis*)	215[b]	34	Aomori, Hokkaido, Miyagi
Pearl oyster (*Pinctada fucata martensii*)	0.03[c]	19	Nagasaki, Ehime, Mie
Other animals	17	9	
Prawn (*Marsupenaeus japonicus*)	2	8	Okinawa, Kagoshima
Sea squirt (*Halocynthia roretzi*)	15	1	Miyagi
Seaweed	484	118	
Nori (laver, *Porphyra yezoensis*)	359	98	Saga, Hyogo, Kumamoto
Tangle (*Laminaria japonica*)	47	8	Hokkaido, Iwate
Wakame (*Undaria pinnatifida*)	62	10	Iwate, Miyagi, Tokushima
Subtotal mariculture	1215	434	
Subtotal freshwater aquaculture	46	52	
Total aquaculture	1261	486	

Note: 1 billion yen = approximately $8,633,088 in August 2006.
[a]Excluding pearl oyster   [b]Including shell weight   [c]Weight of pearls

Red Sea Bream

The centers of aquaculture production of red sea bream are Ehime Prefecture in Shikoku, Mie Prefecture in central Japan, and Kumamoto and Nagasaki Prefectures in Kyushu (Fig. 1). As a high value marine fish, red sea bream has long been of interest to aquaculturists. Although the temporary stocking of live fish in tanks, ponds, or net cages before shipping to market has been practiced for many years, there was no commercial culture of this fish until 1965. Red sea bream culture has since developed into a significant industry. In terms of volume, current yields are second only to yellowtail. Production in 2004 was 81,000 MT.

Oysters

The production of oysters is mainly concentrated in the Seto Inland Sea around Hiroshima Prefecture and on the northern coast of the Pacific Ocean around Miyagi Prefecture (Fig. 1). Japan has a long history of oyster culture. In the traditional method, natural seed

Figure 1. Map of Japan, showing localities that are referred to in this chapter.

oysters attached to bamboo twigs that were fixed in the shallow seabed were either collected as seeds for culturing onto the seabed or harvested after they grew to edible size. In the past 60 years, oyster culture has developed dramatically due to the hanging culture technique and an efficient technique for seed production. The hanging culture technique has made oyster culture possible in places unsuitable for the traditional methods, thus expanding oyster culture areas considerably. This culture technique has also greatly increased the productivity of oysters per unit area. The seed production technique has made it possible to provide a large and steady supply of oyster seeds. In recent years, annual production has become stable at around 230,000 MT including shell weight, equivalent to 37,000 MT meat weight, without shells.

Nori

The seaweed, nori, is cultured along the central to southern coasts of Japan and is an important part of the Japanese diet. Nori was first cultivated in Japan in the seventeenth century, but until after World War II, production of nori remained at low levels, and dried nori was a rather expensive food. Various new techniques established after the war, including net cultivation with an open water system of floating nets, artificial seeding of conchospores, low temperature storage of nursery nets, and mechanization of dried nori manufacturing processes made a rapid increase in nori production possible. The ever-increasing demand for this product has made nori culture one of the most important seawater aquaculture industries in Japan. Production in 2004 reached 359,000 MT wet weight, with a value of 98 billion yen (approximately $0.85 billion).

Regulatory System for Aquaculture

The long tradition of fisheries in Japan, along with an interest in cooperation and reasonably equitable access to resources, has given rise to its unique system of coastal management and legislation (Ruddle 1992). Unlike other countries, in Japan, sea holdings and sea tenure have the same legal status as land holdings and land tenure. The Fisheries Law (1949, as revised in 1962) is the principal law that regulates fishery activities and is administered by the Ministry of Agriculture, Forestry and Fisheries (MAFF), although many tasks are delegated to prefectural governments (FAO 2006b). Under the Fisheries Law, rights within sea areas in a particular geographic location are granted by a prefectural governor (usually, of a coastal prefecture) to a Fisheries Cooperative Association (FCA), which distributes the rights to its members (the local community of fishermen), and the rights are exclusive to that association (FAO 2006b). The FCA is a key organization for the implementation of official fisheries projects, linking central and prefectural governments with individual fishermen (Ruddle 1992).

Sea Area Fisheries Adjustment Commissions, under joint jurisdiction of the MAFF and the prefecture governments, and a Central Fisheries Adjustment Council address matters of policy, implementation, and enforcement and ensure that prefectural fisheries development is coordinated within the overall national framework (FAO 2006b). Under the Fisheries Law, "special demarcated fishery rights" are granted when numerous fishermen would like to conduct different types of aquaculture within a fairly large but sheltered location (i.e., relatively prone to pollution), and in which activities with differing environmental quality requirements must be managed in a compatible and equitable manner. "Demarcated fishery rights" are granted for pond aquaculture that occupies a defined and fixed site, and which demands little coordination with other, potentially incompatible activities (FAO 2005).

The Fisheries Law is the basis for granting licenses to the FCAs. A jury organized of public election committees and those selected by the prefectural governor examines an application for a license, in which the type of mariculture, location and extent of the farm, duration of mariculture and so on are described, and submits a report to the governor. Based on the report, the governor decides whether the license should be granted. The license for pearl oyster aquaculture is valid for 10 years, and that for large-scale fish farming and other aquaculture is valid for 5 years.

Within the framework set by the prefectures and in terms of the local conditions, each FCA establishes its own regulations regarding control and specific items of operation, such as the area, duration, and method of mariculture. Interpretation of the rules and regulations is given wide latitude, and application of the guidelines is left to the FCAs (Ruddle 1992). Thus, within a framework of policy guidelines, planning, management, and monitoring that is subject to higher-level regulation, the FCAs control the day-to-day operations of the Japanese fisheries sector (Ruddle 1992; FAO 2006b).

Environmental Quality Standards

Accompanied by the rapid economic growth during the 1960s in Japan, the inflow of industrial wastes and sewage effluents resulted in eutrophication of coastal waters. Within the MAFF, the Fisheries Agency is responsible for preserving and managing marine biological resources and fishery production activities (FAO 2006b). The Fisheries Agency recognized eutrophication as a serious threat to inshore fisheries, and requested the Japan Fisheries Resources Conservation Association (JFRCA)[1] to devise Environmental Quality Standards (EQS) in inshore fishery grounds for the assessment of the environments. In 1983, JFRCA established the "Environmental Quality Standards at coastal fisheries grounds," based on three indicators of water quality (i.e., dissolved oxygen, chemical oxygen demand, and acid volatile sulfides) (Table 2, JFRCA 1983). Shortly afterwards, the JFRCA proposed an "Organic Pollution Index" (JFRCA 1985).

Dissolved oxygen (DO) is one of most important factors controlling life in aquatic organisms. The JFRCA recommends maintaining a DO of >6 mg L^{-1} in the bottom layer in coastal waters to ensure the healthy growth of aquatic animals. A DO content of 4.3 mg L^{-1} (3.0 mL L^{-1}) was established as one of environmental quality standards for the minimum limit in inshore fisheries grounds, and a DO of <2.9 mg L^{-1} (2.0 mL L^{-1}) indicated critical conditions for the survival of benthic animals.

---

[2] JFRCA is a non-profit corporation composed of members of prefectural governments, municipal authorities, the National Federation of Fisheries Associations, prefectural federations of fisheries associations, fisheries cooperative associations, and individual fisheries associations.

Table 2. Environmental quality standards for coastal fisheries grounds (JFRCA 2000).

Indicator	Criteria
Dissolved oxygen in bottom water	
Healthy environments for aquatic animals	>6 mg L^{-1}
Minimum limit for fisheries grounds	4.3 mg L^{-1} (3.0 mL L^{-1})
Critical conditions for survival of benthic animals	<2.9 mg L^{-1} (2.0 mL L^{-1})
Chemical oxygen demand of sediment	
Slightly deteriorated environment	20 to 30 mg g^{-1}
Highly deteriorated environment	>30 mg g^{-1}
Acid volatile sulfides of sediment	
Slightly deteriorated environment	0.2 to 1.0 mg S g^{-1} (dry sediment)
Highly deteriorated environment	>1.0 mg S g^{-1}
Organic Pollution Index[a]	
Normal sediments	<0
Polluted sediments	>0

[a]Complex combination of three or four environmental factors.

Chemical oxygen demand (COD) represents the amount of organic matter in sediments. The JFRCA proposed >20 mg g^{-1} (dry sediment) and >30 mg g^{-1} of COD as EQS to indicate slightly deteriorated environments and highly deteriorated environments, respectively. An environment is defined as slightly deteriorated when the effects of eutrophication begin to appear in the benthic community as phenomena such as the occurrence of organic pollution indicators and a decrease in species diversity. A highly deteriorated environment is one in which eutrophication has serious impacts on the benthic community, resulting in exclusive dominance of pollution indicators, a decrease in biomass and, ultimately, azoic conditions. These EQS values are widely adopted in Japan except in the northern part, where environmental deterioration seems to be less conspicuous than in central and southern parts of the country, even in areas with high COD values due to the low water temperatures.

Acid volatile sulfides (AVS) are produced when hydrogen sulfide, generated when organic matter decomposes under anoxic conditions, reacts with ions of metals such as iron. As the organic loading rate increases and deoxygenation proceeds, the AVS content in sediments increases. Thus, AVS content is widely used as an indicator for assessing environmental deterioration in coastal waters in Japan. The JFRCA proposed >0.2 mg S g^{-1} (dry sediment) and >1.0 mg S g^{-1} of as EQS to indicate slightly deteriorated and highly deteriorated environments, respectively. The absorbent-column method (Gastec Corporation, Ayase, Kanagawa, Japan) is a convenient method for measuring AVS.

The *Organic Pollution Index* was first calculated from a selection of bottom quality oriented environmental factors, including COD, AVS, ignition loss, total nitrogen, total phosphorus and mud content of the sediment, the Shannon-Weaver's species diversity index of macrofauna (H'), and from a principal component analysis of the environmental data from 10 representative enclosed areas (JFRCA 1985, 1995). Improvements have been made in the calculation methods, and several formulae composed of a reduced number of environmental factors (e.g., COD, AVS, and mud content) have been proposed (JFRCA 2000). The calculation methods and some problems are discussed in Ohwada (2001).

Japanese environmental legislation is closely tied to legal safeguards for coastal fisheries (Ruddle 1992). Ten years after the "Environmental Quality Standards at coastal fisheries grounds" were established, the Basic Environmental Law (1993), was enacted, requiring the government to establish EQS to be achieved and maintained in public waters to protect human health and conserve the living environment (FAO 2006b). Although not specific to aquaculture, the standards take into consideration the potential health hazards associated with the intake of listed substances through drinking water and/or fish and shellfish. In addition, bodies of water, including coastal waters, were classified based on water usage, and EQS values were established for each class (FAO 2006b).

Law to Ensure Sustainable Aquaculture Production (1999)

Intensive culture of finfish and shellfish generates large amounts of waste in the form of feces, pseudofeces, and uneaten feed. This particulate organic matter settles on the seabed under mariculture facilities, resulting in deoxygenation and buildup of sulfides, which sometimes damage the cultured organisms. The large amount of nutrients and dissolved organic matter that originates from mariculture has the potential to lead to outbreaks of harmful red-tide plankton. In Japan, negative effects such as these have become conspicuous since the commencement of large-scale fish farming in the mid 1960s and its subsequent rapid development during the 1970s and 1980s.

To promote the improvement of aquaculture grounds by the FCAs and to prevent the spread of contagious disease of cultured organisms, the "Law to Ensure Sustainable Aquaculture Production" (hereafter the Law) was enacted in 1999. The Law consists of two major parts: the "Aquaculture Ground Improvement Programmes," and measures to prevent the spread of "Specific Diseases" (contagious diseases stipulated under the Decree of the MAFF). The FCAs developed the "Aquaculture Ground Improvement Programmes" and implemented those that were approved by prefectural authorities to ensure sustainable aquaculture. The MAFF issued "Basic Guidelines to Ensure Sustainable Aquaculture Production", which detailed matters relevant to the goal of aquacultural improvement, as a fundamental guide for practical application of the Law. Although this system is legally based on voluntary activities of the licensed FCAs, the Law also stipulates the mechanism for ensuring compliance, i.e., a recommendation made by the prefectural governor. If a FCA does not utilize its aquaculture grounds along the Basic Guidelines, and the environmental conditions of its aquaculture grounds deteriorate, the prefectural governor may recommend that the FCA take measures necessary for improving their operations per the Aquaculture Ground Improvement Program for that prefecture. If the FCA does not follow the recommendation, the prefectural governor may make the environmental status of the FCA's fisheries area public.

Table 3. Environmental criteria adopted in the Law to Ensure Sustainable Aquaculture Production, 1999.

Item	Indicator	Criteria for identifying healthy farms	Criteria for identifying critical farms
Water in cages	Dissolved oxygen	>4. 0 mL L^{-1}	<2. 5 mL L^{-1}
Bottom environment	Sulfide (AVS)	Less than the value at the point where the benthic oxygen uptake rate is maximum	>2. 5 mg S g^{-1} dry sediment
	Benthic animals	Occurrence of macrobenthos throughout the year	Azoic conditions for > 6 months

Under the provision of the Basic Guidelines, the MAFF established environmental criteria using three indicators: DO of the water within fish cages, AVS in the sediment, and the occurrence of macrofauna beneath the fish cages (Table 3). The farm environments are identified as healthy when the values of these indicators are within the thresholds. When the values of these indicators fall outside the threshold values, criteria for identifying critical environments (established by the Director General of the Fisheries Agency) are used to signal that urgent countermeasures are necessary.

The DO value adopted as the criterion for a healthy environment under the Law (Table 3) is based on studies reporting that yellowtail requires more than 4 mL L^{-1} (5.7 mg L^{-1}) of DO for normal growth (Harada 1978). The Law also establishes 2.5 mL L^{-1} (3.6 mg L^{-1}) of DO as a minimum for mariculture farm environments, which represents an intermediate value between 2.0 mL L^{-1} of DO, which is at the extreme margin of survival for yellowtail, and 3.0 mL L^{-1} of DO, when feeding activity of yellowtail begins to decrease (Harada 1978). These criteria are generally accepted by fish farmers, except where the DO of the surrounding water frequently decreases below the standard values, mainly due to sewage and other industrial wastes.

The criterion for AVS in the sediments is based on the "Omori-Takeoka theory." In a model to determine the limit of organic loading to the bottom, Omori et al. (1994) used the rate of benthic oxygen uptake (BOU), defined as the *in situ* oxygen consumption by sediments, as an indicator of the activity of the benthic ecosystem. They found a peak of BOU along a gradient of organic loading, and took this peak as an indicator of the maximum phase in the process of remineralization. Based on this model, Takeoka and Omori (1996) presented a method to determine the assimilative capacity of fish farms by using the AVS content in the sediment, because there is usually a positive correlation between the organic loading and AVS. This concept, the "Omori-Takeoka theory", states that AVS should be less than the maximum value of BOU at each fish farm. Recent studies, however, have found that it is difficult to detect the maximum BOU and to determine the standard value through *in situ* investigations (Yokoyama and Sakami 2002). Abo and Yokoyama (2003) proved the impracticability of this criterion by developing a three-dimensional numerical model. Although the Law establishes 2.5 mg S g^{-1} as a minimum limit for AVS, azoic conditions are often found in sediments with <2.5 mg S g^{-1} (Yokoyama 2002; Yokoyama et al. 2002a).

Macrofauna are sensitive to changes in organic inputs (Pearson and Rosenberg 1978), and they have been often used as a sensitive indicator in environmental monitoring of fish farms in Japan (Tsutsumi 1995; Yokoyama 2002; Sasaki and Oshino 2004). These studies showed that typical effects of fish farming on the benthic community include a reduction in species richness and/or species diversity, the appearance of dense populations of the opportunistic polychaete *Capitella* sp., which often results in the increase in total macrofaunal abundance, a decrease of large-sized species, and disappearance of echinoderms. The macrofaunal criterion of the Law, however, only specifies that the benthic organisms should be alive (Table 3), because the species composition of macrofauna is difficult for most fish farmers to identify. A healthy environment is identified in terms of the existence of live macrofauna throughout the year, while a critical environment is identified from the azoic conditions during half a year or more. Criteria such as these have no biological basis, but they are convenient in terms of ease of monitoring by farmers. It is important to establish more detailed criteria by analyses of the relationships between macrobenthic communities and environmental conditions in the vicinity of mariculture farms.

Measures to Improve Farm Environments

Considerable effort has gone into improving farm environments in the coastal fisheries grounds and/or mariculture farms in Japan. The measures that have been tried are classified into four groups, according to type of approach: engineering, biological, reducing the organic matter load, and assimilative capacity. Only a few of these measures, however, have been put to practical use in mariculture farms in Japan.

Engineering Approaches

Some of the first measures taken to improve farm environments were based on engineering approaches, i.e., controlling a favorable environment for mariculture by physical means, such as digging trenches to create water-routes on the seabed and widening the mouths of bays (Hagino 1980a, 1980b), aeration or vertical stirring of water (Noma 1980), and dredging out enriched silt from the seabed (Yoshimuta 1980). Effects of the latter two approaches, however, were limited to a small area or within a short period of time. In addition, it is difficult to secure sites for the disposal of polluted silt that is dredged up from the seabed.

Lasting effects are achieved by physically modifying a fisheries area. For example, a man-made waterway that was formed by cutting through a sandbar in Saroma-ko Lagoon in the Hokkaido district (Fig. 1) promoted water exchange between a scallop farm in the lagoon and the open sea (Hagino 1980a). Trenches dug into the seabed enhanced water movement around a laver farm in Matsukawa-ura Lagoon, Fukushima Prefecture, and oyster farms in Hamana-ko Lagoon, Shizuoka Prefecture, and Matsushima Bay, Miyagi Prefecture (Hagino 1980b). Generally, however, engineering approaches entail high costs.

Another engineering approach involved intercepting wastes and dead cultured fish from being deposited onto the seabed by means of a canvas fastened under the fish cages. The cage sludge collection system was developed in Norway (Bergheim et al. 1991) and tested on a fish farm in Ooita Prefecture, eastern Kyushu, but its suitability was not confirmed, due to its low efficiency of waste collection (11%-13% of loaded particulate matter) and its maintenance requirements (Ooita Prefecture 1997).

Other engineering approaches were designed to prevent outgassing of hydrogen sulfide and dissolution of nitrogen (N) and phosphorus (P) from bottom sediments by spreading lime (CaO) or chemicals onto the seabed. Lime and similar compounds that contain calcium have been examined for improvement of sediment qualities. Lime inhibits the growth of sulfate-reducing bacteria, resulting in a decrease in the sulfide content in the sediment (Nishimura and Seki 1983). Noticeable effects of lime have been reported from several farms (e.g., Miyahara et al. 1994, for a fish farm in Nagasaki Prefecture). Covering the seabed with allochthonous clean sand was also tried as a method to prevent the loss of nutrients from the sediments, but the effects were short-term and this measure was deemed too expensive.

Biological Approaches

Other measures under development are designed to accelerate the biological decomposition and assimilation of particulate wastes and nutrients. Submarine tilling using beam-trawlers or power cultivators has been tried as a way to increase the concentration of oxygen in the bottom sediments (Kusuki 1979), but the effects appear to be short-term. Another approach is to spread incubated bacteria or macrobenthos over the seabed to decompose organic wastes. Karim et al. (2003) found two promising bacterial strains (*Enterobacter* sp. and *Pseudomonas* sp.) that decompose organic matter effectively, from sediments under fish cages in Uranouchi Bay, Kochi Prefecture. Chareonpanich (1993) found assimilation of fish feed pellets by the polychaete *Capitella* sp. in a laboratory experiment, and suggested that spreading a laboratory breeding population over the seabed under fish cages would be useful for remineralization of organic wastes. These two latter laboratory-based methods, however, have not yet been used in practical mariculture farms.

Projecting solar radiation through optical fibers onto the seabed has also been suggested as a way to enhance the growth of benthic microalgae that produce oxygen (Ruangdej and Fukami 2004), but the technology is expensive and the effects are limited within a small area.

Another measure based on a biological approach is to construct an artificial midlayer seafloor on which biotic communities are formed. Kochi Prefecture (1997) tried to reduce the organic load from a fish cage by placing net sacks above the seabed in Uranouchi Bay, in which a number of small plastic vessels (empty bottles of a soft drink) were placed, and suggested that benthic animals and microorganisms living on or in the vessels decomposed the organic wastes. Kawaguchi et al. (2004) also found that a similar device, made of oyster shell, reduced by 6.6% the organic load from oyster rafts. Such artificial midlayer-seafloor systems may accelerate the biological decomposition of wastes, but there is concern about the possibility of inhibiting vertical water movement and the long-term maintenance of the device.

Integrated aquaculture, in which co-cultured organisms assimilate wastes, is another approach that has been proposed for improving farm environments. Although the effectiveness of integrated aquaculture has been reported from many parts of the world (Troell et al. 2003), and its effects have been confirmed from experimental fish farms in Kagoshima Prefecture (Hirata 2002; Kitadai and Kadowaki 2003), this system has not been adopted on a commercial-basis, probably due to the lack of financial reward for the farmer's additional work to implement such measures.

Site rotation, which results in assimilation of wastes by natural biota during fallow periods, is one of most effective ways for environmental management of mariculture farms. In Japan, however, this measure has not yet been adopted, due to limited licensed areas for farming and the scarcity of quantitative information on its effects. The use of site rotation requires further scientific assessment.

Approaches Based on Reducing Organic Matter Load

The most practical way of implementing environment-based management of fish farms is to implement measures aimed at reducing the organic matter load, e.g., by reducing the density of cultured animals or of mariculture facilities. In Japan, fish feed has changed gradually during the past 30 years from trash fish and moist pellets to dry (extruded) pellets. Use of nutritive but "low-pollution" feed pellets, which have a high digestion rate, low nitrogen (N) and phosphorus (P) content, and appropriate buoyancy in fish cages, results in increased N and P assimilation by fish and reduced amounts of feces and leftover feed, as well as decreased N and P loadings to the environment (Watanabe 1991). Measures to control the densities of fish farms in an area and of culture animals on the farms, as well as the use of "low pollution" feeds are currently being implemented in Japan. Feeding methods have also been improved. Recently, a self-feeding system has been developed, in which the least amount of feed is given to cultured fish in response to their appetite, and the effectiveness of the system is currently being examined (Takeuchi et al. 2002).

Assimilative Capacity Approaches

The assimilative capacity of an area is defined as the ability of an area to maintain a "healthy" environment and "accommodate" wastes (Fernandes et al. 2001). Some measures currently being implemented are aimed at conducting mariculture within the range of the assimilative capacity of the surrounding ecosystem by siting farms in deeper, offshore areas. A related approach is to evaluate existing farm environments objectively and conduct aquaculture within the range of the assimilative capacity of their environments.

Suggested Approaches to Data Collection

Mariculture should be conducted within the range of the assimilative capacity, which depends on waste dispersal and oxygen supply. Based on this concept, Yokoyama and colleagues (Yokoyama 2003; Yokoyama et al. 2002a, 2002b, 2004) have attempted to develop guidelines for the suitable siting of fish farms by proposing two indices, "ED" (Embayment Degree) and "ISL" (Index of Suitable Location). The ED is expressed by the formula:

$$ED = (L_1/W_1 + L_2/W_2)(a/Ds)(b/Dm)$$

where Ds is the water depth at a sampling site or, if present, the depth of any sill that exists between the site and the mouth of the bay, Dm is the maximum depth at the mouth of the bay, a is the mean depth of all the sampling sites, and b is the mean depth of the mouth of the bay in the research area (Yokoyama et al. 2002a; Yokoyama 2003). Yokoyama et al. (2002a) adopted $a = 20$ and $b = 45$ in their case study conducted in bays along the coast of Kumano-nada (Fig. 1).

Yokoyama et al. (2002b) classified the fish-farm environments into healthy, cautionary, and critical zones, based on the macrofauna and chemical factors of the sediment (Table 4). They proposed a method of determining the upper limit of fish production and suitable siting for fish-farm grounds by placing the mariculture sites in a grid of ED versus fish production

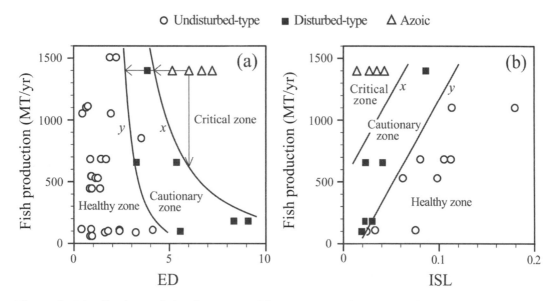

Figure 2. Distributions of the three assemblage groups of the macrofauna in a gradient of ED versus fish production (a) and in a gradient of ISL versus fish production (b). Symbols represent undisturbed-type assemblages (○), disturbed-type assemblages (■), and azoic stations (Δ), respectively. See text for ED and ISL (adapted from Yokoyama et al. 2002b, 2004).

Table 4. Three zones of the fish farms in Kumano-nada based on the macrofauna and chemical factors (adapted from Yokoyama et al. 2002b, 2004).

Zone	Macrofauna	Chemical factors
Healthy zone	Undisturbed-type assemblage: High species diversity throughout the year; variable species composition	High levels of dissolved oxygen throughout the year; low levels of sediment enrichment; low values of sediment sulfide content
Cautionary zone	Disturbed-type assemblage: Predominance of *Prionospio pulchra*, an indicator of eutrophic and hypoxic conditions, in summer; low values of biomass, density, and species richness in summer; increased densities in winter, but not as high as in the critical zone	Hypoxic conditions of the bottom water in summer; high levels of sediment enrichment; high values of sediment sulfide content
Critical zone	Azoic in summer; in winter, extremely high density (Mean = 24,400 m^{-2}) with a high proportion (Mean = 66%) of *Capitella* sp., a worldwide indicator of organic pollution	Anoxic conditions of the bottom water in summer; extremely high levels of sediment enrichment; extremely high values of sediment sulfide content

(Fig. 2A). For instance, if a mariculture farm that annually produces 1,400 MT of fish is located in the critical zone with an ED value of 6, the farm should be moved to the area having ED values smaller than 4, or the annual production should be lowered to less than 600 MT, to alleviate the critical conditions.

The ED is easy to calculate from a nautical chart, and it is an effective means of comparing the suitability of sites for fish farming among neighboring areas with similar oceanographic conditions. The ED, however, may be less suitable for comparing fish farms presenting a variety of topographic situations under different oceanographic and/or geographic conditions.

The ISL is expressed as:

$$ISL = DV^2$$

where D is the water depth (m) at a fish farm site and V is the time-averaged current velocity (m/s) (Yokoyama et al. 2004).

Table 5. Values of benthic components for identifying cautionary and critical conditions of fish-farm environments (adapted from Yokoyama et al. 2004).

Benthic components	Cautionary condition	Critical condition
Sediment		
Total organic carbon (mg g^{-1} dry)	20 to 30	> 30
Total nitrogen (mg g^{-1} dry)	2.5 to 4	> 4
Total phosphorus (mg g^{-1} dry)	4 to 6	> 6
Chemical oxygen demand (mg g^{-1} dry)	30 to 75	> 75
Acid-volatile sulfide (mg g^{-1} dry)	0.5 to 1.5	> 1.5
Macrobenthos		
Biomass* (g m^{-2})	< 10	0
Density (individuals/m^2)	< 1500	0
Number of species (#/0.04 m^2)	< 20	0

* Wet weight of animals, excluding the shells of molluscs.

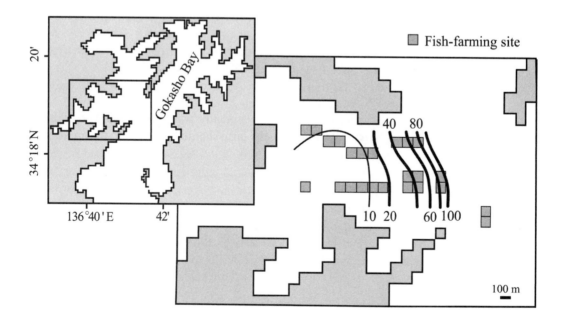

Figure 3. Isopleths of the limit value of organic matter loading rate (μmol O$_2$ cm^{-2} day^{-1}) in Gokasho Bay, based on the three-dimensional model (after Abo and Yokoyama 2003).

Thus, ISL incorporates more direct variables, i.e., the water depth and current velocity, which control waste dispersal and loading and oxygen supply. The fish farm sites were also categorized as being in healthy, cautionary, or critical zones (Fig. 2B). The ISL has a wider potential application for assessing assimilative capacity under a variety of topographical conditions. These proposed indices, which were based on the concept that dispersive environments are less susceptible to environmental degradation than semi-enclosed systems, are readily applicable for use in decisions about the siting of fish farms.

Since benthic impacts are integrated over time, chemical factors of the sediment and community parameters of the macrobenthos are convenient for environmental monitoring. Yokoyama et al. (2004) also estimated the threshold values of these factors and parameters to classify fish farm environments as healthy, cautionary, or critical (Table 5).

Abo and Yokoyama (2003) developed a three-dimensional numerical model, which takes advection, dispersion, deposition, and decomposition of organic matter from the mariculture system into account. This model not only proved the impracticability of the AVS environmental quality criteria used in the Law, as noted earlier, but also indicates the upper limit of organic matter loading to each of the calculation grids (100 x 100 m) of the mariculture ground in terms of equivalent weight of oxygen (Fig. 3). If the validity of the model is confirmed by field surveys, this method will be adopted for practical usage in determining suitable sites for mariculture farms.

Literature Cited

Abo, K. and H. Yokoyama. 2003. Examination of the environmental criterion for mariculture based on benthic oxygen uptake rate and an attempt to evaluate assimilative capacity, by using a three-dimensional numerical model [in Japanese with English abstract]. Bulletin of the Japanese Society of Fisheries Oceanography 67: 99-110.

Bergheim, A., J.P. Aabel, and E.A. Seymour. 1991. Past and present approaches to aquaculture waste management in Norwegian net pen culture operations. Pages 117-136 *in* C.B. Cowey and C.Y. Cho, editors. Nutritional Strategies and Aquaculture Waste. University of Guelph, Guelph, Ontario, Canada.

Chareonpanich, C., S. Montani, H. Tsutsumi, and S. Matsuoka. 1993. Modification of chemical characteristics of organically enriched sediment by *Capitella* sp. I. Marine Pollution Bulletin 26: 375-379. FAO (Food and Agriculture Organization of the United Nations). 2006a. Fishery Statistics. Fishery Information, Data, and Statistics Unit (FIDI), Food and Agriculture Organization of the United Nations, Rome, Italy. http://www.fao.org/figis/servlet/static?dom=org&xml=FIDI_STAT_org.xml.

FAO (Food and Agriculture Organization of the United Nations). 2006a. Fishery Statistics Fishery Information, Data and Statistics Unit (FIDI), Food and Agriculture Organization of the United Nations, Rome, Italy. http://www.fao.org/figis/servlet/static?dom=org&xml=FIDI_STAT_org.xml.

FAO (Food and Agriculture Organization of the United Nations). 2006b. National aquaculture legislation overview: Japan. FAO Fisheries (Aquaculture). Fisheries Global Information System, FAO, Rome, Italy. http://www.fao.org.

Fernandes, T.F., A. Eleftheriou, H. Ackefors, M. Eleftheriou, A. Ervik, A. Sanchez-Mata, T. Scanlon, P. White, S. Cochrane, T.H. Pearson, and P.A. Read. 2001. The scientific principles underlying the monitoring of the environmental impacts of aquaculture. Journal of Applied Ichthyology 17: 181-193.

Hagino, S. 1980a. Water exchange in semi-enclosed bays [in Japanese]. Pages 34-44 *in* T. Deguchi and M. Nakamura, editors. Engineering of Mariculture Grounds. Japan Fisheries Resources Conservation Association, Tokyo, Japan.

Hagino, S. 1980b. Water-route making [in Japanese]. Pages 52-61 *in* T. Deguchi and M. Nakamura, editors. Engineering of Mariculture Grounds. Japan Fisheries Resources Conservation Association, Tokyo, Japan.

Harada, T. .1978. Yellowtail and amberjack [in Japanese]. Pages 463-503 *in* N. Kawamoto, editor. Details of Fish Culture. Koseisha-Koseikaku, Tokyo, Japan.

Hirata, H. 2002. Systematic aquaculture: yesterday, today, and tomorrow. Fisheries Science 68 (supplement 1): 829-834.

JFRCA (Japan Fisheries Resources Conservation Association). 1985. Guidelines for the implementation of sediment quality improvement [in Japanese]. Japan Fisheries Resources Conservation Association, Tokyo, Japan. 110 pp.

JFRCA (Japan Fisheries Resources Conservation Association). 1995. Water quality criteria for the protection of aquatic living resources (the 1995 edition) [in Japanese]. Japan Fisheries Resources Conservation Association, Tokyo, Japan. 69 pp.

JFRCA (Japan Fisheries Resources Conservation Association). 2000. Water quality criteria for the protection of aquatic living resources (the 2000 edition) [in Japanese]. Japan Fisheries Resources Conservation Association, Tokyo, Japan. 96 pp.

Karim M.A., K. Fukami, and A.B. Patel .2003. Enhancement of inorganic nutrient regeneration in a eutrophic sediment-bottom water complex system by adding effective indigenous bacteria. Fisheries Science 69: 1146-1157.

Kawaguchi, O., T. Yamamoto, O. Matsuda, T. Hashimoto, and H. Takayama. 2004. Artificial midlayer seafloor: Simple and new devices to reduce organic loads from oyster rafts to the sediment [in Japanese with English abstract]. Bulletin of the Japanese Society of Scientific Fisheries (Nippon Suisan Gakkaishi) 70: 722-727.

Kitadai, Y. and S. Kadowaki. 2003. The growth process and N, P uptake rates of *Laminaria japonica* cultured in coastal fish farms [in Japanese with English abstract]. Suisanzoshoku 51: 15-23.

Kochi Prefecture. 1997. Investigation for the treatment of deposits from fish farming by an artificial midlayer seafloor system [in Japanese]. Pages 13-76 *in* A Report on Investigations for the Treatment of Deposits from Fish Farming. Japan Seawater Fishery Cultivation Association, Tokyo, Japan.

Kusuki, Y.1979. On the effect of cultivating oyster growing grounds [in Japanese]. Bulletin of the Hiroshima Fisheries Experimental Station 10: 15-26.

Miyahara, J., Y. Kitagawa, S. Todoroki, and K. Matsuo. 1994. Effects of grounds improving chemicals to fish farming grounds [in Japanese with English abstract]. Bulletin of the Nagasaki Prefecture Institute of Fisheries 20: 55-59.

Nishimura, A. and M. Seki. 1983. Effects of lime for the improvement of mariculture grounds [in Japanese with English abstract]. Bulletin of the Japanese Society of Scientific Fisheries (Nippon Suisan Gakkaishi) 49: 353-358.

Noma, T. 1980. Purification of water by using electric and mechanical powers [in Japanese]. Pages 90-100 *in* T. Deguchi and M. Nakamura, editors. Engineering of Mariculture Grounds. Japan Fisheries Resources Conservation Association, Tokyo, Japan.

Ohwada, K. 2001. Diagnosis of environmental quality of enclosed water areas related to aquacultural activities in Japan –an example of coastal management of environmental condition using principal component analysis. Pages 15-20 *in* Proceedings of the Workshop on the International Symposium on Protection and Management of the Marine Coastal Ecosystems. United Nations Environment Programme.

Omori, K., T. Hirano, and H. Takeoka. 1994. The limitations to organic loading on a bottom of a coastal ecosystem. Marine Pollution Bulletin 28: 73-80.

Ooita Prefecture. 1997. Investigation for the treatment of deposits from fish farming by a cage sludge collection system [in Japanese]. Pages 77-106 *in* A Report on Investigations for the Treatment of Deposits from Fish Farming. Japan Seawater Fishery Cultivation Association, Tokyo, Japan.

Pearson, T. H. and R. Rosenberg. 1978. Macrobenthic succession in relation to organic enrichment and pollution of the marine environment. Oceanography Marine Biology: An Annual Review 16: 229-311.

Ruangdej, U. and K. Fukami. 2004. Stimulation of photosynthesis and consequent oxygen production in anoxic bottom water by supply of low-intensity light through an optical fiber. Fisheries Science 70: 421-429.

Ruddle, K. 1992. Administration and conflict management in Japanese coastal fisheries. FAO Fisheries Technical Paper No. 273. Food and Agriculture Organization of the United Nations, Rome, Italy. http://www.fao.org/DOCREP/003/T0510E00.htm

Sasaki, R. and A. Oshino. 2004. Environmental conditions relevant to aggregative distribution of macrobenthos below coho salmon culture cage. Bulletin of Fisheries Research Agency, Supplement 1: 19-31.

Takeoka, H. and K. Omori. 1996. Methods of determining the limit of suitable fish culture based on the oxygen consumption rate by the sediment [in Japanese with English abstract]. Bulletin of the Japanese Society of Fisheries Oceanography 60: 45-53.

Takeuchi, T., T. Akiyama, and Y. Yamagata. 2002. Trend occurring high reduction technology of organic compound loading in marine aquaculture areas [in Japanese]. Journal of Resources and Environment 38: 801-810.

Troell, M., C. Halling, A. Neori, T. Chopin, A. H. Buschmann, N. Kautsky, and C. Yarish. 2003. Integrated mariculture: Asking the right questions. Aquaculture 226: 69-90.

Tsutsumi, H. 1995. Impact of fish net pen culture on the benthic environment of a cove in south Japan. Estuaries 18: 108-115.

Watanabe, T. 1991. Past and present approaches to aquaculture waste management in Japan. Pages 137-153 *in* C.B. Cowey and C.Y. Cho, editors. Nutritional Strategies and Aquaculture Waste. University of Guelph, Guelph, Ontario, Canada.

Yokoyama, H. 2002. Impact of fish and pearl farming on the benthic environments in Gokasho Bay: Evaluation from seasonal fluctuations of the macrobenthos. Fisheries Science 68: 258-268.

Yokoyama, H. 2003. Environmental quality criteria for fish farms in Japan. Aquaculture 226: 45-56.

Yokoyama, H. and T. Sakami. 2002. Examination of the benthic oxygen uptake rate as an environmental criterion for fish farms in Gokasho Bay [in Japanese with English abstract]. Bulletin of the Japanese Society of Scientific Fisheries (Nippon Suisan Gakkaishi) 68: 15-23.

Yokoyama, H., M. Inoue, and K. Abo. 2004. Estimation of the assimilative capacity of fish-farm environments based on the current velocity measured by plaster balls. Aquaculture 240: 233-247.

Yokoyama, H., A. Nishimura, and M. Inoue. 2002a. Influence of aquaculture and topographic conditions on the macrobenthos and the sediment in fish farms along the Kumano-nada coast [in Japanese with English abstract]. Bulletin of the Japanese Society of Fisheries Oceanography 66: 133-141.

Yokoyama, H., A. Nishimura, and M. Inoue. 2002b. Evaluation of fish farm environments by identifying community types of the macrobenthos [in Japanese with English abstract]. Bulletin of the Japanese Society of Fisheries Oceanography 66: 142-147.

Yoshimuta, C. 1980. Improvement of enriched sediments [in Japanese]. Pages 137-161 *in* T. Deguchi and M. Nakamura, editors. Engineering of Mariculture Grounds. Japan Fisheries Resources Conservation Association, Tokyo, Japan.

SOUTH KOREA

5

Executive Summary

Aquaculture of seaweed, shellfish, and finfish are important industries in the Republic of Korea (South Korea), representing about 30% of total fisheries production by weight. The Korean government is currently developing a comprehensive ecosystem-based marine management program as part of its strategy to develop marine resources in a sustainable manner. Estimation of the carrying capacity of an aquaculture area is necessary to maintain sustainable production and to protect the environment through culturing activities. The National Fisheries Research and Development Institute, South Korea, and the University of Georgia Sea Grant College Program, USA, are conducting a cooperative study to model carrying capacity of specific sites in South Korea for ecosystem-based aquaculture management.

In this chapter, the status of two implementation projects, in Gamak Bay and Jeju, South Korea, is reviewed and outlined. The modeling necessary for good decision-making is also considered.

Introduction

Commercial aquaculture of seaweed (*Porphyra* sp.) and oysters (*Crassostrea gigas*) in Korea began about 300 years ago. Results of research conducted by the National Fisheries Research and Development Institute (NFRDI) and Pukyong National University since the late 1920s on the production of freshwater fish, such as tilapia (*Oreochromis niloticus*) and carps (*Ctenopharyngodon idella, Hypophthalmichthys molitrix*), were instrumental in the development of hatchery-based seed production technology and of mariculture in Korea (NOAA Central Library 2005). With government support and public subsidies, the marine aquaculture industry is growing rapidly. Around 90% of the near shore aquaculture production is along the southern coast of Korea. The major provinces of aquaculture production are Chollanam-Do and Gyungsangnam-Do (Fig. 1).

Production Data

Aquaculture production is about 30% of South Korea's total fisheries production by weight. Since 1969, the long-established traditional method of culturing oysters in intertidal beds has been replaced with suspended-culture methods. In its early stages, oyster production increased rapidly due to better methods and maximized in the mid-1980s. Between 1999 and 2003, shellfish production increased about 30%, while seaweed production decreased about 4% (Table 1). Aquaculture of fish species has increased dramatically since the 1980s. Production of marine finfish more than doubled between 1999 and 2003 (Table 1). Production trends for aquaculture of the major species of marine finfish and shellfish are shown in Table 2.

Contributors: Kim, Y., I.K. Chung, I.K. Jang, J.U. Lee, Y.-U. Kim, and H.T. Oh
In J.P. McVey, C.-S. Lee, and P.J. O'Bryen, editors. Aquaculture and Ecosystems: An Integrated Coastal and Ocean Management Approach. The World Aquaculture Society, Baton Rouge, Louisiana, United States.

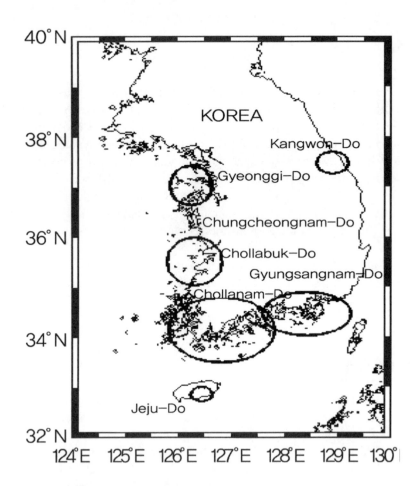

Figure 1. Map of South Korea, showing locations of Chollanam-do and Gyunsangnam-do, major provinces of aquaculture production.

Table 1. Overview of marine aquaculture production, in metric tons (MT), 1999-2003.

Type of aquaculture	1999	2000	2001	2002	2003
Fishes	33,453	25,986	29,297	48,073	72,393
Crustaceans	1,180	1,158	2,081	1,403	2,324
Shellfish	221,031	222,608	217,078	212,433	291,063
Other animals	35,916	29,165	33,833	22,053	8,411
Seaweeds	473,672	374,456	373,538	497,557	452,054
Total	765,252	653,373	655,827	781,519	826,245

Table 2. Current aquaculture production (MT) trends of major marine finfish and shellfish.

Finfish	1999	2000	2001	2002	2003	Average
Olive flounder (*Paralichthys olivaceus*)	21,368	14,127	16,426	23,343	34,533	21,959
Black rockfish (*Sebastes schlegelii*)	9,459	8,473	9,254	16,548	23,771	13,501
Grey mullet (*Mugil cephalus*)	347	968	1,415	3,898	4,093	2,144
Sea bass (*Lateolabrax japonicus*)	797	605	873	2,006	2,778	1,412
Sea bream (*Pagrus major, Acanthopagrus schlegeli*)	176	412	641	960	4,417	1,321
Subtotal finfish	33,453	25,986	29,297	48,073	72,393	41,840
Shellfish						
Oysters (*Crassostrea gigas, Pinctada fucata*)	177,259	177,079	174,117	182,229	238,326	189,802
Manila clams (*Ruditapes philippinarum*)	16,135	17,927	16,433	19,652	27,494	17,728
Blue mussels (*Mytilus edulis*)	15,042	11,713	13,653	13,201	15,785	13,879
Ark shells (*Anadara satowi, A. broughtonii*)	8,550	10,618	7,359	4,745	4,696	7,194
Cockles (*Anadara granosabisenensis, A. subcrenata*)	2,511	820	3,842	413	2,440	2,005
Subtotal shellfish	221,031	222,608	217,078	212,433	291,116	232,853
Total marine finfish and shellfish	254,484	248,594	246,375	260,506	363,509	274,693

The majority of cultured production is consumed domestically. When seaweed production is high, market prices decrease due to the over-supply. The preference of most Korean consumers is for raw fish, so the majority of cultured fish are marketed in live form. Various types of fresh processed fish, however, have recently been introduced into the domestic market.

Cultured fisheries products make up a very small percentage, in terms of weight and revenue, of the total fisheries product export industry. About 20% of the flatfish (mainly olive flounder, *Paralichthys olivaceus*) produced are exported. Oysters are the leading export species, accounting for 4% of total exports by weight and 8% of the total revenue. About 10% of South Korea's oyster production is exported. Almost half of the cultured ark shells (*Anadara broughtonii, A. satowi*) and baby clams (*Tapes japonicus*) produced are exported. Of the seaweeds that are cultured, 6% of the sea mustard (*Undaria pinnatifide*) and 4% of the laver (*Porphyra* spp.) are exported (Fig. 2). Recent changes in production of the major cultured fisheries species that are exported are summarized in Table 3. The export of fisheries products and cultured species (except laver and sea mustard) has decreased.

Regulatory System for Aquaculture

The Fisheries Act (1990, as amended), regulates fishing ground utilization and development, fishing licenses (including aquaculture), fish processing and transport, and measures for conserving and protecting fisheries resources (FAO 2005). A variety of marine-

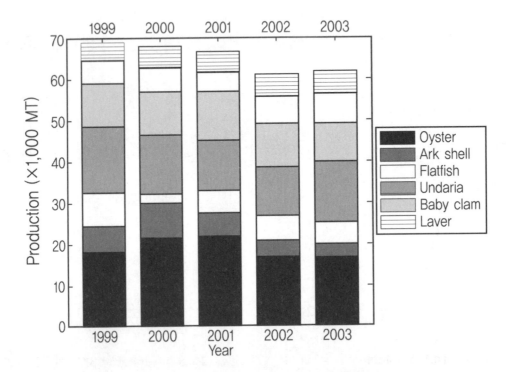

Figure 2. Export fisheries production by weight, 1999-2003.

Table 3. Changes in fisheries export production, 1999-2003.

Species	1999 Weight	1999 $1K	2000 Weight	2000 $1K	2001 Weight	2001 $1K	2002 Weight	2002 $1K	2003 Weight	2003 $1K
Oyster (*Crassostrea gigas, Pinctada fucata*)	18,563	111,141	22,296	129,577	22,544	125,656	17,217	76,122	16,610	74,699
Ark shell (*Anadara broughtonii, A. satowi*)	6,211	49,472	7,059	52,866	5,128	42,231	3,717	29,226	3,322	25,548
Flatfish[a]	8,125	42,697	2,941	39,575	4,988	43,817	5,479	41,721	4,163	47,947
Sea mustard (*Undaria pinnatifide*)	15,855	33,774	12,951	29,748	9,709	21,160	10,218	20,400	13,271	21,900
Baby clam (*Tapes japonicus*)	10,340	23,553	11,546	27,212	12,656	29,370	9,510	24,148	8,322	21,177
Laver (*Porphyra* spp.)	4,414	25,426	5,178	31,015	6,348	40,069	6,275	37,709	6,969	41,646

[a]Includes species such as *Paralichthys olivaceus, Psetta maxima,* and *Hippoglossus hippoglossus.*

related functions, including marine policy, fisheries, and international cooperation, which were formerly managed by diverse government agencies, were integrated under the Ministry of Maritime Affairs and Fisheries (MOMAF) in 1996 (MOMAF 2004). The MOMAF is the central authority for planning and implementing fisheries policy and overall fishery management, but local provincial, municipal, and district-level governments are also involved in the conservation of marine areas and development and management of fisheries resources (FAO 2005).

Other legislation relevant to aquaculture development includes the Framework Act on Marine Development (1987, as amended), which provides direction for South Korea's basic policy for the rational development, utilization, and preservation of sea and marine resources, the Aquaculture Ground Management Act (2000), with its goal of improving productivity of farm sites, and the Culture-Based Fishery Promotion Act (2002), which requires the Government to establish a framework to promote culture-based fisheries every five years (FAO 2005).

Under its "Basic Plan for the Development of Nurturing Fisheries," the MOMAF fosters development of the high value-added aquaculture industry. Under this plan, about 1.1 trillion South Korea Won[1] will be invested by 2008 to implement core tasks, such as restructuring aquaculture fisheries, developing aquaculture technologies, and improving the environment of fishing areas. Under the plan, the aquaculture fishery industry will be restructured to establish optimal production systems and enhance competitiveness. The number of aquaculture facilities will be reduced by about 10% over the next five years, and new licenses will not be issued for such products as laver, sea-mustard, and over-produced finfish species. In contrast, new technologies for harvesting tuna (e.g., *Katsuwonus pleanis, Thunnus albacares, T. tonggol*), mackerel (e.g., *Scomber ausriasicus, Rastrelliger kanagurta, Trachuras symmetricus*), and other high value species will be developed. In addition, to establish a cultivated fishery supply that is consumer-oriented, aquaculture techniques for high-demand fish such as tuna, yellow corvina (*Cynoscion phoxocephalus*), and horse mackerel (*Trachurus japonicus*) will be developed and promoted. By turning to more advanced aquaculture fisheries within the next five years, the MOMAF plans to encourage the industry to reduce production costs to become more competitive with imported products.

Specific Working Scenario: Gamak Bay

Background

At the Second Korea-United States Joint Coordination Panel Meeting for Aquaculture Cooperation, held in Honolulu, Hawaii in March 2004, the delegations agreed to cooperatively conduct studies on carrying capacity for ecosystem-based management. A Korea-United States working group was formed to broaden and deepen collaboration under an existing framework, and both sides continue to share scientific and technological information to develop aquaculture from an ecosystem-based management perspective. In June 2004, the

---

[1] Approximately $1.17 billion at rates effective in May 2006.

University of Georgia Sea Grant College Program (UGA), USA, and the NFRDI of MOMAF, agreed to initiate the project by modeling carrying capacity for ecosystem-based management. The UGA scientific team visited NFRDI research laboratories and was informed about on-going research at the NFRDI. In November 2004, the UGA-NFRDI working group visited the Gamak Bay study site to subsequently develop a research plan. The working group will focus on assessing carrying capacity for aquaculture, and exchanging visiting scientists, aquaculture data, and other relevant information.

Description of the Area

Gamak Bay is a closed bay surrounded by the Yeosu peninsula to the west and Dolsando Island to the east (Fig. 3). Gamak Bay is 15 km long and 12 km wide, with a total surface area

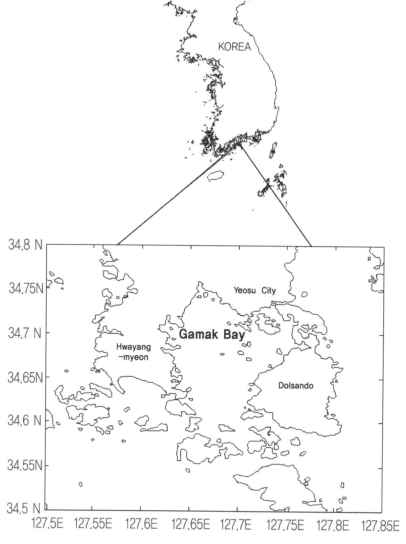

Figure 3. Overview of Gamak Bay.

of 112 km². Mean water depth is 6.3 m. The tidal range is about 3 m, with seawater exchanged through two channels into the bay. At high tide, water flows through Yeosu Harbor channel in the north and the mouth of the bay in the south.

The United States Food and Drug Administration designated area of Gamak Bay, a conditionally approved area where shellfish harvesting is prohibited for 24 hours after rainfall over 15 mm, is located at the southernmost part of Gamak Island in the middle of Gamak Bay, 6-8 km from the shoreline of Yeosu City, north of the drainage area. The designated area is also at least 200 m from the shoreline of Hwayang-Myeon and Dolsando Island, the right and left drainage areas, respectively.

Current Use

The major shellfish products of Gamak Bay are oysters (*C. gigas*), hard-shell mussel (*Mytilus edulis*), and Manila clam (*Ruditapes philippinarum*). In 2001, there were 96 permitted shellfish farms in the designated area. Most of these farms produce oysters (74 farms, 573.4 ha) and ark shells (3 farms, 33 ha). Other shellfish (19 farms, 381 ha) are also being cultured. In 2001, farms in the designated area produced 1,960 metric tons (MT) of oysters, 900 MT of blood shells, 400 MT of Manila clams, and 450 MT of various other shellfishes.

In 2002, the population in the drainage area of Gamak Bay was 257,453, with 63.3% residing on the east side of Yeosu City and 26.7% residing on its west side (Fig. 4). The eastern part of Yeosu City, where a commercial quarter and a residential district are located, had the highest density population in the area (1,301.9 individuals km⁻²). Dolsando Island, Hwayang-Myeon, and Baekyado Island had a combined total population of about 26,000.

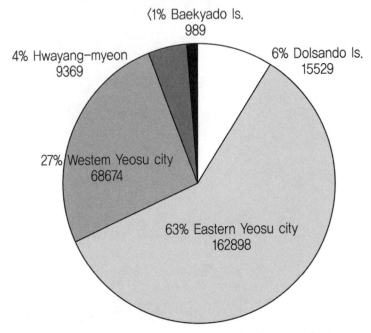

Figure 4. Population distribution (2002) in the Gamak Bay area.

The total number of domestic animals in the area was 148,433. Chickens are the largest group, followed by dogs, pigs, cattle, and goats. Large-scale chicken farms are located in Weonpo-Ri and Hwayang-Myeon. Most of the cattle are raised on Dolsando Island and in Hwayang-Myeon. The majority of pigs and goats are also raised in Hwayang-Myeon. Dogs are distributed fairly evenly throughout the area (Table 4).

Table 4. Domestic animals in the drainage area of Gamak Bay

Section No.	Administrative district	Type of animal						
		Chicken	Dog	Pig	Cattle	Goat	Others	Total
1	Dolsando Island	667	1,301	2,368	717	1,061	320	6,434
2	Yeosu City, eastern part	615	3,348	4	139	157	175	4,438
3	Yeosu City, western part	1,575	1,662	163	132	401	173	4,106
4	Hwayang-Myeon	145,405	3,397	1,864	2,247	1,302	232	154,447
5	Baegyado Island	171	95	5	126	162	5	564
Total		148,433	9,803	4,404	3,361	3,083	905	169,989

The total drainage area of Gamak Bay consists of 236.02 km², with mountainous topography at 20-388 m above sea level. Thus, 61.4% of the area is forested land. Agriculture is not developed in this area, with only 22.6% of the total area utilized as farmland. Dolsando Island and Hwayang-Myeon, located at the right and the left of the designated area, account for 68% of the total land in the drainage area (Table 5).

Table 5. Use of the drainage area of Gamak Bay.

Section No.	Administrative district	Area (km²)					
		Drainage area	Forest	Farmland	Rice paddies	Residential sites	Other
1	Dolsando Island	71.76	48.78	10.53	5.35	1.96	5.14
2	Yeosu City, eastern part	29.52	13.41	4.03	1.29	5.43	5.36
3	Yeosu City, western part	20.74	8.10	2.68	2.39	4.09	3.48
4	Hwayang-Myeon	70.14	47.92	10.57	6.09	1.17	4.39
5	Baegyado Island	4.23	2.67	1.20	0.17	0.09	0.10
Total		196.39	120.88	29.01	15.29	12.74	18.47

Chemical fertilizers commonly used in the drainage area contain nitrogen, phosphoric acid, potassium, or other nutrients. In 2002, annual usage of nitrogen, phosphoric acid, and potassium in Yeosu City was 2,395, 1,224, and 692 MT ha^{-1}, respectively. A greater amount of fertilizer was used in Hwayang-Myeon and Dolsando Island, where there are larger areas of farmland (Table 6).

Table 6. Usage and types of chemical fertilizers in the drainage area of Gamak Bay in 2002.

Section No.	Administrative district	Farmland (ha)	Amount used (MT)				
			Nitrogenous fertilizer	Phosphate fertilizer	Potassium fertilizer	Others	Total
1	Dolsando Island	15.88	502	205	208	919	1,834
2	Yeosu City, eastern part	5.32	98	42	43	127	310
3	Yeosu City, western part	5.07	157	58	64	375	654
4	Hwayang-Myeon	16.66	342	145	157	650	1,294
5	Baegyado Island	1.37	66	32	34	103	235
Total		44.30	1,165	482	506		4,327

The amount of sewage discharged from Yeosu City was about 177.90 kiloliters (kL) day^{-1}, of which 45.9 kL was treated in sewage treatment plants, although the capacity of the plants is 230 kL day^{-1}. The two sewage treatment plants in Yeosu City are located in Weolrae-Dong and in Sinweol-Dong. The final discharge from the Sinweol-Dong plant flows into Gamak Bay (Table 7).

Table 7. Sewage treatment plants in Yeosu City.

	Facility 1[a]	Facility 2[b]
Treatment method	Chemical	Chemical
Capacity	150,000 L day^{-1}	80,000 L day^{-1}
Disposal rate	130,000 L day^{-1}	70,000 L day^{-1}
Dilute water	300 m^3 day^{-1}	80 m^3 day^{-1}
Electricity usage	380 kW month^{-1}	230 kW month^{-1}

Source: Yeosu City Statistical Year Book (2003).

[a]Located at #197-22, Shinweol-Dong, Yeosu City.
[b]Located at #200-4, Weolrae-Dong, Yeosu City.

Since 1996, surveys have been conducted at streams and sewers that flow directly into Gamak Bay and were thought to affect the microbial composition in the water. Except for Yeondeung Stream, most of the streams showed drought water levels during the survey period. Moreover, 89% of the total discharge of the drainage area was domestic wastewater from densely populated Yeosu City (Table 8). Discharges from streams and sewers partially contaminated the shore area, but had no significant effects on the microbial composition of the water in the designated area.

Table 8. Streams and sewers identified in the drainage area of Gamak Bay.

Section No.	Drainage area	No. of streams and sewers		Discharge volume
		Flowing	Non flowing	L min^{-1}
1	Dolsando Island	11	24	13,150
2	Yeosu City, eastern part	9	19	168,487
3	Yeosu City, western part	6	13	26,494
4	Hwayang-Myeon	11	38	6,133
5	Baegyado Island	5	5	3,664

In Gamak Bay, seawater moves inside and outside the bay by strong tidal movements through a narrow channel in the north between Yeosu City and Dolsando Island and an entrance of the bay in the south. The maximum current velocity is variable by season and time. The current velocity in the channel between Yeosu City and Dolsando Island was found to be 125-182 cm sec^{-1}, and 50-87 cm sec^{-1} at the entrance to the bay. Current velocity was always stronger in a north-south direction.

In Gamak Bay, 87% of the total water mass is changed through the mouth of the bay in the south, and the other 13% is changed through the Yeosu Harbor channel in the north. The exchange rate of seawater in the Gamak Bay area was found to be 22%-43% per day. In addition, 77%-88% of the changed seawater moves through the bay mouth in the south, which may affect the microbial composition of the water. The moving and exchange rate of seawater is variable with time. In particular, rainfall was shown to directly affect the seawater exchange rate.

Challenges

Economic Factors

Based on major economic indicators, the income of the average aquaculture fishery household in 2002 decreased due to increased fishery production expenses and household debts (Table 9). Families engaging in finfish aquaculture suffered due to decreased supplies of feedstuffs and the increased cost of imported feeds. Producers' price indices for olive flounder, laver, and oysters probably decreased due to overproduction in 2002 (Table 10).

Table 9. Average income of aquaculture fishery households, 1998-2002 (Unit: 1,000 Won).

Year	Non-fishery Income	Transfer Income	Gross Fishery Receipts	Fishery Production Expenses	Sub-total[1]	Fishery Household Income
1998	7,283	3,015	20,728	9,049	11,680	21,978
1999	6,067	3,708	28,055	13,758	14,297	24,073
2000	7,155	4,025	30,767	16,555	14,211	25,392
2001	9,035	5,529	32,167	16,684	15,483	30,046

[1] Sub-total = Gross Fishery Receipts – Fishery Production Expenses.

Table 10. Changes in the relative producers' price indices, based on the year 2000.

Year	Marine products	Freshwater fish	All flatfish	Olive flounder	Oyster	Manila clam	Laver	Other seaweed
1998	89.5	87.1	100.0	88.4	93.3	82.0	117.0	109.3
1999	96.6	95.9	100.5	94.8	104.7	80.2	106.9	102.4
2000	100.0	100.0	100.0	100.0	100.0	100.0	100.0	100.0
2001	101.9	102.0	112.4	88.6	105.0	121.5	92.5	101.0
2002	111.7	112.9	117.7	79.6	99.3	156.3	94.0	102.4

Policies

The Ministry of Marine Affairs and Fisheries is implementing a national ocean governance strategy, "Ocean Korea 21" (OK 21), to instill confidence of the public in the health and productivity of the seas surrounding Korea, and to help Korea emerge as a leading sea power in the twenty-first century. An important part of OK 21 is its vision, "Enhancement of National Sea Power through the Blue Revolution," which has the following three basic objectives: (a) promoting the vitality of South Korea's territorial waters, (b) developing a knowledge-based marine industry, and (c) developing marine resources in a sustainable manner. To attain its vision and meet its objectives efficiently, OK 21 has set specific goals to be achieved through numerous special projects, including plans to decrease capture fisheries and increase culture-based production by establishing sustainable fishery production fundamentals. As part of the policy initiatives for sustainable development, the Korean government is developing a comprehensive program for conservation of the marine environment (MOMAF 2004; Jamieson and Zhang 2005).

Next Steps

Suggested Solutions to Problems

Aquaculture of finfish and shellfish are important industries in Korea. As mentioned previously, aquaculture of marine finfish has increased dramatically in recent years. Oyster production, however, has slowly decreased since the mid-1980s due to several factors, including unstable settlement of spat, lack of food related to intensive culture, and eutrophication of the coastal areas. In some suspended oyster culture grounds in the southern coastal bays of Korea, the condition and size of the oysters change from year to year. As a result, it takes longer to obtain a marketable product.

To maintain sustainable aquaculture production and to protect the environment, it is necessary to have an understanding of the carrying capacity of the environment. An ecosystem model based on physical factors and eutrophic processes in the coastal bay (Nakata 1991) was modified to estimate the carrying capacity for oyster culture systems and applied to Goseong Bay, one of the important oyster culture sites in Korea. Simulated values of oyster growth rate, chlorophyll α, and dissolved inorganic nitrogen concentration were confirmed with observations.

Calculations based on the model demonstrated that intensive culture had resulted in the decline of the oyster growth rate. Based on product meat weight, there were no clear differences in growth rates of oysters seeded at 12 individuals (ind) m^{-3} and 32 ind m^{-3}, but growth rates clearly decreased in oysters seeded at more than 40 ind m^{-3}. Moreover, growth rates remained stagnant at 300 ind m^{-3}. An adequate seeding density at which to obtain a marketable size oyster at the end of the culture period was found to be 16 ind m^{-3}. Based on these results and on the assumption that oysters are being cultured in the whole water volume, the optimum carrying capacity of Goseong Bay was estimated to be 12,300 MT. The available surface area for oyster culture in Goseong Bay, however, is only 13%, so the carrying capacity of this bay was estimated to be 1,500 MT meat weight, in terms of oyster culture.

Suggested Approaches to Data Collection

The NFRDI has been using physical-biological models for ecosystem-based management since the 1990s. Hydrodynamic models simulate the three-dimensional physical field in the coastal bay and predict the long-term variability of currents, tides, water temperature, salinity, and the pattern of particle tracking time (see Nakata et al. 1983 for a description of the numerical development and algorithm of the hydrodynamic models). Briefly, the model includes time-dependent tidal forcing, surface wind, and local density gradients, together with realistic coastal topography and bathymetry (Walne 1972). Model equations are based on the equation of motion, continuity, conservation of heat, and salt. The vertical mixing process is parameterized with a turbulence model of second moment closure (Ezer and Mellor 2004), which determines local distributions of the turbulent kinetic energy, k, by means of well-established k-equations.

Ecological models simulate the flux of the elements carbon, nitrogen, and phosphorous plus the mechanism of oxygen production and consumption in the pelagic system from the viewpoint of its being plankton-based (Hibbert 1977). The model applied to our present work is essentially the same as the one well described by Nakata et al. (1983). It was developed to evaluate the physical-biological interactions and water quality in an estuarine ecosystem (Haven and Morales-Alamo 1972). The model contains eight state variables called "compartments": four organic compartments expressed in carbon stock (phytoplankton, zooplankton, detritus, and dissolved organic matter), two nutrients (phosphate, nitrogen), plus dissolved oxygen and chemical oxygen demand.

Application of Ecosystem-Based Aquaculture Management

Gamak Bay Project

Implementation is the most important part of the Gamak Bay scenario within the concept of ecosystem-based aquaculture management. The results of ecosystem-based management studies in Gamak Bay will be used as the basis for enlarging and broadening the scope to other aquaculture sites in the third stage of the project. The following plan is designed to control and manage the inner shore aquaculture sites and near-shore land areas, and implements the ecosystem-based management study in aquaculture:

First Stage (2004–2005): Initial survey and evaluation of modeling needs

- NFRDI and UGA agreed to initiate carrying capacity modeling for ecosystem-based management by 2006.

- U.S. scientific team visited NFRDI and assessed project needs for models and existing data, November 2004.

- Existing data from Gamak Bay adapted to fit the Princeton Ocean Model (Mellor 2004), August 2005.

- NFRDI scientists visited UGA, USA to complete adaptation of the Princeton Ocean Model to Gamak Bay, July to August 2005.

- NFRDI to conduct monitoring and analyze water in Gamak Bay and pollutant loading near Gamak Bay, and obtain location and a time series of ocean currents, 2005.

- Appropriate water quality model to be selected to link to the Gamak Bay hydrodynamic model.

- Existing data on oysters from Gamak Bay to be evaluated for a preliminary assessment of reasons for the decline of aquaculture production. In cooperation with local universities, NFRDI will provide data on species composition and phytoplankton dynamics in Gamak Bay, 2005.

Second Stage (2006-2008): Development of a carrying capacity model for Gamak Bay

- Proposal submitted to the National Oceanic and Atmospheric Administration (NOAA) National Sea Grant College Program (USA) to support the Carrying Capacity Modeling Project, February 2005.

- NFRDI scientist to travel to UGA to work for six months on coupling the hydrodynamic and water quality model, 2006, if funds are available.

- Carrying capacity studies and ecosystem model to be used to develop an ecosystem management approach to aquaculture in Gamak Bay (Working Group), 2008.

Third Stage (2009-2010): Development of an ecosystem approach to aquaculture

- Carrying capacity studies and ecosystem model to be used to develop an ecosystem-based approach to aquaculture management in Korea (Working Group), 2008.

- Implementation of the ecosystem management plan (NFRDI), 2008-2010.

Jeju Offshore Aquaculture Project

To protect the environment and develop a sustainable aquaculture industry, aquaculture in Korea is moving towards ecosystem-based management. Korea is looking at the advantages of offshore aquaculture technology to reduce the impacts from nutrients in near-shore areas. Korean working groups, in cooperation with NOAA, will focus on offshore aquaculture as sites for new facilities, assess environmental effects, and improve guidelines.

First Stage (2005-)

- Southern Jeju was selected as the most suitable site for offshore aquaculture (Fig. 1).

- Three 3,000-m^3 offshore aquaculture units, at a depth of 40-45 m, were set up 2.898 km (1.8 miles) offshore from Jeju in May 2005. One unit is for parrotfish, *Oplegnathus fasciatus*, (one year); the others are to be two-year studies, and the target fish will be tested.

- Scientists from NOAA with expertise in offshore aquaculture attended an offshore aquaculture workshop in Jeju in July 2005.

Second Stage (2007-)

- Results of offshore aquaculture during the first stage are to be evaluated, and the possibility of offshore aquaculture will be assessed. If the offshore finfish aquaculture is successful as an economical and ecological evaluator, offshore shellfish aquaculture will be set up.

- Offshore-related guidelines to be revised if needed.

Literature Cited

Ezer, T. and G.L. Mellor. 2004. A generalized coordinate ocean model and comparison of the bottom boundary layer dynamics in terrain-following and in Z-level grids. Ocean Modelling 6: 379-403.

FAO (Food and Agriculture Organization of the United Nations). 2005. National Aquaculture Legislation Overview - Republic of Korea. FIGIS-Fisheries and Global Information System. Aquaculture. FAO, Rome, Italy. http://www.fao.org/figis/servlet/static?xml=nalo_korea.xml&dom=legalframework.

Haven, D.S. and R. Morales-Alamo. 1972. Biodeposition as a factor in sedimentation of fine suspended solids in estuaries. Pages 121-130 *in* B.W. Nelson, editor. Environmental Framework of Coastal Plain Estuaries. Vol. 133. Geological Society of America. Memoirs. Geological Society of America, Boulder, Colorado, USA.

Hibbert, C.J. 1977. Energy relations of the bivalve *Mercenaria mercenaria* on an intertidal mudflat. Marine Biology 44: 77–84.

Jamieson, G. and C.-I. Zhang, editors. 2005. Report of the study group on ecosystem based management science and its application to the North Pacific. PICES (North Pacific Marine Science Organization) Scientific Report No. 29. PICES, Sidney, British Columbia, Canada. 77 pp. http;//www.pices.int/publications/scientific_reports/.

Mellor, G.L. 2004. Users Guide for A Three-Dimensional, Primitive Equation, Numerical Ocean Model. Program in Atmospheric and Oceanic Sciences, Princeton University, Princeton. New Jersey, USA. 56 pp.

MOMAF (Ministry of Maritime Affairs and Fisheries). 2004. The Ministry of Maritime Affairs and Fisheries. http://www.momaf.go.kr/eng/main/main.asp.

Nakata, K. 1991. A model of the formation of oxygen depleted waters in Tokyo Bay.KAIKOU 5(2): 1-26.

Nakata, K., F. Horiguchi, K. Taguchi, and Y. Setoguchi. 1983. Three dimensional tidal current simulation in Oppa Bay. Bulletin of the National Research Institute of Pollution Resources 12(3): 17-36.

NFRDI (National Fisheries Research and Development Institute). 2002. Sanitary Survey of the Designated Area of Shellfish Production for Export. Report No. NFRDI-11-1520671-000008-12. NFRDI, Busan, Korea. 61 pp.

NOAA (National Oceanic and Atmospheric Administration) Central Library. 2005. Korea – US Aquaculture. United States – Korea Aquaculture Webpage. Aquaculture Information Center. Office of Oceanic and Atmospheric Research, NOAA, Washington, DC, USA. http:// www.lib.noaa.gov/docaqua/frontpage.htm

Walne, P.R. 1972. The influence of current speed, body size and water temperature on the filtration rate of five species of bivalves. Journal of the Marine Biological Association of the UK 52: 345–374.

On-line sources of statistics presented in tables and text:

- Fishery Production Survey [in Korean]. Ministry of Maritime Affairs and Fisheries, Korea. http://fs.fips.go.kr/main.jsp-.

- Korean Statistical Information System [in Korean]. Korea National Statistical Office. http://kosis.nso.go.kr.

- National Fisheries Research and Development Institute, Busan, Korea. http://nfrdi. re.kr/home/eng-nfrdi/.

- 2004 Statistical Year Book of Maritime Affairs and Fisheries [in Korean]. Ministry of Maritime Affairs and Fisheries. http://www.momaf.go.kr/doc/2004%20stat/index. html.

- Yeosu City Statistical Year Book [in Korean]. 2003. http://www.yeosu.go.kr.

THE UNITED STATES

6

Executive Summary

Faced with static capture fisheries production, relatively slow growth of the aquaculture sector, a steadily increasing trade deficit for seafood, and federal directives to implement ecosystem-based management, the United States must develop and implement strategies for aquaculture expansion that are consistent with the goals of integrated coastal and ocean management. A description of the current status and future potential of near shore molluscan shellfish culture and offshore culture of both finfish and shellfish in the Gulf of Maine region of the United States is used to illustrate the process for planning, development, and management of aquaculture within the context of ecosystem based management. Presented in this scenario are the historical perspective of fisheries and aquaculture in the region, the current and proposed policy and regulatory structure; social, economic and technical challenges; and steps that may be taken to address the most critical issues. The authors conclude that it is possible to integrate state-of-the-art aquaculture facilities within the coastal zone such that there are not only minimal negative effects but also substantial ecosystem benefits that may accrue in addition to the more obvious economic benefits.

Introduction

Status of Fishery and Aquaculture Sectors in the United States

Territorial waters of the United States have historically supported bountiful natural fisheries resources. Systematic exploitation of the fisheries began when the first European settlers began fishing Atlantic cod (*Gadus morhua*) and other cold-water species in the Northwest Atlantic in the sixteenth century. Over the next four centuries, as the remainder of the continental United States was colonized, fisheries, essentially unrestricted by any regulatory and management structure, were established for a wide variety of species in all coastal areas of the country and fishing effort and landings grew rapidly. Even as late as the early twentieth century, fisheries scientists believed that fish stocks were inexhaustible, and little effort was made to manage fishing effort. By the 1960s, however, it became obvious that overfishing, inadequate management measures, coastal pollution, and habitat destruction had caused critical declines in native stocks of marine fish. Fish stocks in all regions of the United States have declined, although in the Northwest Atlantic, this has been the most severe and caused the greatest disruption of coastal economies.

Cod, perhaps the most important fishery in the United States for nearly four centuries, best illustrates the extent of fisheries collapse. In 2003, cod landings were 25% of the total landed in 1890. Government sponsored trawl surveys, which were initiated in 1960, indicate an 85% decline in cod biomass over the past 45 years (NOAA 2005). Similar statistics exist

Contributors: Langan, R., R.I.E. Newell, J.P. McVey, C. Newell, J.W. Sowles, J.E. J. Rensel, J. Grant, and C. Yarish

In J.P. McVey, C.-S. Lee, and P.J. O'Bryen, editors. Aquaculture and Ecosystems: An Integrated Coastal and Ocean Management Approach. The World Aquaculture Society, Baton Rouge, Louisiana, United States.

for other species such as Atlantic swordfish (*Xiphias gladius*), tunas (*Thunnus* spp.), Pacific rockfishes (*Sebastes* spp.) and Gulf of Mexico snappers (*Lutjanus* spp. and *Rhomboplites aurorubens*) and groupers (*Mycteroperca* spp. and *Epinephelus* spp.). Some areas of the United States still maintain fairly significant capture fisheries production; the notable example being the Alaskan pollock (*Theragra chalcogramma*) fishery, which accounts for nearly half of the nation's landings, and which in 2003 totaled 4,309,128 metric tons (MT) valued at $3.2 billion (NOAA 2005). Management measures for overexploited fisheries have been implemented and recovery for some stocks is expected, although the timeframe for achieving fully recovered status is unknown. It is also expected that even if stocks do recover, fishing effort will continue to be strictly controlled and overall landings will not increase significantly.

United States aquaculture contributes less than 10% of the total domestic edible seafood supply, with 2003 production of approximately 420,000 MT valued at just under $1 billion. Therefore, as a percentage of the total, U.S. aquaculture production is far below the global portion, which is now approaching 40%. In addition, only a small fraction of U.S. aquaculture production comes from marine species. Channel catfish (*Ictalurus punctatus*), grown primarily in ponds in the southern United States, accounts for 80% of the total weight and 64% of the total domestic aquaculture production value. Aquaculture production of marine and estuarine species, primarily molluscs (oysters, clams, mussels), salmon and shrimp, is valued at $150 million, with nearly $120 million of the total coming from mollusc culture (NOAA 2005). The combined domestic production of aquaculture and capture fisheries is well below the demand. The United States imports more than 70% of the seafood consumed. This reliance on imports has resulted in an ever-increasing trade deficit for edible seafood products, which now approaches nearly $9 billion annually.

Commercial finfish aquaculture has been slow to develop, particularly for marine species. Channel catfish culture in freshwater was initiated in the 1960s, primarily to provide crop diversity for inland agriculture, and rapidly helped improve the economy of land farms. Channel catfish is the most important freshwater species, although other species such as trout (*Oncorhynchus* spp. and *Salmo trutta*), tilapia (*Oreochromis* spp.) and hybrid striped bass (*Morone chrysops* x *M. saxatilis*) are produced in raceways, ponds, and tanks. While the United States has a long history of hatchery production of Pacific salmon (*Oncorhyncus* spp.) for stock enhancement, commercial farming of Atlantic salmon (*Salmo salar*) did not begin until the late 1960s. Through the 1980s, advances in husbandry techniques and the development of commercial feeds led to a rapid expansion of the industry worldwide. In the United States, most of the farmed salmon production was concentrated in the sheltered coastal waters of northeastern Maine and Washington State, where environmental conditions were favorable for year round production. Domestic production increased steadily throughout the 1980s and 1990s and peaked in 2001 at a farm gate value just under $100 million. Along with this tremendous growth, however, came increasing environmental concerns. It soon became apparent that poorly sited and poorly managed operations were causing adverse environmental impacts. Incidents of seafloor pollution from uneaten feed and fish wastes, outbreaks of diseases, use of antibiotics and biocides, and escapement of fish from sea cages led to increasing opposition to the expansion of salmon farming.

In response to criticism and subsequent regulatory scrutiny, the salmon farming industry began to improve management practices to address environmental concerns. Better feed formulations and careful monitoring of the feeding behavior of fish resulted in improved feed conversion ratios and less waste. Vaccines drastically reduced the use of antibiotics. Fallowing cage sites allowed impacted benthic communities to recover. These improvements, however, were incremental, and for the industry's detractors, they came too late. Strong opposition to salmon farms persists, and if anything, has increased in recent years, often focusing on issues that to a large extent have been solved. So, despite these improvements, opposition to salmon farming in the United States remains strong, and approval of new farm sites is difficult and costly.

Harvesting natural mollusc populations, particularly oysters, has a relatively long history in the United States, and oyster cultivation practices date back to the mid nineteenth century. At the turn of the twentieth century, the United States was the largest oyster producer in the world. Oysters were regularly consumed by all segments of the domestic population and substantial quantities were exported. Early on, the industry was concentrated in the mid-Atlantic, Gulf of Mexico, and in the Pacific Northwest. In Virginia, some of these harvested oysters were relayed onto private leased oyster bottom where they were held until retail prices were more favorable. In some states, small oysters were planted onto leased bottom and grown to harvest size, but such private aquaculture production was always minor compared to the wild fishery. Overfishing and disease decimated east coast production, which today is a fraction of historical levels. The east coast shellfish industry now consists of small to medium sized farms, producing oysters, clams, and smaller quantities of mussels. The Gulf of Mexico, and specifically, the state of Louisiana, where extensive bottom culture of wild produced oyster seed is the primary means of production, is the leading producer of oysters in United States. Intensive aquaculture of hatchery produced Pacific oysters (*Crassostrea gigas*) along the Pacific coast has blossomed over the past 60 years. Today, the State of Washington, which also has substantial aquaculture production of several species of clams and mussels, is the overall top producer of shellfish in the United States. Mollusc culture is more broadly accepted in the United States as an environmentally benign if not beneficial activity, and consequently, enjoys less opposition to expansion than finfish culture, though resistance for aesthetic reasons from shorefront property owners continues to be a factor limiting expansion.

Several species of macroalgae are harvested from the wild in the United States, although cultivation of edible seaweeds is uncommon. *Porphyra* sp. (nori) cultivation in the northeast United States is thought to have the single greatest potential for generating a viable seaweed mariculture industry. A commercial venture of nori cultivation began in Portland, Maine in the late 1990s. Due to financial repositioning, however, the farm sites were abandoned and the company ceased operations. Recent field experiments (Chopin et al. 1999; McVey et al. 2002) indicate that *Porphyra* sp. culture integrated with salmonid culture can successfully remove excess nutrients generated by salmon farming. Recognizing that algae can reduce nutrient impact in waters around salmon farms and provide an additional harvestable crop, researchers and the salmon aquaculture industry are continuing to experiment with integrated culture of *Porphyra* sp. and salmon.

Production Data and Goals

The 2003 production data for the fisheries and aquaculture sectors presented above are the most recent figures for which there is confirmed documentation. If trends that have been observed over the past few years continue, little change in capture fisheries landings, modest growth in the shellfish sector, and continued decline in salmon production are expected. There are several initiatives that have been put forward that, if successful, may influence the growth of aquaculture production in the United States. In 1999, the U.S. Department of Commerce (parent organization of the National Oceanic and Atmospheric Administration or NOAA) issued an Aquaculture Policy recommending an increase in aquaculture production five-fold from $1 billion to $5 billion by 2025. This ambitious goal would depend upon investments in science, technology, and industry infrastructure that have not occurred since the passage of the policy. A report produced by the three-year study conducted by the U.S. Commission on Ocean Policy (USCOP 2004) recognized the growing importance of aquaculture, and cites the potential for industry growth in offshore waters. The report recommends that Congress should designate NOAA as the lead federal agency for marine aquaculture, and that more resources should be made available for aquaculture research, technology development, technology transfer, training, and education. Research activities supported by NOAA to date have resulted in technological advancements that have shown good prospects for large scale increases in finfish production in offshore waters with minimal environmental consequences. With offshore technology advancing, and data indicating the environmental effects in offshore locations are greatly reduced, the United States has begun to address regulatory impediments to offshore development. The Department of Commerce submitted the National Offshore Aquaculture Act to Congress in June 2005. This bill would establish a much-needed regulatory framework for permitting aquaculture operations in the U.S. Exclusive Economic Zone (EEZ). If this legislation is approved by Congress, permits for offshore farms may be issued as soon as 2007.

Whatever goals are established for increased domestic aquaculture production, activities that will be implemented to achieve them will need to be conducted in a manner that is consistent with broader goals for integrated ocean management. The NOAA is now implementing plans for ecosystem-based management for environmental, fisheries, and aquaculture activities. This view of a holistic and integrated management system incorporates the use of seafloor mapping and geospatial technologies, social sciences, environmental and fisheries models based on hydrographic, biological, and nutrient considerations, and an interconnected understanding of the roles of physical, biotic, and human activity factors in ecosystems. To do this, NOAA has adopted the concept of matrix management to address key coastal resource management issues. Matrix management involves the contributions of all stakeholders on any one issue in a coordinated way. This integrated management approach combines environmental, engineering, biological, and socioeconomic factors that can be adjusted and optimized as outcomes develop. For marine aquaculture, this management approach can be employed such that the benefits of aquaculture can be maximized while minimizing user conflict and negative environmental impact.

Regulatory Structure for Marine Aquaculture

Regulatory jurisdiction for aquaculture activities in waters that extend out from the shoreline for 4.83 km (3 miles) resides with individual states, and in the U.S. EEZ that extends from 4.83 km (3 miles) out to 322 km (200 miles), with the federal government. Aquaculture policy, regulatory structure, and the permitting process vary from state to state. Some states require separate permits from several agencies and even from municipalities. A federal permit from the U.S. Army Corps of Engineers (ACOE) is required regardless of state policy and regulatory structure. This permit triggers review by other federal agencies and by the state's Coastal Zone Management entity for federal consistency. The ACOE also solicits comments from the Regional Fishery Management Councils that were established under the Magnuson-Stevens Fisheries Conservation and Management Act (1976). Review by the Councils often results in misapplication of statutes and policy intended for managed wild fisheries. Finfish aquaculture operations for farms exceeding annual production of 45,000 kg (100,000 lbs) must also obtain a National Pollution Discharge Elimination System (NPDES) discharge permit. Some states are vested with permitting authority by the U.S. Environmental Protection Agency (EPA), and in other states, the EPA issues permits, with state agencies only being involved in compliance review. In all states, the process of obtaining a permit (or permits) frequently takes years because of numerous state, federal, and local agencies involved, in addition to requirements for public hearings to address local concerns by the public, community officials, and environmental groups. At present, there is no regulatory process for aquaculture within federally managed waters (EEZ) and consequently, there are no commercial aquaculture facilities in the EEZ. Greater detail on federal and state agencies with regulatory or decision making authority is presented in Appendix 6-1 at the end of this chapter.

Specific Working Scenario: The Gulf of Maine

Description of the Area

The Gulf of Maine (Fig. 1) is a semi-enclosed sea in the western North Atlantic Ocean, bounded on the west by the states of Massachusetts, New Hampshire, and Maine and to the north by the Canadian Maritime provinces of New Brunswick and Nova Scotia. The seaward boundary is defined by the relatively shallow Brown Banks to the east and Georges Bank to the south. The Gulf's ocean currents are driven by a flow of cold arctic water from the Labrador current that enters the Gulf from the northeast, flowing over the Scotian Shelf and Browns Bank and through the Northeast Channel, creating a counterclockwise gyre that gains momentum from the world's most powerful tidal surges released from the Bay of Fundy, and from the fresh water that flows into the Gulf from the major rivers of its watershed. The Gulf of Maine is classified as a macrotidal water body, with diurnal tides that range from 2 m in the southwestern Gulf to more than 20 m in the Bay of Fundy.

The Gulf of Maine's bathymetry consists of the outer banks (Browns and Georges) and deep basins in the central portion that are interrupted by shallow subsea ridges and peaks. The uneven bathymetry and complex hydrography generate upwelling of nutrient rich bottom

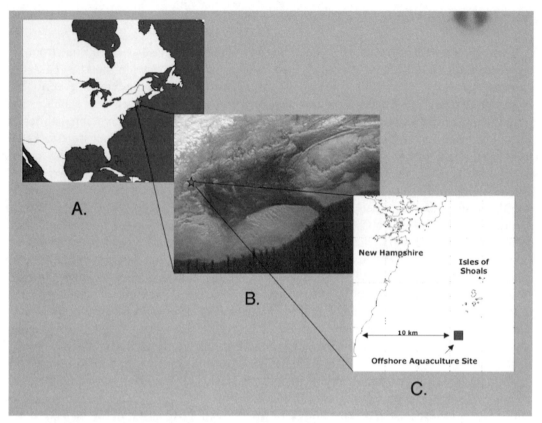

Figure 1. Map of the U.S. East Coast (A), a bathymetric map of the Gulf of Maine (B), and a map showing the location of the offshore aquaculture site described in the U.S. scenario (C)

water that fuels high productivity at all trophic levels. The shoreline consists of expanses of exposed open coastline interspersed with protected embayments and drowned river valley type estuaries, the largest and most numerous of which are located in the northeast portion of the coast. Land use along the coast ranges from highly urbanized in the southwest portion to rural in the northeast, although in the U.S. portion of the Gulf, there is rapid coastal development and a change in the demographics and economic base along the entire coastline. The Gulf of Maine supports a diversity of water dependent activities, including commercial and recreational fishing, recreational boating, commercial shipping, and ecotourism.

Historical Background

The Gulf of Maine historically supported valuable fisheries for species such as Atlantic cod, haddock (*Melanogrammus aeglefinus*), and flounder (*Hippoglossoides platessoides, Pseudopleuronectes americanus, Limanda furruginea, Glyptocephalus cynoglossus*). These fisheries were an important contributor to the region's economy until overfishing and wasteful fishing practices collapsed the stocks by the mid 1990s. Current conservation management is allowing fish stocks to gradually rebuild, although it is considered unlikely that they will ever recover to historically high levels. Human activity in the watersheds of many of the rivers that flow into the Gulf of Maine (e.g., construction of dams, agricultural development, industrial pollution, etc.) has irreversibly degraded much of the pristine habitat required to support populations of many estuarine and diadromous species, adding to the adverse effects of over-fishing. Today, the most important commercial fishery is trap fishing for lobsters (*Homarus americanus*). Other active fisheries include dragging for sea scallops (*Placopecten magelanicus*) and seine and trawl fisheries for lower trophic level pelagic fish species such as herring (*Clupea harengus*) and mackerel (*Scomber scombrus*).

Since the implementation of the Clean Water Act (1973), government regulations have succeeded in reducing discharges of untreated sewage and industrial pollutants. In the Gulf of Maine, the resulting improvements in water quality have allowed a steady increase in blue mussel (*Mytilus edulis*) and eastern oyster (*Crassostrea virginica*) aquaculture over the past three decades. This was fostered by the development of hatchery seed production and improvements in bottom culture methods for oysters and mussels. Environmental, fishery, and aquaculture laws are well developed in the state of Maine, and locations without severe conflicts with existing fisheries, navigation, and recreational users are generally approved for on-bottom shellfish aquaculture. In the mid-1990s, mussel suspension culture was also adopted, although permits for surface-referenced suspension culture are more difficult to obtain than for on-bottom culture. Most of the shellfish farms in the region are small to medium size and the industry now produces about $20 million annually.

Marine finfish aquaculture in the Gulf of Maine region began in the late 1960s, when Atlantic salmon farms were established in Cobscook Bay, Maine. The industry grew rapidly, though most farms were restricted to Northeast Maine, where human population density is low, unemployment is high, and conditions are most favorable for salmonid culture. In 2001, production peaked at a value $100 million, but has since declined appreciably due to a number of factors, including infectious salmon anemia disease, foreign competition, and a highly restrictive regulatory environment.

Description of Current Production Sectors: Inshore Molluscan Shellfish Culture

In the northeastern portion of the Gulf, there are numerous sheltered bays and estuaries that can support expansion of molluscan shellfish culture. The best locations for on-bottom cultivation of suspension feeding bivalves have firm sandy/mud sediments that prevent burial of the shellfish. Optimum mean water current velocities of 10-30 cm sec^{-1} provide sufficient food flux for rapid animal growth and enough oxygen to maintain aerobic sediments (see Appendix 6-2 at the end of this chapter). For suspended bivalve culture, mean velocities of 7-15 cm sec^{-1} are adequate (Panchang et al. 1997; Dudley et al. 2000). Locations sheltered from wind and ocean waves are a general prerequisite for shellfish aquaculture using the currently employed raft-culture technologies.

The initial sites for suspension culture of blue mussels were established in locations where the wild harvest produced high yields and there was an absence of blooms of the dinoflagellate *Alexandrium tamarensis*, the organism responsible for paralytic shellfish poisoning. Promising sites were further characterized by measuring water current and modeling water flow, and a single mussel raft was then installed at the 10 best potential locations. Production data from these rafts were then used to select five sites with highest annual production. At these sites, further development, including strengthening the rafts and mooring systems, and refining sea duck exclusion netting, has allowed annual production of 400,000 kg live weight from 12 rafts, with production expected to triple within five years.

The five raft culture sites in coastal Maine are good examples of combined activities of a wild blue mussel fishery, mussel culture on and off-bottom, fisheries, and tourism. Eelgrass (*Zostera marina*) beds in this region are important for primary settlement of blue mussel larvae (Newell et al. 1991; Grizzle et al. 1996) and so aquaculture sites have to be managed to protect these beds. At all shellfish lease sites, monitoring has shown increases in biodiversity of the animal community, including several species of invertebrates on mussel ropes (sea cucumbers, sea urchins, polychaete worms, shrimp) and under the rafts (crabs and starfish) as well as sea ducks and fish. Mussels that fall from the ropes are consumed by benthic predators that also bioturbate and oxygenate the sediments. The shells from these fallen mussels serve as habitat for other benthic species, further increasing benthic biodiversity. Such secondary benefits have frequently been observed in off-bottom mussel aquaculture (Grant et al. 1995). Conflicts with riparian landowners are now being minimized by making mussel rafts less visually obtrusive by reducing their vertical profile and locating them over 300 m from shore. Locating rafts in deep water overlying soft sediments that are not ideal lobster habitat has solved conflicts with the lobster fishery, which prefers unrestricted access to all bottom waters inhabited by lobsters.

Shellfish culture for human consumption requires water that is not affected by sewage or industrial effluents. The positive economic impact of the shellfish aquaculture industry on coastal communities has provided impetus for improving and protecting water quality. The potential for job creation in the shellfish cultivation and processing sectors has motivated state agencies to increase their efforts to eliminate point-source discharges. These activities have received broad public support and many water quality-monitoring volunteers now aid the State of Maine in identifying pollution sources and reclassifying growing waters.

In the southwestern portion of the Gulf, where many of the bays and estuaries are impacted by anthropogenic nutrient enrichment, molluscan shellfish and seaweed culture could be used for mitigation eutrophic conditions, providing a viable alternative to costly nutrient reduction measures (see Appendix 6-2 at the end of this chapter).

Description of Current Production Sectors:
Offshore Finfish and Shellfish Pilot Project

In 1999, the University of New Hampshire (UNH), in partnership with other regional research institutions, commercial fishermen, and aquaculture firms, established a 12 ha offshore aquaculture demonstration facility in the Gulf of Maine (Fig. 1). There are many advantages of working in the open ocean, including excellent water quality and tremendous water flow for dispersion and assimilation of wastes. Despite the advances that have occurred over the past several years, challenges still remain before significant investment in offshore aquaculture is justified. These include conflict with commercial fishing activities, poorly defined economic risk, the lack of a regulatory framework for offshore leasing, and resistance from the environmental community.

This offshore aquaculture demonstration facility was designed to develop and demonstrate technologies for the cultivation of several native finfish species in submerged cages and native shellfish species tethered to submerged longlines. A facility was established 10 km from shore and near a group of small offshore islands known as the Isles of Shoals. These islands are shared by the states of Maine and New Hampshire and extend their respective boundaries to approximately 12 km from the mainland. This location provided an opportunity to establish an aquaculture site representative of open ocean conditions, yet still within the state boundary. The advantage of being within state jurisdiction is that there is an established procedure for obtaining state aquaculture permits. Currently, this project is the only aquaculture operation in the open ocean environment in the Northeast United States, although there are comparable demonstration/commercial facilities operating elsewhere, including Hawaii and Puerto Rico.

The offshore installation includes a submerged grid mooring system that occupies approximately 12 ha of seafloor and can accommodate up to four submersible finfish cages. Adjacent to these sea cages, shellfish can be suspended from two submerged longlines that occupy an area approximately 400 x 12 m (Fig. 2). The submerged longlines used to cultivate shellfish are better able to withstand the rough offshore waters than the rafts used for near shore cultivation of blue mussels. Surface structures include two automated feeders that deliver pelletized fish food, and an environmental monitoring buoy. To date, three sea cages have been used to produce small quantities (5,000 kg live weight) of Atlantic halibut (*Hippoglossus hippoglossus*), haddock (6,000 kg), and a larger quantity of Atlantic cod (32,000 fish initially stocked) that will be harvested in fall 2005 with an estimated market value of $200,000. With four 3,000-m^3 cages operating at full stocking capacity, this site is capable of producing 300,000 kg live weight of fish annually. Depending on the species cultivated, annual gross revenues could range from $1.3 million to $1.6 million. The two shellfish longlines have been used for experimental blue mussel and sea scallop culture. At full production capacity for blue mussels, the installation would yield 11,000 kg live weight annually, valued at $30,250. Some experimental sea urchin cage culture has also been conducted at the site.

The sea floor beneath the offshore site is primarily muddy sand, with patches of gravel and small rock outcroppings. Due to the water depth (52 m), there are no benthic macrophytes in the immediate vicinity. Benthic macrofaunal communities consist of epifaunal crustaceans (shrimp, lobster, and crab), echinoderms (predominantly asteroids), and molluscs (sea scallops). The infaunal community is dominated by polychaetes, but also includes crustaceans, molluscs, and hydrozoans (burrowing anemones). Demersal fish (gadoids and flounders) frequent the area, as do pelagic (herring, mackerel) and migratory species (striped bass, bluefish, [*Pomatomus saltatrix*], tuna). Marine mammals (seals, whales) and seabirds of many species are also observed in the vicinity of the site. Adverse interaction with these species is avoided by maintenance of taut lines and nets that do not allow entanglement.

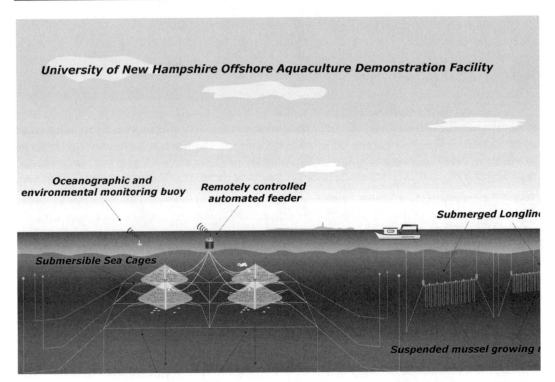

Figure 2. A drawing showing components of the offshore aquaculture site described in the U.S. scenario.

The aquaculture infrastructure (moorings, cages, etc.) provides substrate for a wide variety of colonizing organisms including hydroids, molluscs, small crustaceans, and polychaetes. Similarly the three-dimensional habitat and the food resources present in the invertebrate community attract small fish (e.g., cunner [*Tautogolabrus adspersus*], herring, and juvenile pollack [*Pollachius virens*]). These small fish then attract larger piscivorous fish, such as striped bass, bluefish and tuna. The planktonic communities are typical of the Gulf of Maine, consisting of zooplankton dominated by copepods, with seasonally high abundances of larval forms of fish and benthic invertebrates; and a phytoplankton community dominated by diatoms and flagellates.

One of the requirements for obtaining state and federal permits was detailed physical and biological characterization of the offshore site and an assessment of the potential impacts of the proposed activities. The assessment was conducted over a one year period and included:

- Physical characteristics: bathymetry, bottom substrate, waves, currents, water column profiles of oxygen, turbidity, and dissolved nutrients;

- Biological communities: epifauna, infauna, marine mammals and turtles, water column primary productivity;

- Simulation modeling of dispersion and fate of wastes; and

- Assessment of the risk of entanglements by marine mammals and turtles.

This characterization provided fundamental information about the suitability of the site for culturing fish and shellfish and served as a baseline for monitoring potential impacts of the aquaculture activities. Eight monitoring stations were established prior to the commencement of fish culture and have been maintained for the past six years. Stations upstream (2) of the sea cages, in the predicted depositional zone (4), and downstream (2) of the sea cages were initially sampled on a monthly schedule and are now sampled quarterly. The primary indicators that are used to track potential impacts include:

- Water column: dissolved nutrients, chlorophyll concentration, turbidity, dissolved oxygen

- Sediments: grain size, total organic content, depth redox potential zone

- Infaunal benthos: species diversity, density, and biomass

- Epifaunal communities: presence-absence and relative abundance

The monitoring program has been unable to detect any changes in any of the measured parameters over the six-year operational period. For water column nutrients, the lack of any nutrient output signal from the operation is likely due to masking by the naturally nutrient-rich waters of the Gulf. Estimates made by Sowles (2001) of the nitrogen inputs (Table 1) clearly show that natural offshore nutrients overwhelm any contribution by finfish aquaculture in the open ocean waters of the Gulf of Maine. This is typical of many offshore locations. The general increased carrying capacity of offshore waters is one of the main reasons for considering offshore locations for fed aquaculture species.

Table 1. Sources of Nitrogen to the Gulf of Maine (from Sowles 2001).

Nitrogen Sources to the Gulf of Maine	Rate: 10^3 M ton yr^{-1} (% total)
Offshore	2512 (94 %)
Precipitation	130 (4.8 %)
Point Source	25 (0.9 %)
Riverine	11 (0.4 %)
Finfish Aquaculture	3 (0.1 %)
Non-Point	Not estimated
Total	2681

Challenges

Socioeconomic, Cultural, and Ecological Factors

Though some types of aquaculture have been conducted in the region for more than four decades, industry expansion is still viewed with skepticism by some sectors in coastal communities. Many traditional capture fishermen view aquaculture as a competitor for territory and market share, and object to private "ownership" of the water and seafloor. Some fishermen, however, now combine aquaculture activities with their seasonal fisheries. For example, one fisherman in Maine is restricted to 51 days of finfish trawling annually. He is supplementing his fishing income with two blue mussel rafts in Frenchman Bay, and a seeding and maintenance contract on nearby mussel rafts using his 25 m fishing vessel. The Maine Aquaculture Training Institute was established to re-train commercial fishermen to run mussel and oyster farms, and many of its 25 graduates have now established shellfish farms in Maine. This training, combined with a state program for start-up aquaculture companies that allows for annual aquaculture licenses for small plots and for two-year experimental leases for larger operations, has helped expand the regional aquaculture industry. Since 1998, partnerships between commercial fishermen and a large, commercial mussel producer have been growing mussels on rafts along the Maine coast.

Blue mussel longline culture technology developed by the University of New Hampshire offshore aquaculture demonstration project has been transferred to the local fishing industry. Commercial fishermen have established two offshore mussel farms at a site 5 km from the UNH demonstration site and began production in spring 2005. Initial production will be limited to 60,000 kg ($165,000) annually, however, the success of these operations will likely result in new farms and expansion of the existing sites. Supplemental revenue from mussel culture could allow some nearshore fishermen to remain in the fishing industry through the current and expected future restrictions on fishing days. A potential build-out scenario for the immediate New Hampshire coast is annual production of 700,000 kg ($1.9 million), and for the entire Gulf of Maine, annual production of approximately 4 million kg ($11 million) is a conservative estimate.

Tuna penning is another enterprise where traditional fishermen and aquaculturists may find common ground. The U.S. fishery for Atlantic bluefin tuna (*Thunnus thynnus*) has experienced economic hardship in recent years due to depressed export prices. It may be possible to hold fish in offshore pens for a short period and to harvest the captive fish when markets are favorable. This strategy could provide substantially higher returns for the fishermen.

Additional social challenges have arisen due to the changing demographics of coastal towns. Over the past two decades, coastal communities have experienced an influx of people that have purchased waterfront property and built expensive vacation homes and in some cases permanent residences. This dynamic has resulted in a tremendous increase in waterfront property value, making it difficult to maintain the waterfront infrastructure needed to support marine resource industries and displacing long-time residents that work in these industries. In addition, homeowners often object to aquaculture operations for aesthetic reasons and have had substantial influence through expensive litigation and appeals of permitting decisions.

Ecological and environmental challenges include both the effects of aquaculture on the environment (details presented in Appendix 6-2 at the end of this chapter) and the effects of the environment on aquaculture. While some of the impacts described in Appendix 6-2 have been documented for U.S. aquaculture operations, a great deal of progress has been made in addressing many of these issues. Effective tools for proper siting of aquaculture facilities are available, and the U.S. salmon farming industry has successfully improved management practices to address environmental concerns. Better feed formulations and careful monitoring of feed loss has resulted in improved feed conversion ratios and less waste. The introduction of vaccines has greatly reduced the use of antibiotics. All salmon farming sites in Maine and Washington State presently meet NPDES performance standards for retention of all adverse benthic impacts within 30 m of the sea cages, and in Washington, all the farms are operated continuously (Rensel 2001; Nash 2001). Maine has similarly overseen a monitoring program that provides fast feedback to growers when signs of excessive benthic loading have been detected (Normandeau Associates, Inc. and Batelle 2003). Optimum loading or fallowing cage sites has allowed benthic communities to assimilate wastes suitably or recover rapidly if overloaded. Further refinement of culture practices will no doubt lead to increasingly sustainable production.

Unfortunately, groups and individuals opposed to aquaculture continue to distribute inaccurate and outdated information to the media that has adversely influenced public opinion (e.g., that antibiotics continue to be widely used). Regulatory agencies have difficulty making informed decisions when faced with such public pressure. The movement of finfish aquaculture to offshore environments has been proposed as a solution to some of the environmental problems and data obtained to date from the few active offshore operations in the United States may support this assumption. Environmental activist groups, however, contend that moving cage culture of fish to the open ocean is simply moving the problem from one place to another, and they have launched a campaign to impede offshore development. In the face of this criticism, which seems to have a great deal of influence on public opinion and government policy, a new approach to aquaculture development must be considered.

Natural and human induced environmental conditions also pose challenges to aquaculture operations and to industry expansion. Pollution from land based activities poses the greatest threat to molluscan shellfish culture. Continued development and the proliferation of impervious surfaces in coastal watersheds, coupled with the lack of effective storm water management, have resulted in increased non-point source contaminant loading to near-shore waters. Naturally occurring harmful algal blooms on the Northeast and Northwest coasts cause temporary closure and suspension of shellfish harvest activities. Some areas in Maine are subject to closure for extended periods, restricting their suitability for shellfish culture. Disease and parasite transmission to farmed species from wild hosts can result in mass mortalities and additional costs for treatment. Predation on both finfish and shellfish has resulted in crop losses and damage to culture systems. In locations where predators are present, exclusion measures must be taken. Though technology for offshore culture has advanced in recent years, high-energy offshore environments still pose challenges for profitable operations. More robust moorings and cages, longer transit time for vessels and personnel, and extensive use of SCUBA diving all contribute to higher operating costs.

An additional challenge for aquaculture development is the lack of government investment in research and development and the lack of private sector capital for industry expansion. Investment by the U.S. federal government is far below that of other developed countries and must increase substantially. The private sector has been hampered by U.S. regulatory structure. Prospects may improve for investment in offshore aquaculture development if Congress approves the National Offshore Aquaculture Act.

User Conflicts

Siting aquaculture facilities in estuarine and protected coastal waters of the United States continues to be a contentious issue. In these locations, aquaculture must compete with many other activities, including commercial shipping, recreational uses, and commercial fishing. Additionally, there are significant conflicts over aesthetics between aquaculturists and coastal landowners who object to the "visual pollution" of aquaculture operations. Since aquaculture is relatively new compared to more traditional uses such as commercial fishing, it has failed to achieve a level of legitimacy equal to more established activities. In the open ocean, the primary user conflict is with commercial fishing. In addition to site-specific conflicts, commercial fishing interests have an expectation of free and open access to the ocean and have a cultural and philosophical objection to private "ownership" and exclusive use of the seafloor and water column. Conflicts between wild-harvest fishers and aquaculturists can be an impediment in permitting aquaculture, depending on the type of local fishery gear employed. For example, where trawling is prevalent (e.g., Maine) or fish gill netting widespread (Puget Sound, Washington), serious conflicts may occur, but these can be mitigated through planning and stakeholder meetings before the formal permit process is initiated. Local and regional fisheries managers in many cases have published maps showing the location of prime fishing grounds and these can be consulted prior to aquaculture site selection to minimize conflicts. Some fisheries sectors have begun to realize unanticipated benefits of aquaculture installations. The sport and commercial Dungeness crab (*Cancer magister*) fishery in Puget Sound actually focus their fishing activity near some sea cages, because the catch per unit effort is usually much better. In Maine, draggers have found greater densities of scallops around salmon cages. In New Hampshire, lobster fishers report better catch rates when setting gear adjacent to the offshore demonstration farm. If the fishing industry can be convinced that some amount of direct or indirect benefit can be gained from aquaculture, conflict between these two production sectors can be substantially reduced.

Policymaking and Consolidation of Agencies

As stated in the introductory section of this chapter, the U.S. policy and regulatory structure for aquaculture suffers from fragmentation, complexity, and inconsistency, resulting in a difficult, time consuming, and costly application process. The extensive list of agencies and their roles in aquaculture permitting and review (Appendix 6-1 at the end of this chapter) is ample proof that the current structure needs consolidation and streamlining. Some states have moved toward implementing a more streamlined permitting process, but this remains the exception rather than the rule. Decisions on policy and regulatory changes for state waters must be made within the individual states, though federal permits (e.g., ACOE permit) would still be required regardless of any policy changes enacted at the state level. Ideally, states would establish a lead agency and require a single permit application that would satisfy the requirements of all the federal, state, and local agencies involved in permitting and review.

As previously mentioned, there is currently no process in place for permitting aquaculture operations in the EEZ. The National Offshore Aquaculture Act submitted to Congress in 2005 represents an opportunity to develop a more efficient process. This legislation would establish the Department of Commerce (and very likely NOAA) as the lead agency and the central point of contact for applicants, and the liaison to other agencies that require additional permits (e.g., NPDES), and those with responsibility for review and comment. This act responds directly to the U.S. Commission on Ocean Policy's recommendations for NOAA to develop a comprehensive, environmentally sound permitting and regulatory program for offshore aquaculture, and fulfills the Administration's commitment, in the U.S. Ocean Action Plan, to propose national offshore aquaculture legislation in the 2005 Congressional session.

Next Steps

Suggested Solutions to Problems

With little prospect for increased production from capture fisheries, the United States must increase the domestic aquaculture sector to reduce its reliance on seafood imports. Given the current state and projected future direction of ocean management and policy, it is clear that for marine aquaculture to succeed, it must be fully integrated with the collective efforts to implement ecosystem-based management and included in the broader Integrated Coastal Management framework. Therefore, strategies for management of existing operations and new development must not only embrace the social and economic goals associated with seafood production, but also be consistent with broader goals to restore and sustain the health, productivity, and biological diversity of the oceans.

Ecosystem-based management is an integrated approach to management that considers the entire ecosystem, including humans. The goal of ecosystem-based management is to maintain an ecosystem in a healthy, productive, and resilient condition, maintaining diversity and abundance of natural flora and fauna as well as providing for human use of resources and services. Ecosystem-based management differs from current approaches that usually focus on a single species, sector, activity or concern; it considers the cumulative impacts and interactions between sectors.

The primary purpose of marine aquaculture is commercial food production. Related purposes include fisheries enhancement, ornamental fish, aquarium supply and medicinal-biochemical production. It should be recognized that while products of aquaculture are similar to those of capture fisheries, it is a different activity and must be managed accordingly. For aquaculture production to be consistent with the concept of ecosystem-based management, it must be undertaken in a way that results in acceptable changes to the local environment, i.e., it must be sustainable. Therefore, to be consistent with this paradigm, a strategy must be implemented for developing the policy and regulatory framework and management structure that will promote long-term sustainability and compatibility with other goals.

The concept of using aquaculture species to provide either new ecosystem services or replace those lost from the decline of natural populations is the basis of managed ecosystem aquaculture (Chopin and Yarish 1999; Chopin et al. 1999; McVey et al. 2002; Neori et al. 2004). Managed ecosystem aquaculture may require adjusting production goals of farms that have previously focused on working at maximum production capacity (Smaal et al. 1998). To achieve the benefits associated with managed ecosystem aquaculture, production goals should be determined by the assimilation capacity of a given location. Natural capacity can be augmented by integrating multiple trophic levels of cultured organisms. By using extractive aquaculture species such as seaweeds and bivalve molluscs to remove some of the nutrients inputs from fed aquaculture, it is conceivable that a system in which economic returns are maximized and environmental impacts are minimized can be established (McVey et al. 2002). (See Appendix 6-2 for more complete details).

The biomass of extractive organisms, such as macroalgae and bivalves (may be cultivated, or exist in natural populations), necessary to remove the nutrients introduced from fed aquaculture and other sources of nitrogen is difficult to determine precisely because it is so dependent on local environmental factors. Consequently, knowledge of the processes involved can be combined with local environmental conditions to parameterize predictive ecosystem models. Such models will allow managers to estimate the biomass of each aquaculture component required to balance the nutrient budget. A perfect balance may not always be necessary because well-flushed coastal ecosystems have an innate natural capacity to assimilate increased levels of nutrient enrichment without exhibiting adverse effects. As long as environmental conditions remain in an optimum range to support aerobic conditions in benthic sediments and the water column, the living communities can provide the processing capacity for the nutrients in the system.

Suggested Solutions to Data Collection

Successful implementation of ecosystem based management for marine aquaculture as well as for other management goals for fisheries, biodiversity, and environmental quality, requires detailed scientific knowledge of the ecosystem, including the interactions between physical, chemical, and biological components, as well as the effects of human activities on these systems. Because of the complexities of this new approach to managing living marine resources and environmental quality, effective methods for ecosystem assessment and prediction will be needed. These, in turn, rely on data collection systems, data integration and analysis methods, and modeling tools. Fortunately, most of the components of an effective data collection system already exist and in some cases, have already been applied to site selection and site monitoring. Capabilities for detailed seafloor mapping, remote sensing, in-situ observing, geographic information systems, and forecasting and prediction can be more broadly applied to site selection. Examples for effective site monitoring already exist (e.g., Maine, Washington, the UNH offshore aquaculture demonstration project) and standard methods for environmental monitoring and compliance reporting can be established. Ultimately, the Integrated Ocean Observing System model of a regional network of computer-based, command centers that process multiple data streams and create products that are useful to resource managers could serve as the data source for aquaculture decision-making.

In addition to the need for standardized data collection and analysis in support of aquaculture management, continued research and technology development is needed to address biological, engineering, socioeconomic, and environmental issues. A list of potential research topics is presented in Appendix 6-3 at the end of this chapter.

Recommendations for Ways to Apply Ecosystem-Based Management

The most effective way to apply ecosystem-based management to aquaculture is within a broader framework for ocean and coastal management. If implemented, the recommendation by the U.S. Commission on Ocean Policy (USCOP 2004) to establish regional ocean councils would provide the ideal framework for aquaculture management. A decision-making entity within a regional management structure might include appropriate federal and state government agencies and the U.S. Coast Guard; stakeholders that include the aquaculture and fishing industries, the scientific community, environmental groups, recreational interests, shipping and energy industries, and financial institutions. A process for implementation might include the following steps:

- Identify management area boundaries;

- Reach consensus on universal principles/vision;

- Reach consensus on environmental, social, production, economic, and management goals;

- Establish Aquaculture Task Force Teams that would establish specific goals and objectives, set action plans, establish timelines and performance measures, and develop mechanisms for interaction between teams and with the broader management structure.

Literature Cited

Anderson, D.M., P. Andersen, V.M. Bricelj, J.J. Cullen, and J.E. Rensel. 2001. Monitoring and Management Strategies for Harmful Algal Blooms in Coastal Waters, APEC #201-MR-01.1. Asia Pacific Economic Program, Singapore, and Intergovernmental Oceanographic Commission Technical Series No. 59. Paris, France. 264 pp.

Chopin, T. and C. Yarish. 1999. Seaweeds must be significant component of aquaculture for an integrated ecosystem approach. Pages 35-37 *in* Proceedings of the Workshop on Coldwater Seaweed Aquaculture Held at Aquaculture Canada '98. Bulletin of the Aquaculture Association of Canada. St. Andrews, New Brunswick, Canada, March 1999.

Chopin, T., A.H. Buschmann, C. Halling, M. Troell, N. Kautshy, A. Neori, G.P. Kraemer, J.A. Zertuche-Gonzalez, C. Yarish, and C. Neefus. 2001. Integrating seaweeds into mariculture systems: a key towards sustainability. European Journal of Phycology 37(6): 975-986.

Chopin, T., C. Yarish, R. Wilkes, E. Belyea, S. Lu, and A. Mathieson. 1999. Developing *Porphyra*/salmon integrated aquaculture for bioremediation and diversification of the aquaculture industry. Journal of Applied Phycology 11: 463-472.

Chung, I., Y.H. Kang, C. Yarish, G. Kraemer, and J. Lee. 2002. Application of seaweed cultivation to the bioremediation of nutrient-rich effluent. Algae 17(3): 187-194.

Cloern, J.E. 2001. Our evolving conceptual model of the coastal eutrophication problem. Marine Ecology Progress Series 210: 223-253.

Coen, L.D., M.W. Luckenbach, and D.L. Breitburg. 1999. The role of oyster reefs as essential fish habitat: A review of current knowledge and some new perspectives. American Fisheries Society Symposium 22: 438-454.

Dudley, R.W., V.G. Panchang, and C.R. Newell. 2000. Application of a comprehensive modeling strategy for the management of net-pen aquaculture waste transport. Aquaculture 187: 319-349.

Everett, R.A., G.M. Ruiz, and J.T. Carlton. 1995. Effect of oyster mariculture on submerged aquatic vegetation: an experimental test in a Pacific Northwest estuary. Marine Ecology Progress Series 125: 205-217.

Gowen, R.J. and N.B. Bradbury. 1987. The ecological impacts of salmonid farming in coastal waters: A review. Oceanography and Marine Biology Annual Review 25: 563-575.

Grant, J., A. Hatcher, D.B. Scott, P. Pocklington, C.T. Schafer, and G.V. Winters. 1995. A multidisciplinary approach to evaluating impacts of shellfish aquaculture on benthic communities. Estuaries 18: 124-144.

Grizzle, R.E., F.T. Short, C.R. Newell, H. Hoven, and L. Kindblom. 1996. Hydrodynamically induced synchronous waving of seagrasses: Onami and its possible effects of larval mussel settlement. Journal of Experimental Marine Biology and Ecology 206: 165-177.

MacKenzie, C.L. 1996. History of oystering in the United States and Canada, featuring the eight greatest oyster estuaries. Marine Fisheries Review Fall 1996.

Mazouni, N., J.-C. Gaertner, and J.-M. Deslous-Paoli. 2001. Composition of biofouling communities on suspended oyster cultures: An in situ study of their interactions with the water column. Marine Ecology Progress Series 214: 93-102.

McVey, J.P., R. Stickney, C. Yarish, and T. Chopin. 2002. Aquatic polyculture and balanced ecosystem management: New paradigms for seafood production. Pages 91B-104 *in* R.R. Stickney and J.P. McVey, editors. Responsible Marine Aquaculture. CABI Publishing, Oxon, UK.

Miller, D.C., R.J. Geider, and H.L. MacIntyre. 1996. Microphytobenthos, The ecological role of the "secret garden" of unvegetated, shallow-water marine habitats. II. Role in sediment stability and shallow-water food webs. Estuaries 19: 202-212.

Nash, C. 2001. The net-pen salmon farming industry in the Pacific Northwest. NOAA Technical Memorandum NMFS-NWFSC-49. National Oceanic and Atmospheric Administration (NOAA), Washington, DC, USA.

Newell, C.R., H. Hidu, G. Podniesinski, B.J. McAlice, L. Kindblom, and F. Short. 1991. Recruitment and commercial seed procurement of the blue mussel, *Mytilus edulis*. Journal of the World Aquaculture Society 22: 134-152.

Newell, R.I.E. 2004. Ecosystem influences of natural and cultivated populations of suspension-feeding bivalve molluscs: A review. Journal of Shellfish Research 23: 51-56.

Newell, R.I.E. and E.W. Koch. 2004. Modeling seagrass density and distribution in response to changes in turbidity stemming from bivalve filtration and seagrass sediment stabilization. Estuaries 27: 793-806.

Newell, R.I.E, J.C. Cornwell, and M.S. Owens. 2002. Influence of simulated bivalve biodeposition and microphytobenthos on sediment nitrogen dynamics: A laboratory study. Limnology and Oceanography 47: 1367-1379.

Newell, R.I.E., T.R. Fisher, R.R. Holyoke, and J.C. Cornwell. 2005. Influence of eastern oysters on Nitrogen and Phosphorus regeneration in Chesapeake Bay, USA. Pages 93-120 *in* R. Dame and S. Olelin, editors. The Comparative Roles of Suspension Feeders in Ecosystems. NATO Science Series: IV - Earth and Environmental Sciences. Kluwer, Dordrecht, The Netherlands. http://hpl.umces.edu/faculty/newellcv.html.

Neori, A., T. Chopin, M. Troell, A.H. Buschmann, G.P. Kraemer, C. Halling, M. Shpigel, and C. Yarish. 2004: Integrated aquaculture: rationale, evolution and state of the art emphasizing seaweed biofiltration in modem mariculture. Aquaculture 231: 361-391.

NOAA (National Oceanic and Atmospheric Administration). 2005. Fisheries of the United States – 2003. NOAA, Washington, DC, USA. http://www.st.nmfs.gov/st1/fus/fus03/index.html.

Normandeau Associates, Inc. and Battelle. 2003. Maine Aquaculture Review 4. Prepared for Maine Department of Marine Resources, West Boothbay Harbor, Maine, USA. 59 pp. http://www.maine.gov/dmr/aquaculture/reports/MaineAquacultureReview.pdf.

Panchang, V.G., G. Cheng, and C.R. Newell. 1997. Application of mathematical models in the environmental regulation of net-pen aquaculture. Estuaries 17: 210-230.

Peterson, C.H., J.H. Grabowski, and S.P. Powers. 2003: Estimated enhancement of fish production resulting from restoring oyster reef habitat: Quantitative valuation. Marine Ecology Progress Series 264: 249-264.

Ragnarsson, S.A. and D. Raffaelli. 1999: Effects of the mussel *Mytilus edulis* L. on the invertebrate fauna of sediments. Journal of Experimental Marine Biology and Ecology 241: 31-43.

Rensel, J.E. 2001. Salmon net pens in Puget Sound: Rules, performance criteria and monitoring. Global Aquaculture Advocate 4(1): 66-69.

Rensel, J.E. and J.N.C. Whyte. 2003. Mariculture and harmful algal blooms. Pages 693-722 *in* D. Anderson, G. Hallegaeff, and A. Cembella, editors. UNESCO Manual on Harmful Marine Microalgae. UNESCO - IOC monograph on Oceanographic Methodology No. 9.

Sahoo, D. and C. Yarish. 2005. Mariculture of seaweeds. Pages 219-237 *in* R. Andersen, editor. Phycological Methods: Algal Culturing Techniques. Elsevier, Amsterdam, The Netherlands.

Sahoo, D., X. Tang, and C. Yarish. 2002. *Porphyra*-the economic seaweeds as a new experimental system. Current Science 83(11): 1313-1316.

Silvert, W. and C.J. Cromey. 2001. Modeling impacts. Pages 154-181 *in* K.D. Black, editor. Environmental Impacts of Aquaculture. CRC Press, Boca Raton, Florida, USA.

Simenstad, C.A. and K.L. Fresh. 1995. Influence of intertidal aquaculture on benthic communities in Pacific Northwest estuaries: Scales of disturbance. Estuaries 18: 43-70.

Smaal, A.C., T.C. Prins, N. Dankers, and B. Ball. 1998. Minimum requirements for modeling bivalve carrying capacity. Aquatic Ecology 31: 423-428.

Sowles, J. 2001. Nitrogen in the Gulf of Maine: Sources, susceptibility and trends. Appendix 1 *in* Workshop Report 2001: Managing Nitrogen Impacts in the Gulf of Maine. National Oceanic and Atmospheric Administration/University of New Hampshire Cooperative Institute for Coastal and Estuarine Environmental Technology (CICEET), Gulf of Maine Council on the Marine Environment, and National Ocean Service, National Oceanic and Atmospheric Administration, Washington, DC, USA. http://www.gulfofmaine.org/council/committee/eqmc/NitrogenWorklshopReport.pdf.

Troell, M., C. Halling, A. Neori, A.H. Buschmann, T. Chopin, C. Yarish, and N. Kautsky. 2003. Integrated mariculture: Asking the right questions. Aquaculture 226: 69-90.

Tsutsumi, H. 1995. Impact of fish net pen culture on the benthic environments of a cove in south Japan. Estuaries 18: 108-115.

USCOP (United States Commission on Ocean Policy). 2004. An Ocean Blueprint for the 21st Century. U.S. Commission on Ocean Policy Final Report. USCOP, Washington, DC, USA. 522 pp. + Appendices. http://www.oceancommission.gov/documents/full_color_rpt/welcome.html.

USFDA (United States Food and Drug Administration). 2003. Guide for the Control of Molluscan Shellfish, 2003. National Shellfish Sanitation Program. FDA/Center for Food Safety and Applied Nutrition, U.S. Department of Health and Human Services, Washington, DC, USA. http://www.cfsan/fda/gov/~ear/uss2-toc.html.

USFDA (United States Food and Drug Administration). 2005. Hazard Analysis and Critical Control Point. FDA/Center for Food Safety and Applied Nutrition, U.S. Department of Health and Human Services, Washington, DC, USA. http://www.cfsan.fda.gov/~lrd/haccp.html.

Appendix 6-1: U.S. Federal and State Agencies and Their Roles in Aquaculture

U.S. Department of Commerce/National Oceanic and Atmospheric Administration (NOAA)

Under the Magnuson-Stevens Fishery Conservation and Management Act, NOAA has responsibilities for regulating and managing commercial fishing operations. Because harvesting living resources in federal waters by U.S. vessels constitutes fishing under the Act, aquaculture operations may be considered commercial fishing operations under the Act. Regulations implementing the Marine Mammal Protection Act specifically include aquaculture in their definition of "commercial fishing operation" (50 C.F.R. §229.2 1999).

Under the authority of the Fish and Wildlife Coordination Act, the Endangered Species Act of 1973, and the Marine Mammal Protection Act of 1972, NOAA is entitled to comment on any project under review by the U.S. Army Corps of Engineers (ACOE) or other agency if there is federal involvement in the project (i.e., a permit, license, funding, etc.).

A Letter of Acknowledgement by NOAA is required to conduct research in federal waters. A permit called the Exempted Fishing Permit is required to hold juvenile (undersize) fish in federal waters.

U.S. Department of Agriculture (USDA)

The National Aquaculture Act (1980), as amended, established the Joint Subcommittee on Aquaculture (JSA), chaired by the USDA. The JSA produced the National Aquaculture Development Plan, which identified the roles of the major agencies (U.S. Departments of Agriculture, Commerce, and the Interior) and established strategies and priorities for development. The JSA does not issue aquaculture permits.

The Animal and Plant Health Inspection Service within the USDA enforces regulations to prevent the spread of aquatic animal diseases from a foreign country or between states.

U.S. Department of the Interior/Fish and Wildlife Service (USFWS)

Under the authority of the Fish and Wildlife Coordination Act, the Endangered Species Act of 1973, and the Marine Mammal Protection Act of 1972, the USFWS is entitled to comment on any project under review by the ACOE or other agency if there is federal involvement in the project (i.e., a permit, license, funding, etc.). The USFWS does not issues aquaculture permits.

The U.S. Army Corps of Engineers (ACOE)

The authority of the ACOE under the Rivers and Harbors Act (1899), Section 10, to preserve unhindered navigational access of the nation's waters was extended into the Exclusive Economic Zone (EEZ) by the Outer Continental Shelf Lands Act (1953). Under 43 U.S.C. §1333(a), (e) 1999, the ACOE now regulates "installations and other devices permanently or temporarily attached to the seabed, which may be erected thereon for the purpose of exploring for, developing, or producing resources" from land to the outer continental shelf.

The U.S. Environmental Protection Agency (EPA)

Under Section 318 of the Clean Water Act, the EPA asserts its jurisdiction to require point source pollution discharge permits for aquaculture projects in the open ocean. The regulations are found under the National Pollutant Discharge Elimination System (NPDES) 40 C.F.R. §122.24. The EPA may delegate authority to the states for implementation.

Under the Ocean Dumping Act, 33 U.S.C. §1412, 1999, the EPA is authorized to permit the dumping of material into U.S. waters when such dumping will not unreasonably degrade or endanger human health or the marine environment, ecological systems, or economic potentialities. The permits are called National Pollutant Discharge Elimination System (NPDES) Permit and, when necessary, the Ocean Discharge Permit.

Fishery Management Councils

Eight regional Fishery Management Councils (FMCs) were established under the (1976) Magnuson-Stevens Fishery Conservation and Management Act with responsibility to manage fishery resources beyond the jurisdictional limit of state waters to the 322 km (200-mile) limit of the EEZ. Because aquaculture operations are considered to constitute fishing under the Act, the FMCs have authority to manage aquaculture in the EEZ. Although none of the FMCs currently issues an "aquaculture permit" per se, exempted fishing permits have been issued to two experimental aquaculture projects in the Gulf of Mexico. In addition, each FMC may comment on proposed operations as part of the review process for applicants seeking other permits, such as a Section 10 permit from the ACOE, and, where necessary, make relevant amendments to any fishery management plan.

The U.S. Coast Guard (USCG)

The USCG is responsible for the regulation and enforcement of various activities in the navigable waters of the United States and requires that aquaculture-related structures be marked with lights and signals in order to ensure the safe passage of vessels. Installation and maintenance of markers is the responsibility of the aquaculture operators as long as the structures are located in navigable waters. The requirements for the markers are specified by the USCG. No permit is required from the USCG, but conformity with USCG regulations for markers is stipulated in the permits approved by the ACOE and/or the EPA.

Minerals Management Service (MMS)

The MMS has authority to lease sites for minerals development on submerged lands on the outer continental shelf under jurisdiction of the Outer Continental Shelf Lands Act. The MMS does not issue aquaculture permits, but aquaculture facilities using oil and gas platforms require MMS approval for the removal of a platform or transfer of ownership. The MMS may also review and comment on permit applications submitted to the ACOE or other federal agency.

Possible Acts and Regulations Impacting Coastal Management in the United States

Aquaculture Policies in Effect at this Time

At this time, NOAA is operating under a Aquaculture Policy that was created in 1998. The Policy outlines the relative roles of the various line offices under NOAA, such as the National Marine Fisheries Service, The National Sea Grant Program administered by Oceanic and Atmospheric Research, the National Ocean Service, and the National Environmental Satellite and Data Service. The policy focuses on offshore and recirculation marine aquaculture as well as marine stock enhancement and includes specific language on increasing the number of species that can be cultured in the United States.

Connections to Stakeholders

Connections to Fishery Managers

Aquaculture is useful to fishery managers as an alternative source of production at a time when natural fishery stocks are at their maximum sustained yield or overfished. Aquaculture can offset the loss of fishery landings resulting from fishing restrictions in Marine Protected Areas, and Marine Sanctuaries, and provide tools to regain nutrient balances within existing protected areas. When fishery quotas are reduced to allow natural stocks to rebuild, aquaculture can be used to enhance natural populations to reduce the time necessary to rebuild those stocks and provide the market with additional product to maintain availability and optimize value for the managed species. Modern genetics diagnostics makes it possible to ensure that the gene complement of enhancement stocks is equal to that of wild stocks. Aquaculture can provide out of season product for popular species, thus allowing markets to offer product for a longer period and retailers to develop a more permanent clientele. Aquaculture of bivalve species creates critical habitat for many other species, and reproductive products from farmed shellfish are important food for early stages of many species. To be effective, fishery managers need to incorporate all these concepts in their management portfolio. It is much easier to set lower quotas for wild stocks when an alternative source of supply for those stocks is available. Managers who must deal with local politics, however, have to be firm in setting lower quotas if improved populations of wild stocks are to be obtained.

Connections to Coastal Zone Managers

The US Coastal Zone Act of 1996 has specific language relative to the importance of recognizing the legitimate rights of aquaculture in the U.S. coastal zone. Aquaculture is a latecomer to the coastal zone and is generally not considered when establishing zones within the ocean. Given the important role that extractive aquaculture can play in improving nutrient flow and balance in the ecosystem, coastal plans need to include aquaculture to enhance ecological function. In addition, aquaculture can play a very important role in the economic health of coastal communities. Space needs to be set aside for both extractive and fed aquaculture to optimize value from coastal resources.

Connections to Water Quality Managers

Extractive aquaculture by filter feeding shellfish and macroalgae is very important in maintaining healthy ecosystems (McVey et al. 2002; Newell 2004). The challenge is to understand the key biological processes in a particular ecosystem so that aquaculture contributions are in balance with other components of the system. Water quality managers need to be aware that macro-algae can strip inorganic nutrients from the water volume, and filter feeding molluscs can harvest phytoplankton and detritus, thus improving water clarity and removing nitrogen from the system.

Connections to Navigation Managers

The ACOE and the USCG are involved with maintaining coastal designations and aids to navigation. These organizations need to work with coastal zone managers to establish the best locations for aquaculture in the coastal zones to avoid conflicts with navigation. The recent development of submerged, offshore aquaculture required that all structures be below 12.19 m (40 feet) in depth, and in some cases, that lighted marker buoys be maintained.

Connections to Legislative Bodies

Nationally and locally, there are many regulatory and policy adjustments that need to be made to allow aquaculture to be placed and operated in any location. Hawaii had to create legislation that allowed leasing of state waters for aquaculture before offshore marine aquaculture could start. At this time, Alaska has a law prohibiting the culture of finfish. Every other state and many more local jurisdictions have an assortment of regulations that make aquaculture difficult. Coastal zone managers and the developing aquaculture industry must understand and work to adjust aquaculture policy and regulations to reach the goal of economically and environmentally sustainable aquaculture.

Appendix 6-2: Environmental Considerations of Marine Aquaculture

In the following section, the authors review some of the inter-relationships between biotic, hydrographic, and chemical processes relevant to marine aquaculture. This is a review of fundamental processes that are applicable to marine aquaculture worldwide. Specific reference is made to some aspects of these processes that are forming the foundation of approaches for developing managed ecosystem aquaculture in the United States within a comprehensive framework for coastal zone management.

Increased Organic Loading to Sediments

Carnivorous and omnivorous species that require food (particulate organic matter, POM) derived from external sources (e.g., fish meal and cereals) are generally the most valuable aquaculture species. Because food is provided, they can be cultivated intensively. If large amounts of undigested food and feces are transferred to the sediments underlying and surrounding the aquaculture site, this can enhance sediment bacterial community metabolism. This increased benthic respiration may exceed oxygen resupply from the overlying waters and cause the sediments to become anoxic. Anaerobic bacterial communities then start to metabolize the POM, and sulfur-reducing anaerobes produce H_2S, which is highly toxic to the benthos. This adverse effect of fed aquaculture has been the cause for concern from regulatory authorities (Gowen and Bradbury 1987; Tsutsumi 1995) and, consequently, considerable effort has been made to develop techniques to minimize such effects.

The development of specially formulated diets that match the ontogenic changes in fish nutritional demands, and optimizing the way in which these food pellets are delivered, maximizes the ability of fish to capture and digest food. These formulated diets minimize POM from unconsumed food and fecal material from being transferred to sediments underlying the facility. These advances in feeding technology now allow North American salmonid cage culture to have extremely limited adverse effects on benthic communities, with significant changes in benthic communities being limited to a zone of about 30 m from the cage structures. Both Washington State and Maine have performance standards incorporating this distance, with additional zones inside this perimeter in Maine.

Potential adverse effects of waste food and feces deposition can be further minimized by locating the finfish aquaculture cages in locations where there is sufficient current velocity and depth to allow the material to be widely distributed or resuspended (Panchang et al. 1997; Dudley et al. 2000; Silvert and Cromey 2001). The advantage of a deep water column is that the increased particle residence time in the water column allows more time for the waste material to be widely distributed by water currents. This effectively reduces POM areal loading to the sediments to levels that are generally insufficient to stimulate the excess bacterial metabolism that may cause sediment anoxia. Water currents are also beneficial because the continual supply of oxygenated water further reduces the likelihood of surficial bottom sediments becoming anoxic.

Increased Inorganic Loading to Water Column

The inorganic nutrients excreted by cultivated finfish and microbially regenerated from their fecal material increases the dissolved inorganic nutrient pool in the water column. In nutrient-sensitive areas, dissolved nutrients from finfish culture (but also shellfish culture at very high densities) can stimulate phytoplankton blooms, possibly including harmful algal species, although there are few documented cases of this occurring (Anderson et al. 2001; Rensel and Whyte 2003). Consequently, an objective of managed ecosystem aquaculture is to remove these excess nutrients by integrating fed aquaculture with extractive aquaculture (McVey et al. 2002; Troell et al. 2003; Neori et al. 2004). Extractive aquaculture involves growing either macroalgae to take up nutrients directly, or cultivating suspension-feeding bivalves to graze on the enhanced phytoplankton biomass. When the macroalgae and bivalves are harvested, the nutrients incorporated in their tissues are permanently removed from the ecosystem.

The growth requirements of macroalgae and phytoplankton are different. In the temperate zones of the North Atlantic Ocean, marine macroalgae tend to grow best during cooler months, while phytoplankton tend to have highest productivity in warmer summer months. Many perennial marine macroalgae have mechanisms whereby they sequester nutrients in their tissues during the winter, when phytoplankton nutrient uptake is at a minimum. As light becomes available, these nutrients are then used by the macroalgae to support increased growth in the spring. The amount of nutrients (especially nitrogen and phosphorus) sequestered in this way varies depending upon the structural complexity of the seaweed species. Structurally complex seaweeds, such as *Laminaria*, may store large amounts of nutrients, whereas the less structurally complex species, such as *Ulva*, have limited storage capabilities.

Suspension-feeding bivalves are generally inactive during colder winter periods and only start to actively feed and remove phytoplankton from the water column as water temperatures increase in spring (Newell 2004). This pattern of highest phytoplankton production and grazing by bivalves during warmer summer months indicates that to ensure a year round removal of nutrients, extractive macroalgal culture should be used in the winter to complement the growth of suspension feeding bivalves. Macroalgae are valuable as food for other aquaculture organisms (e.g., abalone, *Haliotis* spp.), human food (e.g., *Porphyra* spp. and *Laminaria* spp.), a source of valuable organic compounds (e.g., phycocolloids, omega 3 fatty acids, antioxidants), and organic material for methane production (Sahoo and Yarish 2005). The cultivated bivalves, such as oysters and mussels, are valuable commercial species.

Recent research indicates that biodeposition from shellfish can also lead to enhanced nitrogen and phosphorus burial in aerobic sediments and to the loss of di-nitrogen gas (N_2) to the atmosphere through the bacterially mediated process of coupled nitrification-denitrification (Newell et al. 2002, 2005; Newell 2004). Very high densities of shellfish can lead to excess biodeposition that drive sediments anaerobic, which is the same adverse effect associated with poorly managed finfish aquaculture. Excess bivalve biodeposition leads to loss of benthic fauna. Anaerobic conditions, however, preclude coupled nitrification-denitrification, and buried phosphorus can be released into the water column.

It should be noted that because extractive aquaculture is simply drawing down both dissolved inorganic and particulate organic nutrients from the pool in the water column, the actual source of those nutrients can just as easily be anthropogenic nutrient inputs from the watershed. It is becoming increasingly clear that in many coastal systems, phytoplankton production is extremely high, and is associated with agricultural and sewage inputs (Cloern 2001). Extractive aquaculture can help to curb the adverse effects of such nutrient inputs.

Habitat

An important ecosystem benefit of natural shellfish beds is that they provide habitat for many invertebrate and vertebrate species (Coen et al 1999; Ragnarsson and Raffaelli 1999; Peterson et al. 2003). It seems that similar habitat benefits may be provided by commercial aquaculture gear (e.g., fish net pens, racks and bags for shellfish culture, suspended ropes, etc.), although the exact magnitude of the effect remains to be fully quantified. These aquaculture structures provide a surface for plant and animal colonization (Mazouni et al. 2001) that then provide a food source for many native species within the ecosystem. Both on-bottom and off-bottom aquaculture holding gear also provides the type of spatially complex habitat that is sought by many species of mobile animals.

The extreme periodic disturbances associated with cultivation and harvest practices, especially those required for on-bottom culture of infaunal bivalves, can negatively affect benthic animal communities (Simenstad and Fresh 1995). It has been shown that there are severe reductions in seagrass (*Zostera marina*) beds in the immediate vicinity of Pacific oysters cultivated on the bottom in rack and bags systems and on stakes in Oregon, USA. The causes of this seagrass loss are multi-faceted, including direct shading by the aquaculture gear, enhanced biodeposition reducing sediment suitability for seagrasses, sediment erosion associated with on-bottom racks altering bottom water currents, and severe disturbance associated with husbandry activities (Everett et al. 1995).

Reduction in Turbidity

Stocks of bivalve suspension-feeders in locations with relatively restricted water exchange with surrounding waters can remove sufficient organic and inorganic seston particles to reduce turbidity and increase the amount of light reaching the sediment surface (Newell 2004). This has the effect of reducing the dominance of phytoplankton production and extending the depth to which ecologically important benthic plants, such as seagrasses and microphytobenthos (MPB), can grow. Newell and Koch (2004) developed a simple model of the effects of suspension-feeding bivalves on altering light penetration and the consequent benefits to seagrass beds. This model showed that reestablishing seagrass beds may be facilitated by first rebuilding depleted oyster beds to increase light penetration. It is apparent that high densities of oysters (*Crassostrea virginica*) and mussels (*Mytilus edulis*) that have a high feeding activity could provide similar improvements in water clarity.

The reduction in turbidity associated with bivalve feeding may be sufficient to increase light penetration to the sediment surface to a level that can sustain MPB production. These benthic algae are an important food source for both sessile and mobile benthic herbivorous meiofauna and macrofauna (Miller et al. 1996) that, in turn, are eaten by many carnivorous fish. Consequently, an abundant MPB community can support higher trophic levels. Actively growing MPB absorb inorganic nutrients released from bivalve biodeposits at the sediment water interface and compete with the sediment microbial community for nitrogen remaining in the biodeposits. In locations where sufficient light reaches the sediment surface to permit active MPB growth, bivalve biodeposition may not result in appreciable nitrogen removal via denitrification (Newell et al. 2002). Therefore, if enhanced denitrification is a desired ecosystem service, aquaculture stocks of bivalves should be cultivated in deeper locations where the biodeposits will be transferred to sediments beneath the euphotic zone.

Managed Ecosystem Aquaculture

There is interest in developing extractive aquaculture in the United States for use as part of nutrient trading system in coastal waters, such as Chesapeake Bay (http://www. chesapeakebay..net/trading/html.) and Long Island Sound (http://www.longislandsoundstudy. net/pubs/report/30350report.pdf). Nutrient trading schemes allow industry and municipal wastewater treatment facilities to purchase, at market value, extra nutrient removal capacity from others on the same receiving water body, rather than directly reducing their own nutrient inputs. This is becoming an important issue in the United States, where the EPA is mandated by the Clean Water Act to improve water quality. One regulation devised to help reduce phytoplankton production and thereby enhance water quality, is the Total Maximum Daily Load (TMDL), which is the maximum daily allowable amount of nutrients that may be discharged into a water body from all sources (http://www.epa.gov/waterscience/standards/ nutsi.html). Nutrient trading will allow aquaculturists, who can document the amount of N and P removed, to be paid by those industries that find it less expensive to purchase nutrient removal rather than upgrade their own facilities to meet the TMDL.

The use of extractive plants and animals is a proposed solution to helping attain these water quality standards, because it offers a valuable opportunity to reduce nutrients once they have entered a receiving body of water. This may be especially important in ameliorating the effects of non-point source inputs that are the most difficult to regulate and control.

Appendix 6-3: Topics for Research and Development

The following is a list of potential research and development topics where advances and improvements would help increase the success of an ecosystems approach to offshore aquaculture.

Select Optimal Sites for Aquaculture Operations

- Develop procedures to improve aquaculture site selection relative to the species-specific growth requirements (e.g., characterize current velocities and wave conditions, use remote sensing and integrated ocean observing for environmental data, and integrate all information in Geographic Information Systems [GIS] data layers).

- Characterize the hydrodynamics of the shellfish aquaculture structures (rafts, longlines, on-bottom) and food consumption rates relative to phytoplankton supply and stocking biomass.

- Optimize site selection to minimize or eliminate environmental risk and accrue benefits such as enhancement of benthic species abundance and diversity (concurrently).

- Determine optimum physiological conditions for individual species that reduce stress, improve growth, reduce disease risk, and improve feed conversion ratios.

- Identify specific areas and production systems that provide ecosystem benefits such as essential habitat or enhance natural productivity

- Arrange aquaculture units spatially in ways to optimize yield and environmental quality.

Improve the Design of Infrastructure and Development of Integrated ("Smart") Systems Engineering to:

- Increase efficiency of food delivery and waste management.

- Design systems and/or use materials that minimize the amount and adverse effects of biofouling.

- Design cages and operational systems that facilitate fish sampling and harvesting, automate cage cleaning, and enhance worker efficiency and safety.

- Improve cage construction, design, and operation methods to minimize fish escape.

- Improve mooring and cage designs to further reduce the risk of marine mammal interactions.

- Define optimal habitats for protection of wildlife or fisheries resources.

- Integrate the use of alternative forms of energy such as solar, wind, wave, water current or peiziometric generators at offshore installations.

Develop Best Management Practices

- Improve feeds and feeding practices.

- Manage colonizing organisms (biofouling) to mitigate impacts of effluents and waste discharge from farming activities.

- Determine if integrated aquaculture can be implemented in open ocean systems in a manner that enhances economic benefits, environmental benefits, or both.

- Standardize environmental quality criteria and permit compliance monitoring programs to have fairly reported results.

Incorporate Environmentally Safe Husbandry Practices

- Undertake selective breeding of the cultivated species while insuring adequate variation in genomic makeup.

- Locate pollutant-free and sustainable protein and oil sources for feed formulations.

- Improve fish health management and rearing practices to further reduce or eliminate the need for theraputins.

Optimize Product Quality, Seafood Safety, and Product Value

- Work toward organic, eco-friendly, and quality/nutritional certification for inshore and open ocean farmed fish and shellfish. Develop brand names to allow consumer recognition of high quality and safe aquaculture products.

- Evaluate near-term and long-term market value and assess economic risk for farm-raised seafood.

- Ensure that growers utilize HACCP principles in seafood safety, and shellfish growers utilize NSSP guidelines including sampling for harmful algae blooms.

- Examine strategies that can be developed jointly by the farmed and capture fisheries to obtain maximum value for domestically produced seafood. One such possible strategy is to train fishermen to become aquaculturists, and make capital resources available for investment in facilities.

Work toward Social Compatibility

- Enhance cooperation between aquaculturists and the capture fishing sector to achieve mutually desirable goals.

- Improve the design of aquaculture infrastructure to improve its aesthetic appeal.

- Develop information on the industry practices and environmental interactions that are based on science and fact rather than allowing detractors to mischaracterize the industry.

VIET NAM

7

Executive Summary

The extensive aquatic ecosystems and natural biodiversity of the Socialist Republic of Vietnam (Viet Nam) offer a great potential for sustainable fisheries development. Fisheries, a mainstay of livelihoods in local communities, are a key economic sector of the country, with aquaculture constituting an essential portion of its exports. In the past decade, capture fisheries yields and aquaculture production have increased rapidly, due to expansion of farming areas rather than intensification. Projections for 2010 include aquaculture production to reach about 2 million metric tons, and for about 4.7 million people to be employed in the fisheries sector (including aquaculture). National aquaculture programs promoting the conversion of inefficiently used areas to aquaculture use have increased their economic value 4-10 times, but these gains carry high risks in terms of outbreaks of diseases in cultured aquatic animals and adverse environmental impacts. To promote sustainable fisheries and aquaculture development while protecting coastal and marine environments, the Ministry of Fisheries is conducting pilot studies and implementing collaborative projects in the Ha Long Bay coastal area of Quang Ninh province, using an ecosystem-based approach. Challenges include recovering from the impacts of natural disasters, such as flooding and typhoons, and solving conflicts arising from multi-users and sectoral management. To respond to these challenges, management needs to be inclusive and adaptive. Inclusive management requires the participation of all stakeholders. Adaptive management requires the identification and monitoring of robust indicators of environmental and socio-economic conditions. These indicators should be periodically assessed to determine general environmental and socio-economic trends and, more importantly, to evaluate the effectiveness and efficiency of management strategies and interventions.

Introduction

Aquaculture and Fishery Sectors

Viet Nam is a coastal country, with large sea areas (the Exclusive Economic Zone is 1 million km^2) and wetlands (about 10 million ha). These large sea areas and wetlands are important aquatic ecosystems and they offer a great potential for development of the seafood sector. Because the natural biodiversity provides a large resource base for sustainable fisheries development, many economic sectors and communities exploit these areas. There is a traditional saying, "where water exists, fish species occur," reflecting the traditional viewpoint that the seas and wetlands are a mainstay of livelihoods in local communities, especially among the poorest residents. Besides these benefits, however, the seas and wetlands are also sensitive ecological areas exposed to many risks due to natural changes and impacts from human activities.

Contributor: Chu Hoi, N.
In J.P. McVey, C.-S. Lee, and P.J. O'Bryen, editors. Aquaculture and Ecosystems: An Integrated Coastal and Ocean Management Approach. The World Aquaculture Society, Baton Rouge, Louisiana, United States.

For fisheries purposes, the wetlands are divided into three main types: freshwater, brackish water, and saltwater wetlands. The fisheries/seafood sector of Viet Nam is characterized as an export-oriented, diversified production sector based on aquatic biodiversity and traditionally small-scale fisheries. These characteristics present complicated environmental challenges to fisheries sector development and create specialized sectoral features for environmental management. As part of the framework of Vietnam Agenda 21 (2004), adopted in August 2004, the Vietnamese Government considers fisheries to be a key economic sector that merits a high priority in the move toward sustainable development.

The fisheries sector has a very important role in the national economy. Generally, fisheries contribute about 10% of the total value of national exports. Fisheries provide 47% of the animal protein in the Vietnamese diet, and it provides millions of employment opportunities in rural areas. Throughout the coming years, the fisheries sector is expected to continue to be a key economic sector, in which sufficient and proper investment needs to be made.

Since 1990, capture fishery activities have been centrally conducted in near shore areas. Over-fishing of the near shore areas has led to increased aquaculture during the same period. Since 2000, there has been strong development of aquaculture, mainly in coastal brackish water areas.

Production Data

In the past decade, capture fisheries yields and aquaculture production have increased rapidly in Viet Nam. Since 1993, total aquaculture production has steadily increased, with an average growth rate of about 3.7%. Between 1993 and 1998, aquaculture production averaged about 1.1 metric tons (MT) ha^{-1}. Marine and coastal areas have been converted to aquaculture at about the same rate (average 3.8%). Thus, the increase in aquaculture production is due to the expansion of farming areas, not the result of intensive farming practices.

In 2002, total fisheries production reached 2,410,900 MT, a 71% increase compared to that in 1995. Fisheries exports were valued at $2 billion, an increase of 213% compared to that in 1995. About 955,000 ha were used for aquaculture, mostly of brackish water shrimp (*Penaeus monodon*), which was a major contributor to fisheries exports.

In 2004, total aquaculture production was 1,150,100 MT, which provided 80% of the raw materials for fishery processing and export. The export value of aquaculture production and capture fishery yields was about $2.4 billion in 2004, and $2.67 billion in 2005. Marine aquaculture, conducted in cages along embayment shores and in estuaries, accounted for only a small percentage of total aquaculture production (less than 10%).

Projections for 2010 include a total fisheries production of 4 million MT, about 2 million MT from aquaculture, approximately 1.8 million MT from capture fisheries in the Exclusive Economic Zone (EEZ), and 200,000 MT from freshwater fishing. The total export value of the various species is expected to be $4 billion. In addition, the fisheries sector is predicted to provide employment opportunities for 4.7 million people.

Policy Development

Under the guidance of the Government, the fisheries sector continues to implement socioeconomic development plans toward industrialization and modernization. The National Fisheries Administration, established in 1960, continues to be developed. In 1999, the government approved a national program of aquaculture to support sustainable aquaculture development.

In 2000, the Government enacted the "Economic Structure Change in Agriculture and Rural Development" (Decree No. 09/2000/CP-TTg) to increase aquaculture production. Special emphasis on converting ineffective and low-productivity areas, such as paddy fields, salt production fields, and areas used for planting rushes into areas for aquaculture has increased the economic value 4-10 times over that with their former types of production. The conversion has been carried out widely in almost 29 coastal provinces, initially with the conversion of rice-fields into the brackish water shrimp farming. In addition, marine and intertidal aquaculture (including fish in cages and molluscs in tidal marshes) and shrimp farming in coastal sandy areas have been developed and have showed preliminary economic benefits.

At the Annual Review Meeting of the fisheries sector in 2001, Prime Minister Phan Van Khai emphasized,

> "Viet Nam has a lot of potential for fisheries development and should promote faster and stronger development of the fisheries sector... The final goal of the fisheries sector is to improve the competitive advantage of the country and to provide benefits for its laborers".

In 2004, the World Bank conducted a study on fisheries and aquaculture sectors in Viet Nam. In its final report, four key areas were identified for possible intervention and support by multilateral and bilateral agencies: (a) Integrated coastal management; (b) fisheries management in inland, inshore, and offshore waters; (c) diversified aquaculture development in brackish, marine, and freshwater areas; and (d) marketing.

Due to the above-mentioned efforts in aquaculture development, especially in brackish water areas, the Vietnamese fisheries sector has contributed considerably to poverty reduction and elimination of hunger in coastal and inland areas. Fisheries provide one of the few alternative livelihood options in many poor coastal communes. Overall, the fisheries sector has been inadequately represented in the nation's poverty reduction strategies, and stronger lobbying by fisheries sector institutions is desirable. In parallel, aquaculture development is also expected to reduce the pressures of fishing in near shore areas that are over-exploited.

The Regulatory System for Aquaculture

Environmental monitoring has indicated that aquaculture activities, especially in coastal areas, have caused environmental problems and negative impacts, not only on surrounding areas, but also for the aquaculture operations themselves (e.g., epidemic diseases and economic damage). If these problems remain unsolved and their causes continue to be unregulated, the economic benefits of aquaculture could also be reduced in the near future. From an environmental viewpoint, aquaculture operations are considered to be not only victims, but also culprits. From an economic viewpoint, aquaculture operations bring about both high economic value and high risks. From a social viewpoint, aquaculture can be an effective tool for reducing poverty in local communities, but which can also widen the gap between the rich and the poor. Of course, aquaculture includes a dichotomy of positive and negative attributes. In other words, aquaculture has the potential to bring about economic and social benefits as well as adverse environmental impacts. When aquaculture is sited properly and well managed, it can have few, if any, negative environmental impacts and is likely to have a positive economic influence on surrounding coastal communities.

Environmental concerns relating to aquaculture development in Viet Nam include (WB/MoFi 2004):

- An increase of localized water pollution of marine areas due to discharges of large volumes of fresh and brackish water, and marine cage farms placed without consideration of the carrying capacity of the receiving waters;

- The need for more care to be taken when introducing new exotic species, due to the risks of disease introduction and spread and the negative impacts on aquatic biodiversity;

- Significant loss of mangroves and wetlands due to conversion of coastal areas and estuaries for shrimp farming;

- Outbreaks of diseases of cultured aquatic animals, and water pollution and salinization caused by poorly planned and poorly-managed shrimp farming in sandy and agricultural areas; and

- The recent dramatic rise in the use of trash fish in marine and freshwater aquaculture.

To create a legal corridor and to establish procedures for sustainable fisheries development, Viet Nam's National Assembly adopted the Law of Fisheries (hereafter, the Law) on November 26, 2003, which was then ratified by the Government. The Law has been enforced since July 1, 2004. The Law, which includes 10 chapters and 62 articles, is a historically important benchmark for Viet Nam's fisheries sector toward sustainable fisheries development in relation to integrated coastal management (ICM). This relationship is highlighted in Article 5, Chapter I (Appendix 1) of the Law. Articles 23 to 36 in Chapter IV pertain to aquaculture (Table 1).

Table 1. Sections of Viet Nam's Law of Fisheries pertaining to aquaculture.

Chapter I (Appendix 1): General Issues

Article 5: Sustainable fisheries development

1. The Government's policy is to maintain sustainable fisheries development, encourage, and facilitate institutions and individuals to reasonably exploit and utilize aquatic living resources; to maintain the restoration of aquatic living resources and aquaculture development on seas, rivers, lakes, lagoons, and other natural waters.

. . .

3. The Government develops fisheries economics based on the master plan for the fisheries sector, within the framework of the master plan of socio-economic development for the entire country, suitable with regional and local plans; to maintain constructions along riversides, on coastal lands, or nearly aquaculture areas that do not negatively impact aquatic living resources.

4. The Government must identify the extent of coastal marine areas based on depth, distance from the coastline, and other characteristics in near shore areas to decentralize them into coastal localities to promote ICM linking to fisheries and aquaculture production and trade development.

Chapter IV: Aquaculture

Article 23: Aquaculture development planning

Article 24: Conditions of aquaculture

Article 25: Rights of aquaculture institutions and individuals

Article 26: Obligations of aquaculture institutions and individuals

Article 27: Deliver, rent and recover the land for aquaculture

Article 28: Deliver and rent sea-space for aquaculture

Article 29: Recovery of delivered and rented sea-space for aquaculture

Article 30: Rights of institutions, individuals delivered, and rented sea-space for aquaculture

Article 31: Obligations of institutions, individuals using sea-space for aquaculture

Article 32: Aquaculture central areas

Article 33: Seeds of aquatic living resources

Article 34: Import and export of the seeds

Article 35: Food, medicine, and chemical compounds used in aquaculture

Article 36: Prevention and elimination of epidemic diseases of cultured aquatic species

In accordance with the Law, the Ministry of Fisheries (MoFi) is implementing state governance to protect the environment through an ecosystem-based approach to fisheries and aquaculture. Noteworthy initiatives include:

- Environmental monitoring and disease warning activities have been established and are undertaken yearly, including those for aquaculture. The Danish Government International Development Assistant - Fisheries Sector Programme Support (DANIDA/FSPS) program provides funding to build capacity for these activities.

- A National Steering Committee for Marine Protected Areas (MPAs) was established in 2004 to implement Chapter II (Article 9) of the Law. In addition, plans for a coastal and marine protected area (CPA/MPA) system were prepared for submission to the Prime Minister for approval in 2006.

- A MoFi Coordinating Board for a national program on aquaculture was established to steer aquaculture operations toward targets for sustainability.

- The MoFi is also preparing "The guidelines for sustainable aquaculture planning at local levels in Viet Nam" under DANIDA/FSPS support, as well as "The strategy for sustainable fisheries development in Viet Nam" within the framework for implementing Agenda 21 for Viet Nam.

- The MoFi has established a number of different regulations relative to environmental criteria/standards for effectively managed aquaculture, especially for brackish water aquaculture in coastal areas.

In connection with promoting coastal fisheries and aquaculture development within an integrated coastal management (ICM) framework, the MoFi conducted a project, "Building Capacity for ICM in the Tonkin Gulf, Viet Nam: Case Study in Ha Long Bay Coastal Area, Quang Ninh Province - Phase I." This project is a Viet Nam – USA collaborative effort under the framework of the Scientific and Technology Agreement. The National Oceanic and Atmospheric Administration (NOAA), The World Conservation Union (IUCN), and the MoFi are signatories to the Agreement. The main objectives of Phase I of the project, which was successfully completed in March 2005, were to build Viet Nam's capacity for ICM and conduct pilot studies in the Ha Long Bay coastal area of Quang Ninh province. An intermediate step, with in-country contributions, is being carried out in 2004 -2005. In the proposed Phase II, the scope will expand to include both Quang Ninh and Hai Phong provinces, with a focus on coastal and marine conservation and incorporation of fisheries and aquaculture development into an ICM framework using an ecosystem-based approach.

From the viewpoint of sustainable fisheries management, the MoFi recognizes that aquaculture and small-scale fisheries play an essential role in development activities in coastal areas of Viet Nam, and their sustainability depends on maintaining key coastal marine ecosystems. Interconnectivity of the coastal systems (including the socioeconomic considerations) and of the coastal ecosystems are key factors in coastal sustainability, so effective conservation of these ecosystems will create a "spillover effect" of all abiotic and biotic components (e.g., seeds and larvae of aquatic species, broodstock, nutrients, etc.) from the ecosystem into the surrounding marine areas. Most of the impacts (70%) on coastal ecosystems and aquaculture areas originate from outside, including those from coastal watersheds. Because coastal areas are interactive with all processes, poorly managed coastal aquaculture operations would have negative impacts on other sectors.

Solving conflicts arising from aquaculture development and other types of development in a context of multi-use and sectoral management requires effective management of the ecosystems. It also requires the participation of all stakeholders to solve the various aquaculture issues in a coordinated way. Engineering, geographical information system (GIS), and socioeconomic, biological and environmental data, etc. can be used in an integrated manner to effectively manage ecosystems to maximize the benefits of aquaculture while mitigating any possible negative effects.

The MoFi has also strived to establish and effectively manage the MPA in Nha Trang Bay (Central Viet Nam), which is considered to be the first pilot study in Viet Nam. Although the results of MPA management are difficult to quantify, after four years, some stocks have started to recover and have benefitted the native species with economically high value. A national CPA/MPA management system could supply an increasing number of natural aquatic living resources and promote environmentally sound aquaculture development within and near CPA/MPS sites.

Viet Nam has made an effort to mitigate the effects of an increasing population density in coastal areas of the country, which is affecting coastal water quality and aquaculture production. According to a recent national census, the average population growth rate in coastal areas is higher than the national average (2.3% per year compared to 1.8%). Coastal areas also tend to have a larger percentage of Viet Nam's poorest residents. In 2004, the Vietnamese Government identified 157 coastal communes in central Viet Nam as having the lowest per capita income in the country.

Specific Working Scenario: Ha Long Bay

Description of the Area

Ha Long Bay is located in Quang Ninh province in northeast Viet Nam, and extends from lat 20° 43'- 21°9' N to long 106°56' - 107°37' E. The coastal area of the bay is 1,553 km^2, including 1,969 islands, of which 95% are composed of limestone. Ha Long Bay connects with Bai Chay embayment in the northwest, with Bai Tu Long Bay in the northeast, and with the Tonkin Gulf in the southeast (Fig. 1).

From June to September, the Ha Long Bay area is influenced by monsoons, frequent storms, and typhoons that strongly influence fisheries activities. Historically, fishermen have used Ha Long Bay to avoid storms that occurred while they were fishing at sea. The annual rainfall of the bay is about 1800-2000 mm. High temperatures from May to October range from 25-29 C, and low temperatures from November to April range from 15–23 C. The average monthly humidity is 75%-90%.

Figure 1. Map of Viet Nam, showing location of Ha Long Bay.

Five rivers empty into the bay, with an estimated surface runoff of 806 x 10^6 m³ per year, which accounts for 82% of the total runoff. At present, there are about 10,000 ha of wetlands in the area, most of which are in a very degraded state or exist as simple mud flats in estuaries. The bay is 1-7 m deep (average 5 m). The seabed of the bay is flat and shallow, and covered with fine grain muddy sediments. The tidal flats with mangroves on the western coast of the bay are also covered with muddy sediments.

The daily tidal movement in the bay has a maximum amplitude of about 4.6 m, with a mean tidal level of 2.06 m. The current in Ha Long Bay integrates river flow, wind currents, and tidal currents, among which tidal currents dominate. The direction of the flood tidal current is north-northwest. The ebb tidal current flows south-southeast.

The volume of Bai Chay embayment is estimated to be 6 x 10^7 m³ and that of Ha Long Bay to be 6.3 x 10^9 m³. Assuming that water exchange between the bays is caused only by fresh water flows, waters have a retention time of about one month in the Bai Chay embayment and more than six years in Ha Long Bay (including Bai Tu Long Bay in the northeast).

Historical Background

Ha Long Bay is the home of the ancient Viet people, dating from 25,000 to 2,500 years ago. Hundreds of caves, including over 20 famous caves of particular beauty, are located on the islands in the bay. Ha Long Bay is one of the major limestone karst areas of the world that has been inundated by the sea (Fig. 2). Cat Ba biosphere-reserve is located in the south of the bay, and Ba Tu Long Bay National Park is located north of the bay.

Figure 2. Limestone islands and houseboats in Ha Long Bay.

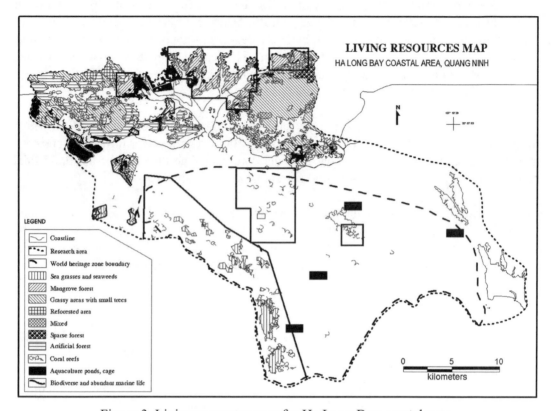

Figure 3. Living resources map for Ha Long Bay coastal area.

In 1994, the United Nations Economic and Social Commission for Asia and the Pacific (UNESCO) adopted Ha Long Bay as a World Natural Heritage for its scenic beauty. In 2000, the bay was further inscribed into the World Heritage list for its unique geology and geomorphology. Currently, the biodiversity and cultural values of the bay are being studied, and management plans have been prepared and implemented. The area of Ha Long Bay World Natural Heritage extends over 434 km^2, and includes 755 limestone islands. Recently, seven unique plant species have been discovered on limestone mountains on the islands.

The bay is also home to a variety of species and is rich in marine biodiversity (Fig. 3). There are also diversity of coastal, marine, and island ecosystems in the bay area, including a remarkable coral reef (120 ha), mangroves (12.7 ha), seagrass beds (14.4 ha), limestone islands, and other wetlands. A preliminary survey recorded about 190 species of fish and shellfish in the bay. There are five important habitats for fishes: mangroves, coral reefs, rocky reefs, bays and embayments, and sand-mud bottom sediments. These are the natural habitats of many rare fisheries targets such as prawns, abalone, pearl oysters, groupers, snappers, and sea cucumbers. There are three spawning areas in Cua Luc, Tuan Chau, and Dau Be for migratory fish; Ngoc Vung and Cong Do are spawning areas for groupers and snappers. There are also six main fishing grounds in the bay: Dau Be, Dau Go, Soi Den-Ngoc Vung, Cua Dua-Cong Do, Tuan Chau, and Cong Tay.

Current Uses and Types of Production

Ha Long Bay is a significant area of economic development with great potential for:

- Development of seaports (e.g., the Cai Lan deep-sea port, the B12 Oil Port, and Hon Gai Coal Port). The waters of the bay are used for various purposes, such as transportation by ships and ferry boats. The navigation channel to Cai Lan port is a unique route cutting across Ha Long Bay. Other uses include floating ports, swimming, and other types of recreational activities.

- Development of aquaculture and fishing in the bay. Floating fishing villages are found even in the core zone of the World Natural Heritage, a no-take zone.

- Development of tourism. Due to Ha Long Bay's beautiful landscapes, outstanding geology and geomorphology, and other attractive destinations in the area, tourism is increasing steadily, with over 1,500 tourist boats operating in the bay.

- Development of industry, especially the coal mining industry that occurs in coastal areas of the bay. Land in this area is a major center of coal production in Viet Nam. Coal production practices, however, include dumping solid wastes and liquid wastes with high concentrations of SO_4, Pb, and other pollutants into coastal watersheds.

- Development of manufacturing for construction materials (limestone, clay, cement, etc.).

- Development of Ha Long city as a socioeconomic and cultural center in the Northern Economic Zone. This development, however, is associated with an increasing discharge of waste into the bay.

Administratively, the study area covers Ha Long Bay, Bai Chay embayment, Ha Long city, and a commune, Hung Thang. About 50% of the households in Hung Thang are located on the mainland and the remaining 50% (over 400 households in 2004) are located on three floating fishing villages. According to a recent survey (NOAA /IUCN/MoFi 2004), the coastal and marine activities of the commune are focused on fishing, aquaculture, coral collection, tourism, and transportation.

Hung Thang commune is a part of Ha Long Bay, and the people in this community depend upon resources of the bay for their livelihood. Hung Thang commune consists of about 320 ha of land, with a coastline of 3 km. There are eight villages; four on the mainland and four on the sea (Ba Hang, Cua Van, Cap De, and Cap La), of which the nearest to land is 15 km from the coast. The farthest is 50 km from the coast (outside the core zone). The Hung Thang commune has had to endure many of the impacts of development, including the urbanization of Ha Long city, and development of tourism, transportation, ports, and mining. Since Ha Long Bay was designated a World Natural Heritage, the socioeconomic conditions of the commune, along with those of the entire province, have changed dramatically. The areas of jurisdiction are diverse, and the population within the commune is widely scattered. People living on the mainland and on the sea influence the general management of the commune.

At present, Hung Thang is home to about 2,360 people in 548 households on the mainland and about 1,290 people in 289 households in floating villages (Table 2). About 60% of the population in the floating villages is illiterate.

Table 2. The total population in communities to May 2003.

Village	Number of Households	Number of people
Number 1	123	467
2	158	708
3	154	624
4	113	560
Ba Hang	34	157
Cua Van	176	733
Cap De	56	286
Cap La	23	111
Total	837	3646

In addition to permanent residents, there are households of immigrants who have come to stay and fish in the communal areas. The migration rate in Hung Thang is somewhat high, at about 5% annually. This is the result of fishermen moving to other regions to fish and live wherever the environment is more favorable and resources are abundant.

Aquaculture is already developed in a number of locations in the Ha Long Bay area, mostly in tidal mangroves and as cage culture in the bay. Brackish water shrimp, fish, and pearl oysters are cultured.

The many different coastal stakeholders include fishermen, aquaculturists, the tourism industry and tourists, traders, service providers, and consumers. The Ha Long Bay Management Board (HLMB) is responsible for managing the Ha Long Bay World Natural Heritage site, but its authority does not extend to the entire bay. The effectiveness of the HLMB, however, is limited, because most impacts to the bay originate from development activities outside the bay (out at sea and in the surrounding land areas).

Legal activities in the commune, such as fishing, aquaculture, tourism, transportation, and especially, Hung Thang's fishing fleet, are developing well. Cage aquaculture on the bay waters has developed over the past few years. Large numbers of cages are in operation and almost every floating village household has at least two cages. Illegal activities such as coral mining and destructive fishing are gradually decreasing, and local authorities are taking steps to prohibit these types of activities altogether.

Fishing and aquaculture are the main sources of income for approximately 1,290 people in the area (i.e., 35% of the population), mostly in the floating villages of Hung Thang. A relatively small number of people depend on other sources of income (Table 3).

Table 3. Main sources of income of the floating village households.

Source of income	Percentage (%)
Fishing	23.3
Fishing and aquaculture	66.7
Aquaculture	6.7
Others	3.3
Total	100

The dependence of coastal communities on fisheries resources is very high, and life in these communities would be severely impacted if these resources were exhausted. Before 1999, immigrant householders in the floating villages depended mainly on fishing, or in a few cases, on transportation and tourism services. A model floating house was introduced in 1999 that was safer and provided more commodious living than other options available at the time. For these reasons, and because floating houses are well suited to operating small aquaculture operations underneath, they have been widely adopted. Now, nearly 100% of the immigrants in the floating villages of Hung Thang commune reside in floating houses. The livelihood of people in the floating houses has improved to the extent that several immigrant householders are considered "billionaires of the sea."

Marine culture activity focuses on cage aquaculture, which developed because it is suitable for the specific conditions of the bay. Net cages are fastened under the floating houses to facilitate their management and care and harvesting of the product. The type of net depends on the culture species. Popular species for aquaculture are high value species such as mangrove red snapper (*Lutjanus argentimaculatus*), grouper (*Epinephelus tauvina*), black kingfish (*Rachycentron canadum*), or crab (*Scylla serrata*). The average floating house has five cages underneath it; larger floating houses may have as many as 12 each.

The main markets for fishery products are the local and Chinese markets. Products are sold to traders, then are transported to other localities or sent directly to fisheries processing plants. A small portion of production is sold to the floating restaurants or for the tourist industry in the region.

In 2004, NOAA/IUCN/MoFi reported the results of a survey they conducted of local people's perceptions relating to environmental issues and the protection of living resources (NOAA/IUCN/MoFi 2004). The results can be summarized as follows:

- 53% of the respondents reported that they recognized the importance of coral to protect coastal areas from storms or waves; the remaining 47% either did not recognize its importance (40%, no comment) or believed the coral reef to be valueless (7%).

- 47% of the respondents did not agree or strongly disagreed with the idea of cutting mangroves to facilitate fishing. The remaining 53% had no comment.

- 75% of the respondents agreed with the statement, "If mangrove forests were not protected, there would be no fish to catch," perhaps because they knew this from personal observations. The remaining 25% of respondents were not sure if they agreed or not.

- 72% of the respondents had no comment about whether coral reefs were only important for fishing or diving activities, perhaps because the concept is relatively abstract, and the wording of the item in the survey may have made it somewhat difficult to understand. Most of the remaining 25% disagreed with the statement.

- 65% of the respondents agreed with the statement, "It is hoped that the next generation can have mangrove and coral." Respondents seemed to realize that mangroves are a habitat of fisheries species, and if the mangroves are destroyed, the loss of habitat will reduce fisheries resources, leading to lower incomes for fishermen. From this perspective, people seem to have a great desire for regulatory authority to improve management of mangroves to restore and develop fisheries resources.

- Only 22% of the respondents knew that seagrass was of some value to humans. About 75% of the respondents indicated that seagrass was valueless for humans.

In general, respondents seemed to be most aware of and have formed clear opinions about resources to which they had the greatest access (e.g., mangroves, coral reefs, or coastal wetlands). Most people seemed to agree that resources could be degraded due to a number of factors, including:

- Urbanization and development of industrial zones and coastal tourism, as well as reclamation of land for shrimp culture that led to destruction of the mangroves. The very serious consequence of these practices was that many fisheries species lost their habitats. Expansion of coastal residential settlements is also exerting pressure on seagrass and mangrove areas, where the average yearly rate of loss is 5.3%. During 1989-2001, it was estimated that 64% of the mangrove areas in Viet Nam had been destroyed.

- Human activities, including fishing with trawl nets, exploitation of the coral reefs for the tourist industry, and pollution from wastes, which have contributed to the destruction of coral reefs, and which have had effects similar to those on mangroves. In 1997, living coral coverage was reported to be 75%. By July 2005, only 25% remained. The structure and diversity of the coral reef community has also changed for the worse since 1997. *Favites* spp., *Pavona* spp., and *Galaxea* spp. corals now dominate coral reefs, especially *G. columna*, an indicator of increased turbidity in the marine environment.

- A generally low level of awareness or knowledge among local people and others about environmental issues and protecting living resources. Despite increased efforts being made in resources management, few people seem to believe that the status of Viet Nam's aquatic living resources is being improved.

Challenges

Ecological and Socioeconomic Factors

Viet Nam in general and the Ha Long Bay area in particular are facing ecological and socioeconomic challenges related to the ongoing and future development of coastal aquaculture.

Unplanned aquaculture operations, in terms of seed production and aquaculture along the sandy coasts of Central Viet Nam and in coastal rice-shrimp fields, have resulted in disease outbreaks that have spread rapidly, greatly reducing the economic effectiveness of aquaculture in some areas. The main reason is that planning and management policies have not kept pace with the demands of the export market and the "mass movement for aquaculture".

Important coastal ecosystems such as coral reefs, seagrass beds, mangroves, etc., which are natural inputs for sustainable aquaculture and fisheries development, have been greatly reduced or destroyed. This has led to a reduced potential for brackish water aquaculture: 70% of the total potential area for brackish water aquaculture has already been used. Coastal and marine living resources and natural seed sources of economically valuable culture species, as well as biodiversity resources, have been lost or polluted due to habitat destruction in coastal bays and lagoons. While the coastal resources/habitats are slowly being rehabilitated, development activities in coastal watersheds continue to increase. In principle, both inshore and coastal living resources depend mainly on the sustainability of coastal ecosystems and habitats. This is an internal conflict within the fisheries sector in terms of its expectations for coastal aquaculture development to reduce the pressures of near shore over-exploitation.

Coastal areas, with their high concentration of aquaculture production activities, suffer from various natural disasters such as flooding, typhoons, erosion, and increasingly, impacts of land-based and sea-based pollution, such as agriculture and industrial wastes, oil spills from shipping, and harmful microalgae blooms. Negative environmental impacts also arise from fisheries activities such as processing and aquaculture.

Coral reefs are a key ecosystem for the maintenance of the ecological function for Ha Long Bay and the surrounding areas. Seagrasses and some small mangroves play a supportive role. Sedimentation, however, has increased, and it is affecting coral reefs and seagrass beds. Although the biodiversity of corals in the bay is rich, the status of coral reef fish in the bay is very poor.

Aquaculture production should not be promoted in coastal areas that are highly sensitive to environmental impacts. Up to now, most coastal aquaculture has been conducted extensively. Intensive farming takes up only about 7% of the total area used for aquaculture. This has led to increased competition for use of coastal areas among small-scale fishermen and aquaculturists.

Commercial hatcheries for shrimp (especially sugpo prawn, *Penaeus monodon*) are developed along the coast of the country, but these provide only a limited supply of shrimp larvae. Hatcheries for mollusc species cultured in the tidal zones/estuaries and for fish grown in cages on the coastal bays are generally lacking. Existing infrastructure for water supply and waste treatment systems for aquaculture ponds/fields are also in need of further development.

Coastal communities are generally poor and lacking in investment capital. Additionally, aquaculture development has increased the income gap in coastal communities for local fishermen, who have no alternative sources of income and whose economic status has not been improved. The permitting process and the few loans available for aquaculture activity in general, and for poor households in particular, are complicated and ineffective.

The competitive advantage of Viet Nam's aquacultural products needs to be greatly improved. Efforts are being made to improve technology for the safe and hygienic control of raw materials and the products of fishery processing. The use of export trade stamps/marks and aquacultural area codes has been initiated, but progress has been difficult. In addition, the fisheries sector has to meet strict requirements in terms of non-tariff barriers (e.g., prices and environmental standards) relating to exported aquaculture products in the context of market mechanisms and globalization.

User Conflicts

Viet Nam's coastal area is rich in resource diversity and has a great potential for multi-use and multi-sectoral development (Table 4). In this context, user conflicts continue to

Table 4. Multiple uses of Viet Nam's coastal areas.

Use
Aquaculture and mariculture
Coastal and near shore fishing
Mining and processing
Oil and gas operations
Development of:
Shipping and ports
Transport
Agriculture
Industries
Reclamation of land and settlements
Urbanization and waste discharge
Scientific and educational activities
Coastal and marine conservation
Tourism
Coastal and marine defense and security
Emergency response activities on the seas

Table 5. Matrix showing the relationship between main benefit conflicts involving multiple uses in the coastal area of Ha Long Bay.

Impact \ Impacted	Port-transportation (1)	Fisheries (2)	Tourism (3)	Agriculture (4)	Coastal industry and mining (5)	Forestry (6)
Port-transportation (1)	x	x	x	x	o	x
Fisheries (2)	x	x	x	x	o	x
Tourism (3)	o	x	x	o	o	o
Agriculture (4)	o	x	o	o	o	x
Coastal industry and mining (5)	o	x	x	o	o	x

x: interactive impact. o: non-interactive.

increase, especially among proponents of aquaculture, tourism, coastal construction, shipping and port development, and conservation. Impacts from land-based (in watershed) and sea-based sources on these activities also play a role in the increased conflicts among users.

Coastal areas of Ha Long Bay have the same types of user conflicts as those in other coastal areas of Viet Nam. Six economic sectors interactively impact each other. Table 5 is a matrix of the relationships between the main beneficiaries involved in conflicts over the multiple-use of coastal areas of Ha Long Bay.

Policy-making and Consolidation of Agencies

The lack of a permitting system for coastal aquaculture and mariculture, as well as the inconsistencies among inter-sectoral and internal policies and institutional frameworks relative to sustainable aquaculture development and management (i.e., tardy enactment of laws, fragmented and scattered regulations, and the lack of enforcement) have had a negative impact on aquaculture productivity. The National Assembly adopted the Law of Fisheries in November 2003, but it did not go into effect until July 2004. While the Law appears to be informative and productive, it has not proved easy to implement at the fisherman's level because of the lack of simplifying rules targeted at the fishermen.

Next Steps

Suggested Solutions to Problems

The Environmental Management Plan for Ha Long Bay

In 1998, the framework for an Environmental Management Plan (EMP) was set up for Ha Long Bay, to maintain the effectiveness of cage aquaculture in the bay while successfully conserving its unique ecosystem. The importance of input factors for sustainable aquaculture and fisheries in the area was also considered.

The fundamental vision behind the EMP is the "environmentally sound and sustainable development of the Ha Long Bay area." Its goals are: (a) to give top priority to protecting the World Natural Heritage; (b) to achieve environmental protection for sustainable economic growth; and (c) to establish an enforcement capability within environmental management.

The following approaches and strategies were suggested:

- Maintain the clean and clear quality of the water in the World Natural Heritage area

- Conserve the natural ecosystem and seascape of the bay, yet allow for sustainable aquaculture and fisheries

- Manage waste disposal into the bay

- Control area-wide pollution loading

- Conserve the natural coast and tidal zones

- Protect forest and water resources

- Build capacity within the responsible agencies

- Set up institutional support to enforce the EMP

Pollutant Loads

Approximately 30% of the sewage from homes in Ha Long city and from on sea activities are discharged into the drainage channels via septic tanks. About 180,000 m³ of municipal solid waste is generated annually in the developed areas, but only about 50% of the population has solid waste collection services.

Specific pollution sources may be classified into four groups, based on activities in the area and/or the type of wastewater discharged: domestic, industrial (including coal mining activities), commercial, and livestock. The estimated pollution loads of biological oxygen

Table 6. Pollution loads flowing into Ha Long Bay.

Items	Pollution loads inflow (MT day[-1])				
	Domestic[a]	Industry	Livestock	Non-specific	Total
BOD	3.0	0.3	1.9	1.9	7.2
COD	4.9	1.9	2.8	12.3	21.9
SS	8.5	22.1	16.3	194.0	241.1
T-N	2.7	0.5	2.5	9.7	15.5
T-P	0.3	negligible	1.5	4.2	6.1

[a]Domestic pollution load includes that contributed by tourism.
BOD: Biological oxygen demand; COD: Chemical oxygen demand; SS: Suspended solids; T-N: Total nitrogen; T-P: Total phosphorus.

Table 7. Mass balance of pollutants in three bays. Unit: Biological oxygen demand, MT/day.

Location	Pollution load inflow	Primary production	Elution	Self-purification	Outflow	Balance
Bai Chay embayment	2.9	45.3	0.6	42.4	6.3	0.1
Bai Chay and Hon Gai	7.6	62.3	0.6	65.0	5.3	0.2
Ha Long Bay	10.3	2,004	13.5	2,010	10.7	7.6

Source: MOSTE and JICA 1998.

Table 8. Projected pollution loads flowing into the bay in 2010 (Unit: MT day[-1])

Time frame	BOD	COD	SS	T-N	T-P
Present	7.2	21.9	241	15.5	6.0
Year 2010	13.0	31.4	274	20.1	6.8
Increments	5.8	9.5	33	4.5	0.8

BOD: Biological oxygen demand; COD: Chemical oxygen demand; SS: Suspended solids; T-N: Total nitrogen; T-P: Total phosphorus.

demand (BOD), chemical oxygen demand (COD), suspended solids (SS), total nitrogen (TN), and total phosphorus (TP) flowing into the bay are shown in Table 6. Domestic pollution accounts for about 50% of the total BOD load. Material circulation and balance in the bay was estimated for an analysis of the mechanisms of organic pollution in the bay. The results are shown in Table 7 (JICA 1998).

A numerical simulation model was used to predict (to 2010) the future water quality of the bay without countermeasures being taken. Projected pollution loads flowing into the bay are presented in Table 8. The total organic pollution load runoff is expected to be 1.8 times current values for BOD, and 1.4 times current values for COD. Total nutrient runoff is predicted to be 1.3 times current values for TN, and 1.1 times current values for TP. These nutrients contribute to primary production by phytoplankton. An increase of organic substances in the water is predicted to lead to a decrease in transparency and in dissolved oxygen (DO). Poorly oxygenated water causes degradation of bottom sediments and adverse impacts on the ecosystem. Additionally, an increase in nutrients would accelerate eutrophication in the bay and cause decreased transparency and an increase in the organic products of primary production. Total SS runoff is predicted to be 1.1 times current values, mainly due to deforestation in the catchment area. Increased sediment runoff would cause adverse impacts on water quality and on the nursery grounds of the aquatic biomass in the bay. Wastes discharged into the bay from cage aquaculture operations would have negative environmental impacts, but may be mitigated due to water exchange in the bay.

Sustainable Aquaculture within Ha Long Bay

Aquaculture is an important economic activity in Ha Long Bay. Some aquaculture activities, such as cage-culture of finfish, generate substantial wastes that impact the marine environment. Actually, the pollution loads from marine aquaculture are trivial compared with those generated from land-based sources around Ha Long Bay, and cage aquaculture is established and highly profitable. It also provides an important alternative source of income for local fishermen. Existing cage aquaculture should be managed to ensure that appropriate environmental quality standards are not exceeded and that good advice and information are available for new opportunities in aquaculture development, e.g., seaweed cultivation. At the same time, the Quang Ninh Province People's Committee (PPC) needs to reevaluate cage aquaculture areas in the bay based on assessments of the carrying capacity of the bay.

Moving Toward Integrated Coastal Management (ICM) in Ha Long Bay

Based on the EMP results and with the support of NOAA/IUCN and MoFi, the project, "Capacity Building for ICM in the Tonkin Gulf: Case Study in Ha Long Bay (Phase I: 2003-2004)," was carried out. Objectives developed under this project include:

- Relocating aquaculture cages from three floating villages in the core zone of the World Heritage to other sides of the bay or surrounding bays.

- Reducing the density of the cages per ha of marine water, primarily by using assessments of carrying capacity.

- Reducing the density of cultivated species in each cage to mitigate aquaculture wastes discharged into the surrounding seas.

- Developing a water quality map, based on the results of monitoring 22 parameters of marine environmental quality in the bay on a quarterly basis since 1995.

- Developing a socioeconomic map for this area, based on SOCMON surveys.

- Mapping habitats and establishing a database of the bay profile.

- Zoning coastal areas according to function using GIS and modeling technology

- Planning for ICM

A number of important environmental impacts on Ha Long Bay are from external sources (i.e., outside the World Heritage [WH] site). These include fishing, marine recreational activities, shipping, the tourist industry and tourism-related activities, and port development and maintenance (dredging and dredged material disposal), especially from land-based sources of pollution. The marine environment and habitats of the WH site are challenged with negative and potential impacts from destructive fishing, coastal development, and waste discharges into the bay from rivers, Ha Long city, ports, and tourist resorts (hotel construction both within and adjacent to the WH site). These development activities can cause adverse changes in seawater quality, sedimentation on reefs, degradation of marine resources, and destruction of key habitats within the WH and the bay. An integrated coastal and marine management approach is required to identify and effectively manage multiple users from multiple economic sectors.

The Ha Long Bay World Heritage Management Board (HLBWHMB) is currently limited to influencing human activities within the WH area, including mainly tourism and aquaculture, but it has no authority to manage cage aquaculture in the bay. As mentioned above, most environmental impacts within the WH site are from human activities outside the boundaries of the WH site. The Quang Ninh PPC should consider, as part of the environmental impact assessment process, a review by the HLBWHMB of development proposals for Ha Long Bay, where impacts from planned development could affect the natural resources, habitats, and local communities of the WH site.

Suggested Approaches to Data Collection

Management of coastal and marine areas should be not only integrated, but also adaptive. Adaptive management requires the identification and monitoring of robust indicators of environmental and socio-economic conditions within Ha Long Bay and the WH site. This information should periodically be assessed to determine general environmental and socioeconomic trends and, more importantly, to evaluate the effectiveness and efficiency of management strategies and interventions. Goals, objectives, targets, and expected outcomes could then be adapted over time based on this information.

A program of monitoring and evaluating function in the bay should become an integral part of management activities of the bay and cage aquaculture in it. The indicators of environmental conditions in the bay relating to cage aquaculture need to be collected every 3 months for the general parameters in some planned transects (from national environmental monitoring activities), and every 6 months for environmental parameters in aquaculture areas. Indicators of socioeconomic conditions in the bay relating to cage aquaculture should be collected yearly (2005-2006). The data collection could be undertaken through thematic workshops, which should be held during implementation of the initiatives (2005-2006). The above monitoring data and on collected available data for wind fields, marine circulation, and water exchange in the bay will be used to calculate the carrying capacity.

Recommendations for Ways to Apply Ecosystem-based Aquaculture Management

Coastal and marine aquaculture in Viet Nam play very important roles in the economic growth of the fisheries sector and in the reduction of poverty. The ICM framework is considered to be a macro-tool for maintaining sustainable aquaculture development in coastal and marine areas. Guidelines, however, need to be developed for ecosystem-based aquaculture management in Viet Nam and for the incorporation of aquaculture into the ICM framework. In addition, Viet Nam, a developing country, will continue to require international cooperation and technical assistance for ecosystem-based aquaculture management and integration of the activities into the ICM framework. In 2007, MoFi, on behalf of the Vietnamese Government, will organize the Second International Workshop on Ecosystem-based Aquaculture Management, in Viet Nam, to be sponsored by NOAA.

Literature Cited

MOSTE (Ministry of Sciences, Technology and Environment) and JICA (Japan International Cooperation Agency). 1998. The Study on Environmental Management for Ha Long Bay. Final report. Archives of the Ministry of Sciences, Technology and Environment, Ha Noi, Viet Nam.

NOAA/IUCN/MoFi (National Oceanic and Atmospheric Administration/World Conservation Union/Ministry of Fisheries). 2004. Final Reports of Phase I on Building Capacity for ICM in Tonkin Gulf: Case Study in Ha Long Bay Coastal Area. World Conservation Union (IUCN) Vietnam, Ha Noi, Viet Nam.

Vietnam Agenda 21. 2004. The Strategic Orientation for Sustainable Development in Vietnam. Office of VIE/01/021, Ministry of Planning and Investment, Ha Noi, Viet Nam. http://www.va21.org.

Most of the sources of information in this chapter are reports kept in various government agency archives:

Chu Hoi, N. 1998. Implementation of the Chapter 17, Agenda 21 in Viet Nam. United Nations Economic and Social Commission for Asia and the Pacific (UNESCAP) Report 04. United Nations, New York, New York, USA. See also http://www.un.org/esa/earthsummit/vietn-cp.htm.

Chu Hoi, N. 2002. Towards sustainable development of fisheries and coastal areas of Vietnam. [in Vietnamese]. Reviews in Fisheries Science Ha Noi, Viet Nam 6: 9-14.

Chu Hoi, N. and H.T. Minh. 2003. The Implementation of the UN Convention of Law of Seas in Fisheries Sector in Viet Nam. Archives of the Ministry of International Affairs, Ha Noi, Viet Nam.

Chu Hoi, N., N. Xuan Ly, D. Khanh, and N. Van Chiem. 2002. The Strategy toward 2020 and Action Plan up to Year 2010 for Environmental Protection of Fisheries Sector in Viet Nam. Draft. [in Vietnamese]. Archives of the Institute of Fisheries Economics and Planning, Ha Noi, Viet Nam.

Chu Hoi, N., N. Dinh Hoe, and H. Minh Tuong. 2004. Coastal and Marine Areas. Pages 99-140 in Viet Nam: The Life and Environment. Political Publishing House, Ha Noi, Viet Nam.

MoFi (Ministry of Fisheries). 2002a. Strategy of Offshore Fishing up to 2010. Draft document. [in Vietnamese]. Archives of the Ministry of Fisheries, Ha Noi, Viet Nam.

MoFi (Ministry of Fisheries). 2002b. Planning for Socio-economic Development of Fisheries Sector up to Year 2010. [in Vietnamese]. Archives of the Ministry of Fisheries, Ha Noi, Viet Nam.

MoFi (Ministry of Fisheries). 2004. Fisheries Sector Summing up Report for Year 2004 and Some Directions for 2005 Activities. [in Vietnamese]. Archives of the Ministry of Fisheries, Ha Noi, Viet Nam.

WB/MoFi (World Bank/Ministry of Fisheries). 2004. Viet Nam: Fisheries and Aquaculture Sector Study. Final report. Archives of the Ministry of Fisheries, Ha Noi, Viet Nam.

ADDITIONAL PERSPECTIVES FOR ECOSYSTEM
APPROACHES FOR AQUACULTURE

ADDITIONAL PERSPECTIVES

8

Executive Summary

Experiences of Chile, Malaysia, Sweden, and Taiwan with ecosystem-based approaches to aquaculture are informative to the process of refining these approaches and addressing environmental and policy development issues. Chile, the second largest world producer of farmed salmon (*Salmo salar, Oncorhynchus* spp.), has experienced a very rapid growth of aquaculture during the past 10 years. Chile's salmon aquaculture industry is one of the world's most advanced culture technologies and processing capabilities, and it is poised to continue to expand, especially into pristine coastal areas in southern Chile. Evidence suggests some negative effects on the sea bottom in licensed culture areas, including: (a) significant losses of benthic biodiversity, (b) salmon escapees, and (c) the probable induction of harmful algal blooms through the discharge of nitrogen into the water by the cultured fishes. The government and salmon companies are developing regulatory policies and other environmental protection protocols for the industry, but a focus on analyzing the effects of salmon culture on a few specific parameters distracts from the goal of protecting the ecosystem as a whole. The complex interaction of salmon farming and the surrounding environment urgently requires a more integrated approach to improve future prospects of an ecosystem-based approach to salmon aquaculture in Chile.

Malaysia fisheries have increased steadily during the past decade, in terms of both yields from capture fisheries and aquaculture production. By 2010, target aquaculture production is projected to have a value of $2.89 billion. Challenges to aquaculture development include the limited availability of suitable culture sites, which has promoted the indiscriminate removal of mangroves, an insufficient supply of high quality seeds for marine and freshwater finfish, and increasing production costs due to the rising cost of feed. One of the recommended first steps for implementing ecosystem-based aquaculture management is to assess the carrying capacity of surrounding waters. For example, around the Dinding River in the Manjung District of the State of Perak, shrimp is cultured in earthen ponds along riverbanks, and in the river waters, finfish are cultured in cages and mussels are cultured on ropes.

Eutrophication of coastal waters is another serious environmental problem with high costs for society. Researchers in Sweden review a proposed method to reduce eutrophication by culturing filter-feeding organisms, such as blue mussels (*Mytilus edulis*), to reduce nitrogen inputs from aquaculture and other sources. The expected effect of mussel farming on nitrogen cycling was modeled for the Gullmar Fjord on the Swedish west coast, and it was shown that the net transport of nitrogen (sum of dissolved and particulate) at the fjord mouth could be reduced by 20%. Nutrient emission trading systems offer an instrument for environmental authorities and coastal managers to use the commercial shellfish industry to improve coastal

Contributors:
Chile–Buschmann, A.H., V.A. Riquelme, M.C. Hernández-Gonález, and L.A. Henriquez; **Malaysia**–Bin Tohiyat, M.D., and J. Hashim; **Sweden**–Lindahl, O. and S. Kohlberg; **Taiwan**–Chen, Y.-S. and C.-Y. Hsu
In J.P. McVey, C.-S. Lee, and P.J. O'Bryen, editors. Aquaculture and Ecosystems: An Integrated Coastal and Ocean Management Approach. The World Aquaculture Society. Baton Rouge, Louisiana, United States.

water quality while offering shellfish farmers an incentive to increase their enterprises. Mussel farming is suggested as an alternative to nitrogen reduction in a sewage treatment plant. Accumulation of biotoxins, however, has been identified as the largest impediment for further expansion of commercial mussel farming in Sweden. A solution may be identified through ecosystem-based techniques and management strategies.

In Taiwan, production of marine species has increased in the past decade, mainly due to marine cage culture, especially of cobia (*Rachycentron canadum*). The recent and continuing expansion of cage farming in inshore areas and the intention to develop offshore potential are challenged by a number of factors, including the environmental impacts of intensive cage farming in the tropics. Ecosystem-based approaches for overcoming some of these challenges include the use of high quality feed, adoption of good feeding and management practices on the farm, and avoidance of unsuitable farming sites. The Taiwan Offshore Aquaculture Association is working with the government in improving the economy of fishing communities, managing natural resources, and protecting the environment. The government is taking steps to protect Taiwan's marine resources by protecting reef habitats, enhancing fisheries stocks, and initiating overall planning of proprietary fisheries for coastal areas, where multiple users and the limited number of suitable culture sites also need to be considered.

Chile

Aquaculture has evolved to become the fourth major economic activity in the Republic of Chile (Chile) after copper, forestry, and fruit production, with a mean production in 2003 of 633,085 metric tons (MT), valued at $1,073,596 (SNP 2004). The main organisms currently being cultivated in Chile are different species of salmon (*Salmo salar, Oncorhynchus* spp.), mussels, oysters, scallops, gastropods, and algae (Buschmann et al. 1996, 2001a; López et al. in press). The salmon industry is now the main aquaculture activity, contributing over 76.9% of the biomass production and 94.9% of the total value of exports. Moreover, the salmon industry has altered the southern Chile landscape.

The development of the salmon industry, however, has created new requirements for government regulations, especially in terms of employment and the environment. When the industry started about 15 years ago, it was almost unregulated in terms of environmental issues, but various governmental regulations and international market demands have generated a new scenario. This chapter covers the growth of the salmon industry as well as the environmental effects that have been recorded during the past 12 years. State policies as well as the influence of the international market on the industry in relation to environmental regulations are also described. Finally, the above issues are used to define major goals, bottlenecks, and possible environmental solutions, through adopting an ecosystem-based approach to maintain the balance of waste inputs and outputs from aquaculture and other sources.

Aquaculture Status and Environmental Issues

In 2004, salmon aquaculture production in Chile reached 311,000 MT (Fig. 1). Chile currently produces 33% of the world production (Fig. 2), making it the second largest world producer. Exports are destined mainly for Japan and the United States as a result of a government policy of active promotion. The salmon industry has gone through several innovation processes and is now counted among the top culture technologies and processing capabilities in the world. For these reasons, the industry is now considered a consolidated economical activity, and Chile is predicted to become the world's largest producer of salmon in the next few years. To grow, the salmon industry must expand its activities further south, reaching pristine areas that have thus far experienced almost no human activity (Fig. 3).

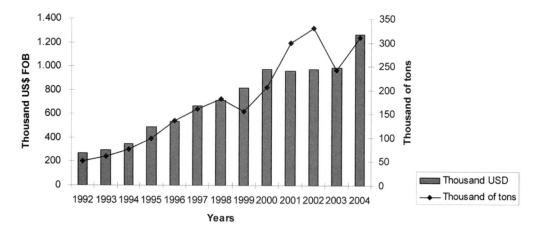

Figure 1. Salmon production (biomass and economic revenue) in Chile, 1994-2004. FOB: Free on board.

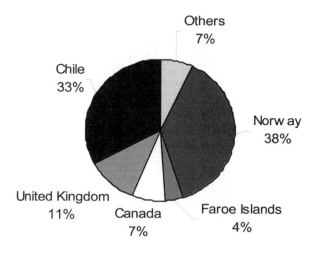

Figure 2. Relative world production of salmon by country, 2003.

Environmental impacts of the industry prior to 1996 were reviewed, but evidence at the time did not suggest any strong effects (Buschmann et al. 1996). After almost 10 years of intensive growth, however, the evidence suggests some effects on the sea bottom in the licensed culture areas, associated with significant losses of benthic biodiversity and changes in the physico-chemical properties of the sediments (Buschmann 2002; Soto and Norambuena 2004). Salmon escapees are another public concern. Evidence suggests that they feed on native species, but the life expectancy of salmon in wild conditions is rather low (< 1 year; Soto et al. 2001). Further research is needed on the net predatory effect of escaped salmon on their prey species in southern Chile.

Another related major concern is the induction of harmful algal blooms (HABs) through the input of nitrogen into the water by the cultured fishes. Ordinarily, no increase can be detected in the concentration of nitrogen in the water column associated with salmon farming (Soto and Norambuena 2004). In a channel in southern Chile used for intensive production,

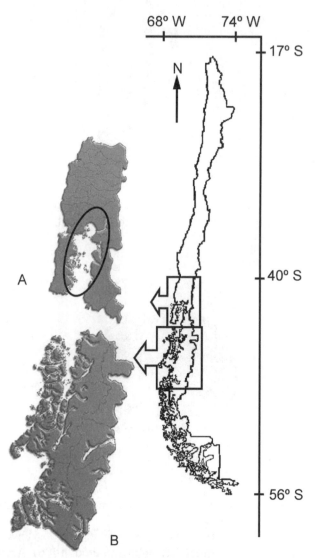

Figure 3. Principal salmon culture region (circled) and the direction of expansion into the southern regions of Chile (arrows).

however, significantly higher concentrations of ammonium were found near the cages in comparison to amounts in an isolated control area located at least 3 km from the cages. The effects of producing 300,000 MT of salmon can be compared, with some restrictions (see Black et al. 1997), to those of a population of 6-8 million human inhabitants (see previous calculation protocol in Buschmann et al. 1996). This analogy offers a perspective on the likely effects of salmon farming, and suggests that nutrient loads as well as nitrogen/phosphorus ratios produced by intensive salmon farming can be significant. These factors must be considered when documenting increases of HABs in the channels and fjords of southern Chile. Although this approach has also been suggested for other regions (Halleagraeff 1993; Smayda 1990), the issue remains controversial (Sellner et al. 2003).

On the other hand, it was observed that the nitrogen content of seaweeds increases when the algae is cultivated near fish pens, suggesting a higher nitrogen availability due to the farming activity (Table 1; Troell et al. 1997). Dinoflagellate population growth in 1,500 L tanks is also enhanced when using the effluents from fish tanks (Table 1). A study carried out using the Before-After Control-Impact (BACI) sampling methodology, described by Underwood (1994), further suggests that in the presence of salmon pens, significant increments of dinoflagellate densities can occur in pulses (Vergara 2001). This latter finding may indicate that a sampling protocol to detect short-term pulses may be necessary for detecting HABs. Lacking the proper sampling protocol may have prevented the detection of a relationship between aquaculture and HABs in a number of cases. Recently, it has been proposed that this finding may be relevant in China. Feng et al. (2004) suggest that when organisms from the higher trophic levels are cultured intensively, the results are eutrophication and there is increased probability of HABs occurring. Based on the above evidence, the authors of this chapter believe that this hypothesis cannot be rejected out of hand for political reasons before it is properly tested. Research is urgently required in Chile, especially because the salmon industry plans to continue expanding south, toward one of the few remaining pristine, biologically unique, and poorly studied coasts of the world (Forsterra et al. 2005).

Table 1. Possible eutrophication effects of salmon aquaculture, based on field observations in southern Chile.

Observation	Source
Significant increase in concentration of ammonium ($p < 0.01$) in the vicinity of salmon cages (< 500 m) in Calbuco Channel compared to sites farther away (< 3000 m).	Cortés-Ebner, personal communication
Growth and N content of macroalgae (*Gracilaria* spp.) cultured near fish pens increased compared to algae cultivated in control areas without fish pens.	Troell et al. (1997)
Effluents from fish farms used experimentally in 1500 L tanks promoted algal blooms and a change in the composition of microflora, favoring dominance of dinoflagellates.	Buschmann, unpublished data
A Before-After Control-Impact (BACI) environmental assessment (following methodology by Underwood, 1994) showed that dinoflagellates increased in abundance in pulses when a salmon farm began operating.	Vergara (2001)

Other studies further emphasize the importance of establishing integrated aquaculture of fed and extractive organisms to establish a recycling of the wastes in coastal environments used for intensive aquaculture (Buschmann et al. 2001a; Chopin et al. 2001; Troell et al. 2003; Neori et al. 2004). The use of filter feeders and seaweeds has been tested in Chile, with positive results (Buschmann et al. 2001a). On the other hand, a more intensive land-based culture module that was developed showed promising technical (Buschmann et al. 1994, 1996) and economic results (Chopin et al. 2001). It seems reasonable that if aquaculture continues to grow, balancing nutrient input from and output of wastes to the environment should be a basic requirement, and integrated culture of extractive and fed organisms in the same water body should be further developed. Nevertheless, integrated aquaculture is not widely practiced in Chile, mainly because eutrophication of coastal waters is still viewed as a remote environmental issue.

Marine birds are also affected by the installation of salmon farms (Buschmann 2002). The abundance of omnivorous, diving, and carrion-feeding birds has been observed to increase three to five times in areas with salmon aquaculture operations than in control areas that have none. The ecological consequences of increased populations of these types of birds have not yet been studied. In addition, the effects of salmon culture on marine mammals have not been established. Due to their possible role in maintaining a healthy environment, however, marine mammals should be included in future studies.

The use of different types of chemical compounds in aquaculture has been of public concern, mainly after high levels of various unwanted chemicals have been detected in a number of other countries. In addition, few studies have investigated the effects of antibiotics on the microbial flora (e.g., Miranda and Zemelman 2002). The importation of antibiotics into Chile strongly suggests that high dosages of these products are being used (Cabello 2003). Related issues, such as the use of malachite green, antifouling paints, and other chemicals are under researched or under reported in the scientific literature. Buschmann and Fortt (in press) suggest that concentrations of copper in marine sediments near salmon cages are related to a reduction of infaunal biodiversity.

Intensive aquaculture may have complex, multiple effects on coastal ecosystems. Without an ecosystem-based approach, understanding the potential effects and making reasonable management recommendations seems unlikely. For Chile's growing salmon aquaculture industry to achieve environmental sustainability requires modifying the conceptual research approaches as soon as possible. An ecosystem-based approach must also incorporate integrated aquaculture, where wastes discharged into coastal ecosystems are balanced with their removal from the environment. Experiences with this approach are reported in the literature (e.g., Buschmann et al. 2001a; Chopin et al. 2001; Troell et al. 2003; Neori et al. 2004), but producers have not yet widely adopted integrated aquaculture as a culture system.

Although aquaculture has been one of the most important economic activities in Chile in the past 10-15 years, its development has been criticized for its impact on the environment. Buschmann and Pizarro (2001) identified salmon farming as an environmentally costly activity (over 30% of fisheries and aquaculture Gross Domestic Product). The possible environmental effects of salmon farming, however, are not well-discussed, due to the low level of knowledge among the general public about salmon farming in general, and an overall impression of its being a low impact activity. A more ecosystem-based and global approach to aquaculture is, at present, found only in the scattered efforts of individual researchers, government agencies, private companies, and other stakeholders. Thus, arriving at a consensus and developing a more integrated approach to salmon aquaculture as a sustainable economic activity in Chile remain future goals rather than recent accomplishments.

Government Policy in Chile

The Chilean government has developed a regulatory plan for addressing environmental issues in Chile. Any new salmon aquaculture operation starting up in Chile is required to submit all necessary information to the National Environmental Commission (CONAMA) for approval. Since December 2001, a second requirement, which falls under a regulation decree (RAMA) administered by the Subsecretary of Fisheries, must also be met, i.e., each salmon culture facility must monitor the environmental conditions in the licensed area. The established norms assume that the main effect of salmon aquaculture (i.e., on the benthic communities) occurs mainly under the fish cages (Table 2). Other aspects of eutrophication (e.g., in the water column) are not addressed by the regulations, nor are the effects on other organisms (e.g., birds, native fishes, marine mammals). Existing evidence strongly suggests that nitrogen input from salmon farms affects nutrient concentrations in coastal zones of southern Chile. For these reasons, the regulations in Chile are criticized for not having a comprehensive ecosystem viewpoint, and for being limited in their application to small areas, without considering many relevant ecological components.

Table 2. Summary of environmental regulations (RAMA) in Chile.

Article Number	Issue	Contents
(none)	General objectives	Provides for the maintenance of the cleanliness and ecological balance of the bestowed zone.
(none)	Laws and regulations	General Law on Fisheries and Aquaculture, No. 18.892 (1991) General Environmental Terms, No. 19.300 (1994)
3, 15, 16, and 17	Instruments for the conservation and assessment of the capacity of bodies of water	Preliminary Site Description (CPS): • Environmental information • Aerobic sediment analysis
4, 8, and 9	Conditions on farms	Maintain the cleanliness of the area and the farm. Dispose of solid and liquid residues or wastes, including blood and dead specimens, in storage deposits. Maintain adequate security systems adapted to avoiding the escapement of farmed resources.

Aquaculture must comply with sanitary policies, which include the sanitary conditions for imported fry, the recommended distances between culture sites to prevent diseases, and the control of chemicals and drugs used by the industry (e.g., parasite control chemicals and antibiotics). Many aspects are covered by current sanitary policies, but farmers have never well understood the policies, and inspections by government agencies remain bottlenecks to achieving better results. It has been found that Chilean salmon farmers use 75 times more antibiotics than the amount used by their Norwegian counterparts (Cabello 2003, 2004). High concentrations of antibiotics and the presence of leucomalachite have been found in exported Chilean salmon, although in comparison with salmon from the Northern Hemisphere, Chilean products contain significantly lower amounts of pollutants (Hites et al. 2004). Nevertheless, the main issues are that the effects of these compounds have not yet been studied and regulations for their use are weak or nonexistent.

Salmon companies developed some self-made environmental compromises with the government (Fig. 4), but their effects are not well understood by the general public. The authors of this chapter submit that the external or "market" regulations are more important (Fig. 4). Because salmon is exported, it must meet international standards. This makes the export market the most important form of control, and it can generate complex situations, such as the retention of shipments because of leucomalachite or antibiotics in foreign ports. In these cases, the Chilean Salmon Association and the government have come together in a unified defense. Technical barriers to exporting products, such as sanitary and environmental standards, among others, are one of the major market controls that affect the exportation of Chilean salmon (Fig. 5).

Despite several existing restrictions, the government has managed to develop some of its own regulations, and the salmon industry has created other environmental protection

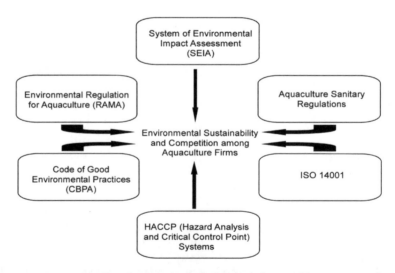

Figure 4. Current governmental and private regulations, codes, and instruments that aquaculture practices use to meet environmental standards in Chile.

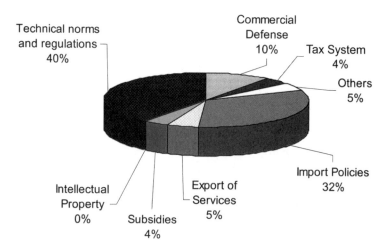

Figure 5. Foreign actions that affect the exportation of Chilean salmon (percent over the total barriers). Source: Anonymous 2005.

protocols. Nevertheless, several omissions exist, such as inspection capacity and the self-regulation of the industry. From the point of view of the authors of this chapter, the main problem is the focus on point effects (e.g., bottom effects, sanitary effects, escapees), an approach that does not address protecting the ecosystem as a whole. Approaches and regulations that do not take the entire ecosystem into consideration (and all the difficulties that this implies) to balance all the inputs and outputs that occur through the various human activities are inadequate to preserve the unique ecosystem of southern Chile (see Forsterra et al. 2005). Examples of how to deal with this issue can be found in the recent literature (e.g., Duarte et al. 2003). Other chapters in this book indicate the real possibility of moving forward into a new management stage for aquaculture, especially if a more integrated approach to intensive aquaculture is adopted.

Future Prospects of Chilean Aquaculture

In summary, two main issues still remain to be addressed to sustain environmentally friendly aquaculture development in southern Chile. First, the development of human activities, such as coastal urban settlements, agriculture, forestry, and aquaculture, without regard to their environmental effects on the inner seas of southern Chile, is unacceptable. The economic development of aquaculture, without taking the environmental and social responsibilities fully into account, thus increases the risk for growth of the aquaculture sector. Economic activities depend heavily upon the ecological services that coastal zones provide, because of the strong effects of human activity on the ecosystems in these areas (Vitousek et al. 1997). This situation is even more evident in Chile, because of the low investment in gathering knowledge, the second main issue with regard to adopting an ecosystem-based approach to aquaculture. Chile is the world's second largest producer of salmon, but only 2.3% of the scientific and technological contributions to the literature on salmon are from Chilean researchers. Thus, research results from Chile are comparatively lacking for diseases and environmental issues that cannot be solved by solutions used elsewhere (Riquelme and Buschmann, unpublished). It is urgent for the government to take a more active role in developing a modern conceptual framework (an ecosystem-based approach) to generate the knowledge needed for the development of proposed models.

On the other hand, if Chile were open to implementing a comprehensive environmental policy and incorporating eco-technologies (e.g., integrated aquaculture), it would allow for an ecosystem-based approach that changed future perspectives. Incorporating integrated cultivation approaches would clearly change the future perspectives of aquaculture, especially those of salmon culture. For a long time, educational programs in Chile have been preparing professionals who are knowledgeable about the various aspects of aquaculture and marine biology. For this reason, the capacity to adopt more modern approaches and regulations already exists. The decision, then, is mainly political, and requires deep and open discussion.

Acknowledgments

The first author acknowledges the help of the workshop organizing committee, as well as the Universidad de Los Lagos and Oceana-Chile for their support. The study for the Chilean salmon section of the chapter was carried out under a grant (No. 105055) from FONDECYT (Chile). The authors wish to thank Sandra Pereda and Cristian Gutierrez for their comments to improve this manuscript, but the authors are solely responsible for the statements and opinions expressed in the text.

Malaysia

The fisheries industry is considered an important sector of the Malaysian economy, contributing 1.37% of its Gross Domestic Product and providing employment to 89,433 fishermen and 21,114 fish culturists. In 1995, capture fisheries yielded 1,198,436 metric tons (MT) of marine fish, valued at $713 million, and aquaculture production was 132,742 MT, with an estimated value of $103 million. By 2003, capture fisheries yields had increased to 1,283,256 MT, valued at $1.06 billion, and aquaculture production had increased to 196,873 MT, with an estimated value of $309 million (Tables 3 and 4).

In 2002, the total export of fisheries commodities was 198,892 MT, with a value of $384.87 million (Table 5). The total amount imported for the same year was 353,794 MT, with a value of $343.87 million, resulting in a trade surplus for fisheries commodities valued at $41 million.

Seaweed production is another important contributor to the economy. In 2001, seaweed exports from Malaysia accounted for 1.4% (estimated value, $5 million) of the global trade of dried seaweed. In 2002, Malaysia exported 2,562 MT of dried seaweed, with a value in excess of $1.16 million (Table 6), accounting for 39% by volume and 4% by value of the total marine aquaculture production solely for the export market in 2002.

Table 3. Marine fish landings and value, 1995-2003. (Source: Annual Fisheries Statistics 2003, Department of Fisheries Malaysia).

Year	Quantity (MT)	Value (in millions of dollars)
1995	1,198,436	713.39
1996	1,126,689	874.25
1997	1,168,973	967.17
1998	1,215,206	1,004.53
1999	1,248,402	1,090.33
2000	1,285,696	1,157.69
2001	1,231,289	1,096.34
2002	1,272,078	1,107.05
2003	1,283,256	1,056.21

Table 4. Estimated value and production from all aquaculture systems, 1995-2003. (Source: Annual Fisheries Statistics 2003, Department of Fisheries, Malaysia).

Year	Quantity (MT)	Value (in millions of dollars)
1995	132,741.61	103.33
1996	109,062.19	121.68
1997	107,983.60	160.28
1998	133,646.64	172.18
1999	166,973.80	203.97
2000	167,893.99	255.35
2001	177,019.17	317.52
2002	191,843.09	284.54
2003	196,873.43	308.50

Table 5. Quantity and value of Malaysia's fishery commodities, 1999-2002. (Source: Annual Fisheries Statistics 2003, Department of Fisheries, Malaysia).

Year	Exports (MT)	Value (in millions of dollars)	Imports (MT)	Value (in millions of dollars)
1999	136,044	303,986,166	307,523	268,397,242
2000	144,590	355,135,941	323,199	307,447,920
2001	161,339	358,930,691	349,265	335,179,571
2002	198,892	384,878,231	353,794	343,871,452

Table 6. Seaweed production in Malaysia, 2000-2003.

Year	Quantity (MT)
2000	4,101.87
2001	4,715.71
2002	2,565.46
2003	2,756.30

Government Policies in Malaysia

There are two main acts that regulate the development of fisheries (including aquaculture) in Malaysia, i.e., the Fisheries Act of 1985 and the Environmental Quality Act of 1974. Section 38(1) of the Fisheries Act of 1985 states that the State Authority or, in the case of the Federal Territories of Kuala Lumpur and Labuan, the Minister may make rules specifically or generally for the proper conservation, development, management and regulation of turtles and inland fisheries in any state in Malaysia or in the Federal Territories of Kuala Lumpur and Labuan. The State Authority or Minister, may, in particular, make rules for all or any of the following purposes: (a) promote and regulate fish culture in riverine waters; (b) provide for the leasing and licensing of lakes, swamps, mining pools and other pools, land, and other areas for the cultivation of fish; (c) prescribe standards for the construction and operation of aquaculture establishments (including the size and depth of ponds); and (d) impose measures for the prevention of fish diseases and controls over particular species of fish that may be produced by cultivation.

While the Fisheries Act of 1985 deals with the fisheries sector per se, the Environmental Quality Act of 1974 covers all sectors, from agriculture and forestry to petroleum and mining. Where aquaculture is concerned, the Environmental Quality Act of 1974 states that an Environmental Impact Assessment Study must be carried out for any project that covers an area of 50 ha or more.

The Third National Agricultural Policy (1998–2010) states that the fisheries industry, particularly deep-sea fishing and aquaculture, will be further developed on a commercial and integrated basis. The development will focus on conservation and utilization of fisheries resources on a sustainable basis. It will be adequately supported with modern fisheries infrastructure, processing, a marketing network, and comprehensive human resource development as well as research and development programs.

According to the Balance of Trade plan formulated by the Ministry of Agriculture Malaysia, by the year 2010, aquaculture production is projected to have a value of $2.89 billion (Table 7). A total area of 330,200 ha has been identified for development to achieve these target production levels (Table 8).

Challenges to Aquaculture Development in Malaysia

Further development of aquaculture will also be required to reach target production levels. Some of the major challenges faced by the aquaculture industry regarding development include:

Table 7. Fisheries production targets for 2010 (Source: Balance of Trade Plan 2000-2010, Ministry of Agriculture Malaysia).

Commodity	Target Production	Value (in millions of dollars)
Fish		
• Fresh, chilled, or frozen	1 billion MT	886.05
• Paste (prepared)	46,000 MT	83.68
• Dried or salted (not smoked)	36,700 MT	48.42
• Fillets	20,400 MT	161.05
• Fry	21 billion individuals	118.16
• Feed	100,000 MT	86.84
• Ornamentals	800 million tails	50.00
Shrimp	250,000 MT	1,333.42
Mussels, cockles, oysters (shell on)	130,000 MT	26.84
Seaweed (dried)	125,000 MT	100.00
Total value		2,894.46

Table 8. Potential areas identified for aquaculture development.

Type of area	Size (ha)	Production (MT)
Inland	105,000	141,230
Open sea	100,000	85,000
Coastal land	28,000	303,980
Freshwater	98,000	64,800
Sheltered marine water	7,200	11,520
Total	330,200	606,530

- Limited availability of land and water bodies. Although Malaysia is blessed with plentiful natural resources, the amount of suitable land and water bodies for aquaculture development is insufficient.

- Indiscriminate removal of mangroves. Following the success of marine shrimp culture in earthen ponds, increasing numbers of people have started up similar ventures. This trend has ultimately led to the illegal removal of mangroves by unscrupulous investors.

- Illegal importation of exotic species, particularly, a marine species, the Pacific white shrimp (*Litopenaeus vannamei*). It is believed that a virulent new pathogen was introduced with this species.

- Food safety. The indiscriminate use of chemicals, drugs, and antibiotics in aquaculture, although apparently on a relatively small scale, is harming the industry.

- High production costs. Due to the high cost of feed, which usually makes up 40% of the total cost of production, aquaculture incurs relatively higher costs than capture fisheries for the same amount of fishery commodities.

- Negative perception of aquaculture. The general public seems to have been given the impression that aquaculture development has caused great pollution and environmental degradation. This perception may be related to the indiscriminate removal of mangroves, as mentioned above.

- Insufficient supply of good quality seeds, especially for marine and freshwater fish.

Proposed Ecosystem-Based Aquaculture Management Site: The District of Manjung

In view of the challenges faced by the industry and the proposed production targets, the District of Manjung in the State of Perak, on the western coast of the Malay Peninsula, Malaysia (extending from approx. lat 4°00' - 4°30' N to long 100°00' - 100°30' E) has been proposed for development of an ecosystem-based approach to aquaculture management. The district has a large diversity of flora and fauna and supports diverse fisheries activities, including both capture fisheries and aquaculture. Currently, 2,998 fishermen, operating 1,185 fishing boats, earn their livelihoods in the District of Manjung (Table 9). A total of 164 investors are involved in various types of aquaculture farms and systems in the area (Table 10).

Table 9. Fishing boats currently operating in the District of Manjung.

Type of Boat	No. of Fishermen
Inshore boats with outboard engines	535
Inshore boats with inboard engines	187
Purse seiners	57
Trawlers	406
Total	1,185

Table 10. Aquaculture systems in operation in the District of Manjung.

Aquaculture System	No. of Investors	Area (ha)
Brackish water ponds	124	1,528.0
Freshwater ponds	31	39.3
Freshwater cage culture	1	0.1
Brackish water cage culture	6	0.8
Rope culture of mussels	2	0.3
Total	164	1,568.5

The Dinding River, which runs through the middle of the district, is the specific site proposed for implementation of ecosystem-based aquaculture management. One bank of the Dinding River is lined with vegetation consisting of mangroves (i.e., *Rhizophora* spp. and *Avicennia* spp.) and oil palm trees (*Elaeis guineensis* Jacq. and *E. oleifera*). The other bank is mainly developed for industries and housing.

Figure 6. Shrimp culture in an earthen pond in Malaysia.

Figure 7. Cage culture of sea bass (*Lates calcarifer*) in the Dinding River, Malaysia.

The main type of aquaculture along the riverbanks is shrimp culture in earthen ponds (Fig. 6). Cage culture of finfish (Fig. 7) and rope culture of green mussels, *Perna viridis* (Figs. 8A-B), are conducted in the river itself. According to a 2004 survey conducted by the Department of Environment, oysters (*Crassostrea* spp.) and green mussels occur naturally in the Dinding River. The dominant algae species are *Pleurosigma* spp., *Rizosolenia* spp., and *Coscinodisus* spp.

A   B

Figure 8. Rope culture of green mussels (*Perna viridis*) in the Dinding River, Malaysia. (A) Lines of floats in the river. (B) Harvesting the product.

Research Needs

There is no record of continuous monitoring of water quality in the river by any of Malaysia's government agencies, nor have any studies been conducted to determine the ecological changes resulting from aquaculture in the Dinding River. In 2004, however, the Department of Fisheries conducted investigations to ascertain whether the area was suitable for oyster farming. The results are summarized in Table 11.

Table 11. Results of a 2004 Department of Fisheries survey of water quality parameters in Dingding River, District of Manjung.

Parameter[a]	Tide Level	
	Low	High
pH	6.78	-
Salinity	15 ppt	20 ppt
Temperature	27.9 C	-
Dissolved oxygen	8.79 ppm	10.21 ppm
Biological oxygen demand	2.09 ppm	4.95 ppm
NH_3	0.173	0.188
NO_3	0.3	0.3
Turbidity	41 cm	110 cm

[a]Samples taken at a depth of 5 m. Ppt: parts per thousand; ppm: parts per million.

Aquaculture plays a major role in providing employment to an estimated 630 local people in the Manjung District, and has contributed $22.0 million in revenue to the economy. Existing aquaculture practices have no apparent conflict with coastal management, except for the indiscriminate removal of mangroves in certain areas. The Perak State Government is taking steps to rectify this problem. As a first step towards ecosystem-based management, a study needs to be carried out to determine the ecological changes and impacts of aquaculture in the District of Manjung. This study should also assess the carrying capacity of the Dinding River to determine whether additional aquaculture systems (new and old) could be introduced into the river.

Sweden

Eutrophication of coastal waters is a serious environmental problem with high costs for society globally. This has resulted in a number of negative effects, e.g., reduced clarity of the water, anoxic bottom conditions, and formation of algal mats in shallow bays, a development that demands immediate environmental action along many coastal sites (Diaz and Rosenberg 1995; Cloern 2001). The goal along the northwest European coasts to reduce nitrogen and phosphorus from anthropogenic, land-based sources to the sea by 50% between 1985 and 2005 (OSPAR Commission 2004) will not be reached. In the Kingdom of Sweden (Sweden), new concepts and management strategies on how to combat coastal marine eutrophication are under development. This involves the introduction of nutrient emission trading, which is presently on trial in the Lysekil area on the Swedish West Coast (Lindahl et al. 2005).

Large-scale mussel farming is a realistic and cost-effective method of decreasing the negative effects of eutrophication. At the same time, healthy marine food is produced at a low level of the food chain. Nutrients are recycled back from the sea to land and new jobs are created. The ecological, environmental, and societal benefits of mussel farming for improving coastal water quality are well documented scientifically (see, e.g., Ryther et al. 1972; Edebo et al. 2000; Newell 2004; Lindahl et al. 2005).

In Sweden, research has been carried out during the past 10 to 20 years to develop and support the shellfish industry and especially mussel farming. The main reason for funding this work was the interest from scientists as well as authorities to use mussel farming to try to counteract the ongoing eutrophication and improve coastal water quality. Mussel production, however, remained more or less at the same small level, at about 1,500 metric tons (MT) annually, and it was concluded that one of the main reasons for this lack of increase was the lack of financial support from society. It was also concluded that mussel farmers received no benefits for the environmental service they provided to society and that society was lacking a direct tool to encourage and support the farming of mussels (Lindahl et al. 2005). To try to improve this situation, the concept of a system of trading nutrient emissions was introduced. Trading nutrient emissions is expected to connect the environmental economy with the market economy, with mussel farming acting as a recycling engine (Fig. 9).

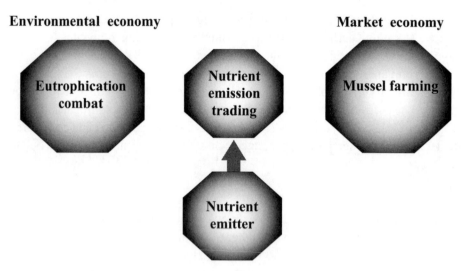

Figure 9. Trading nutrient emissions connects the environmental economy with the market economy.

Trading Nutrient Emissions

The sewage treatment plant (>10,000 personal equivalents) of the town of Lysekil emits 39 MT of nitrogen annually through its outlet pipe north of the town into the sea at a depth of 20 m. As a trial, between 2005 and 2011, the community board of Lysekil is permitted to continue to emit nitrogen from the sewage plant rather than trying to remove it in the plant, presupposing the same amount of nitrogen is "harvested" and brought ashore in 3,900 MT of farmed blue mussels, *Mytilus edulis* (Fig. 10). According to a European Community legal assessment (Staffan Westerlund, personal communication), it is possible to exchange

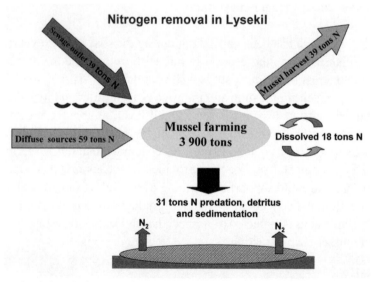

Figure 10. The principle of nitrogen farming, Lysekil, Sweden.

the nitrogen removal done in a sewage treatment plant by mussel farming in the receiving water if the "same" nitrogen can be removed through the harvest of mussels. This has been shown to be possible by placing the farms 1-40 km downstream from the plant outfall. A monitoring program will assure that the harvested mussels are not affected by pathogenic microbes or harmful substances that could affect their safety and quality standards for human consumption.

This system of emission trading is estimated to cost Lysekil about $200,000 annually, which is significantly less than the cost of rebuilding the sewage treatment plant to handle nitrogen removal and its annual operating costs. Lysekil has contracted an enterprise for the mussel business and the community itself does not take on any economic risks. The cost corresponds roughly to $7 kg^{-1} removed nitrogen. Compensation to the mussel farmer is thus about $0.05 kg^{-1} of mussels, or 10% of the necessary sales price to run a mussel enterprise in Sweden. This cost can be seen as compensation to the mussel farmer for taking on the responsibility of harvesting a given amount each year regardless of growth, market, or any other circumstances. At present, other Swedish communities have shown an interest in similar solutions. Mussel farming is a possible method of managing peak nutrient inputs into coastal waters during the summer tourist season, and obviate the need for constructing large sewage treatment plants with capacities that are not required for the major part of the year.

Access to Farm Sites

There are numerous sites along the Swedish west coast with the requisite criteria for mussel farming: availability, reasonable wind protection, water depths between 6 and 25 m, and average current speeds of more than 5 cm sec^{-1}. Other uses, including shipping, yachting, fishing, tourism, and beaches for swimming also have to be taken into consideration. In addition, landowners have the economic rights to the waters within 300 m from their land, so agreements to develop aquaculture must be made between farmers and the landowners. To minimize the risk of conflict, it is important to inform local residents and to consider their views (Ellegård and Ungfors 1999). When this is done, obtaining a farm license is normally not a problem.

Since the mussels are produced mainly for human consumption, farms cannot be located close to any sewage discharge. In the Lysekil area, farms are situated at protected sites 1-40 km from any sewage treatment plant outfall. Discussions with the local professional fishermen and suggestions made during public hearings have led to some locations being excluded and others included as possible sites. Overall, the introduction of large-scale mussel farming to the Lysekil area has been favorably received, and the exploitation of the available marine resources generally accepted. This is particularly the case when the environmental benefits of mussel farming have been made clear to the public.

Modeling the Effect of Mussel Farming on Nitrogen Removal

The expected effect of mussel farming on nitrogen cycling was modeled for the Gullmar Fjord on the Swedish west coast. Gullmar Fjord is 30 km long, with a sill depth of 45 m and a maximum depth of 120 m in the central part. A numerical high-resolution and three-dimensional biogeochemical model was developed for the Gullmar Fjord area (Marmefelt et al. 2000; Svensson 2002). This model was used to predict the amount of mussel farming and harvesting that would be needed to achieve a measurable effect on nitrogen flows and concentration.

In Sweden, long-line farming on vertical suspenders, attached to horizontal lines, is the most common method of growing the blue mussel. A long-line unit typically occupies about 0.4 hectares of the surface of the sea and produces 120 -150 MT of mussels in less than 18 months. A live mussel contains about 1% nitrogen and 0.1% phosphorus (Lutz 1980). In the model, the number of mussel farm units was varied to estimate the ability of the mussels to reduce the seston concentration of the filtered water. According to the model, the mussel farm acts as a sink for plankton, as a source of ammonium, and as both a sink for and source of detritus.

The results of the model simulations showed that when 25 mussel farm units (5,000 MT) were introduced in the fjord and the mussels harvested, the overall sedimentation of particulate organic nitrogen (PON) was reduced by 4% during the period January – October (Lindahl et al. 2005). Naturally, in the areas directly under the farms, the PON increased. The mussel farms had a greater effect on the net transport of nitrogen (sum of dissolved and particulate) at the fjord mouth. The net outgoing transport was reduced by 20%, or by 65 MT, during 10 months, i.e., about one fourth of the input of nitrogen from the major river entering Gullmar Fjord. The conclusion of the modeling was that large-scale mussel farming would have a substantial, positive effect on both the overall sedimentation and the export of nitrogen from the fjord.

Mussel Meal: A New Product for Environmental Sustainability

Since mussels are at the second trophic level of the marine food chain, the use of mussels instead of fish for meal production has a large ecological advantage, since fish mostly feed at higher trophic levels. Further, there is an increasing public opinion that fish, with the exception of industrial offal, should be reserved for human consumption.

In a pilot study, mussels were fed to laying hens, which preferred the mussel fodder to conventional organic hen fodder (Fig. 11) (Lindahl et al. 2005). The color of the egg yolk was intensified and no effect on the taste of the eggs was documented. Mussels contain about 8% fat in dry matter, which is rich in marine omega-3 fatty acids and anti-oxidative pigments. These substances may add extra value to the egg. Trials have demonstrated that production of mussel meal is a rather straightforward technical process. The organic egg production industry in Sweden has shown interest in the use of mussels for fodder, and much larger production volumes can be foreseen if mussels can be used by the fodder industry. The economic potential of making mussel meal for fodder, however, still needs to be developed and evaluated, especially in combination with trading nutrient emissions.

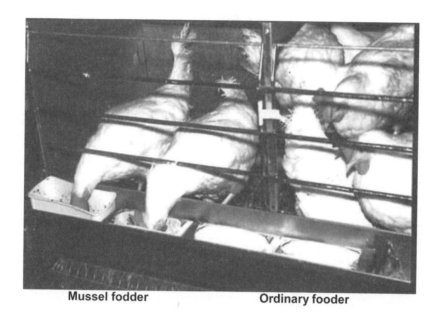

Mussel fodder   **Ordinary fooder**

Figure 11. The hens preferred the mussel meat to conventional fodder.

Biotoxins

Elevated levels of okadaic acid (OA) in blue mussels have been recorded in Swedish marine waters in varying amounts every year since 1983, when the first outbreak was reported (Haamer et al. 1990). Generally, concentrations of diarrheic shellfish toxins (DST) in mussels are low from March to August, and moderate to high from October to January. Some years, farms may be closed to harvesting for six months or more when DST levels exceed the limit for human consumption, i.e., 160 μg kg^{-1} mussel, while the same sites may experience no or only a short interruption of the harvest in other years (Rehnstam-Holm and Hernroth 2005).

Mussels that are DST-toxic and fodder made from toxic mussels was fed to laying hens in parallel with non-toxic mussels and fodder. No harm to the hens was observed, nor was any toxicity found in the eggs (Lindahl and Kollberg, unpublished data; Lotta Jönsson, personal communication). If the results of these preliminary tests were confirmed, it would indicate that the mussel industry would be able to harvest products for a fodder market during periods when the human market would be closed due to toxic shellfish. The resulting economic advantages would provide further incentives to mussel farmers.

Agro-Aqua Recycling of Nutrients

To optimize the environmental effect of mussel farming, all organisms attached to the lines should be harvested and brought ashore. The mussel farm may be regarded as the engine in an Agro-Agua recycling system of nutrients from sea to land (Fig. 12). Not all of the harvested mussels can be used for human consumption. The remainder, consisting of small or damaged mussels, is also important for the removal of nutrients. It can be used for fodder

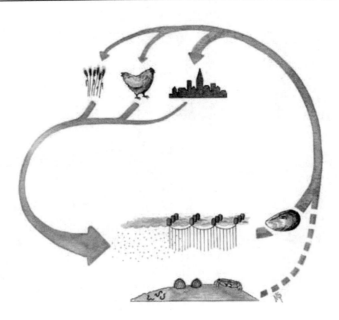

Figure 12. The Agro-Aqua recycling of nutrients, where the mussel farm acts as a recycling engine.

(see above) or as an organic fertilizer. In Sweden, successful use of the wastes from mussel processing lines in organic farming of grain has been documented (Lindahl et al. 2005). At present, composting experiments are ongoing to produce a "mussel fertilizer," which can be stored and used when the farmer needs it and which lacks the disagreeable odor of decomposing mussels.

Ecosystem Effect

A long-line or raft mussel farm acts as a suspended artificial benthic habitat with no or negligible negative effect on the pelagic ecosystem. Mussel farming, however, influences the biogeochemistry and the benthic ecosystem below the farm through an increased load of organic material, including mussels, feces from mussels, and other detritus. The effects, however, are restricted to the farm vicinity and have to be judged in relation to the overall positive effects of using mussels to improve the quality of the coastal ecosystem. In fact, if the mussel farm is operated skillfully, the result is also the removal of nitrogen in the form of N_2 gas by microbially mediated denitrification of the mussel detritus (Newell 2004).

Mussel farming is a win-win solution for society and the environment. Commercial mussel producers currently benefit society by removing nitrogen from coastal waters, for which they are unrewarded. In terms of environmental economics, the nitrogen removal service that mussel farms provide is known as an "external benefit" to society (Pearce and Turner 1990). It is worth noting that an expanded mussel industry could have other benefits and added values, e.g., provide jobs in the region, which is particularly pertinent as many coastal fisheries are under pressure due to low fish stocks.

Since the 1980s, mussel farming has been recognized by Swedish environmental authorities as a possible measure to improve coastal water quality. Useful tools, however, to stimulate the further development of mussel farming have been missing. The authorities should make demands on those who emit pollution through emission quotas that may be traded. The Lysekil case (see above) is the first Swedish example of this system. It is particularly straightforward when nutrients are discharged from a point source, i.e., emissions from a sewage treatment plant or a factory. Nutrient quotas are thus the currency of trade between the market economy and the environmental economy. Nutrients from point sources, however, account for less than 20% of the total nutrient input to Swedish marine waters (SMHI 2001). It is thus important to also find trading solutions for diffuse supplies of nutrients. In principle, the same business approach of trading these nutrients should be possible, but it will be more difficult to define the buyer (= "owner") of a diffuse nutrient emission. (Lindahl et al. 2005).

The benefits of the nutrient emission trading and environmental mussel farming concept can be summarized as follows:

- Marine nutrients recirculated for use on land

- Included readily in a nutrient trading system

- Environmentally friendly

- Cost effective

- Flexible and easy to remove

- New jobs for coastal communities

- Healthy seafood production

Finally, the simple beauty of using nature itself for self-healing, challenges today's focus on high-technological advances to solve all our environmental problems. The usefulness of the mussel concept has significance on a global environmental scale.

Taiwan

Aquaculture has a long history in Taiwan. Before the Chin Dynasty (ca. A.D. 265), the culture of milkfish (*Chanos chanos*) in ponds was introduced from Indonesia, and it has played an important role in the economy and lifestyles of people in local Taiwanese fishing communities ever since. The first major aquatic animals to be farmed were milkfish, carps (*Cyprinus carpio, Aristichthys nobilis, Ctenopharyngodon idellus, Carasssius auratus*), and oysters (*Crassostrea gigas, C. angulata*). With the development of Taiwanese aquaculture technologies, many important species were successfully introduced to global markets, including black tiger prawn (*Penaeus monodon*), eels (*Anguilla* spp.), and tilapia (*Oreochromis* spp.). Currently, more than 100 warm water aquaculture species are farmed commercially.

Seafood production is an important industry. Only one of the 15 counties on the island of Taiwan lacks a shoreline. Penghu County, for instance, is fully surrounded by the sea, and this is reflected in the traditional livelihoods of its residents. Seafood is also a staple of the diet. From 1995 to 2004, per capita consumption of seafood ranged between 30.99 kg and 43.72 kg (Council of Agriculture 2005a), and consisted mainly of finfish (Table 12).

Table 12. Per capita seafood supply, 1995-2004 (Source: Council of Agriculture, Taiwan, 2005a).

Type of seafood	Per capita consumption (kg)									
	1995	1996	1997	1998	1999	2000	2001	2002	2003	2004
Fish	23.72	24.36	23.52	24.55	25.95	22.99	23.45	24.84	26.60	21.14
Cephalopods	5.55	4.87	8.67	6.45	9.29	8.69	4.49	3.59	4.73	1.53
Mollusks	3.77	3.91	4.27	3.72	3.64	3.83	3.35	3.94	4.30	3.97
Crustaceans	3.30	3.35	3.47	2.68	2.62	2.97	2.32	1.55	2.11	2.10
Dried (salted) products	1.54	1.41	1.34	0.73	0.71	0.51	0.48	0.84	1.02	1.04
Other	0.47	0.51	1.03	1.28	1.51	1.23	1.36	1.33	1.21	1.21
Total	38.34	38.42	42.30	39.41	43.72	40.22	35.45	36.08	39.97	30.99

Taiwan is one of the leading contributors to global supplies of seafood. In 2004, more than 1.27 million metric tons (MT) of seafood was produced (Council of Agriculture 2005b), most of which (0.81 million MT) was consumed domestically (Table 13). In the same year, Taiwan exported more than 600,000 MT of seafood, mostly to Japan, and imported 172,000 MT, comprised mainly of lobsters (*Panulirus* spp.), farmed salmon (*Salmo salar*), Greenland halibut (*Reinhardtius hippoglossus*), and fish roe. Since 1994, as production has increased, the amount of seafood that is exported has increased dramatically, while the amount that is imported has increased only slightly (Table 13).

Deep-sea, near shore, and coastal fisheries, as well as inland fisheries (including freshwater and marine aquaculture) all contribute to Taiwan's seafood production. In 2004, deep-sea fisheries yielded 677,703 MT of frozen seafood, most of which was from the long line capture of bigeye tuna (*Thunnus obesus*) and squid (Ommastrephidae) jigging. With the decline of ocean resources in recent decades, however, this sector of the industry is not expected to grow in the future. Near shore fisheries produced 197,722 MT of chilled seafood in 2004, down from 333,799 MT in 1989, due to a rapid decline in resources caused by improper fishing activities. The shortage was made up by inland aquaculture, which produced 299,125 MT, mostly as chilled seafood. Coastal fisheries landings have increased since 2000, due to the use of set nets and long line operations. Since 1999, increased production of marine

Table 13. Taiwan seafood production, exports, and imports, 1994-2004 (Source: Council of Agriculture, Taiwan, 2005b).

Year	Production (MT)	Imported (MT)	Exported (MT)	Domestic supply (MT)	Self-sufficiency rate (%)
1994	1.28×10^6	1.41×10^5	4.50×10^5	9.68×10^5	132
1995	1.32×10^6	1.46×10^5	5.02×10^5	9.60×10^5	137
1996	1.26×10^6	1.47×10^5	4.45×10^5	9.59×10^5	131
1997	1.33×10^6	1.76×10^5	4.45×10^5	1.06×10^6	125
1998	1.36×10^6	1.44×10^5	5.30×10^5	9.78×10^5	140
1999	1.38×10^6	1.56×10^5	4.59×10^5	1.08×10^6	128
2000	1.36×10^6	1.80×10^5	5.39×10^5	1.01×10^6	136
2001	1.32×10^6	1.50×10^5	5.70×10^5	8.99×10^5	147
2002	1.41×10^6	1.77×10^5	6.62×10^5	9.24×10^5	152
2003	1.50×10^6	1.68×10^5	6.48×10^5	1.02×10^6	147
2004	1.27×10^6	1.72×10^5	6.36×10^5	8.08×10^5	157

species has been due mainly to cage culture. Inland fisheries have sharply declined since 1999, due to limitations of freshwater resources.

Inshore Marine Cage Culture in Taiwan

The four major types of aquaculture in Taiwan are: (a) freshwater farming of tilapia, eels, carps, giant freshwater prawns (*Macrobrachium rosenbergii*), freshwater clam (*Corbicula fluminea*, etc.); (b) farming of sea bream (*Pagrus major*), milkfish, grouper (*Epinephelus* spp.), sea bass (*Psammoperca waigiensis*), tiger prawns, and Pacific white shrimp (*Litopenaeus vannamei*) in brackish water ponds; (c) inshore farming of oysters, hard clam *(Meretrix lusoria)*, small abalone (*Haliotis aqualilis*), and fish; and (d) offshore farming of cobia (*Rachycentron canadum*), sea bream, groupers, and yellowtail (*Seriola dumerili*).

The first cage culture operations were started in the Penghu Islands in the 1970s as a way to keep harvests from coastal fisheries. After the collapse of the shrimp farming industry in the late 1980s, however, government support shifted to the development of modern offshore fish farming as a top priority for Taiwan's national aquaculture plan. Penghu Islands, located in the middle of the Taiwan Strait, are one of the major fishing communities, and are known as the birthplace of cobia cage culture. At one time, cage farming had been promoted in inland waters, but operations were suspended in 1996 due to pollution problems in freshwater dams. In the early 1990s, the Taiwanese government recognized the potential for modern marine cage culture as an important industry of the future (Hu 2000). It would ease the pressure on inland freshwater and land resources as well as on capture fisheries, supply high quality seafood to make up for shortages in marine species from capture fisheries, and create jobs in fishing communities. For these reasons, the government authorized the first marine cage-farming zone in 1993 (Hu 2000).

Marine cage culture began to develop as a modern industry in 1993, when the government established exclusive fishery zones for marine cage culture. Progress was initially delayed while researchers looked for a suitable species for this type of culture. After successful breeding techniques were developed for cobia, the industry developed quickly. Sea cage farming sites now include other locations in Penghu (i.e., Chu-Bay, Tung-Liang, and Tsai-Yun) and Pingtung (i.e., Hai-Kuo and Shiao-Liu-Chio, a small island off the west coast of Pingtung). In 2001, production from marine cage culture in Taiwan had a value of $19.3 million. By 2003, 23 cage farms, utilizing less than 160 ha (400 acres) of sea surface area (Table 14), were producing 14 major fish species in cages. Cobia continues to be the major species cultured in cages, with 3,224 MT produced in 2004, valued at $16 million (Fig. 13; Fisheries Agency 2005.

Table 14. Production from marine cage aquaculture in Taiwan, 2003 (Source: Taiwan Offshore Aquaculture Association, unpublished data).

Location	No. of farms	No. of cages	Total volume of cages (m³)	Total surface area of cages (ha)	Production (MT)
Penghu	15	1,004	839,600	104	6,468
Pingtung	5	169	110,912	52	1,650
Total	20	1,173	950,512	156	8,118

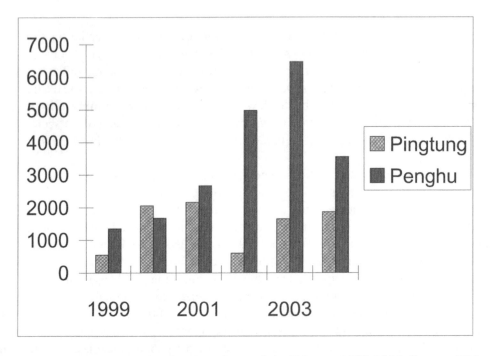

Figure 13. Marine cage production (metric tons) in Taiwan, 1999-2004. Source: Fisheries Agency (2005).

Development of Offshore Sea Cages

The development of net pen systems that are constructed for farming in offshore localities that are exposed to wind, waves, and strong currents may help reduce environmental problems typical of well-protected inshore sites. Several "offshore" concepts have been introduced for the international market, but their application is rather limited. Major challenges include the weight and size of the structures, which make it costly to anchor them and difficult to conduct routine operations in deep seas.

It is essential to develop methods for predicting the effects of fish farms on their surroundings. Although offshore cage farming in its initial stage is unlikely to raise environmental concerns, using current waste dispersion models to predict waste loading and estimate the carrying capacity or stocking density of the site would be very helpful. Being able to predict aquaculture wastes from a fish farm is beneficial to both the farmer and the government regulator. Farmers could predict the feed used to grow their fish, while the government or regulators could use the model to predict environmental enrichment resulting from the operation of farms in their jurisdiction. Careful site selection can ensure minimum impact on sensitive areas, visually, in terms of the ecosystem, individual species, and the increasingly popular eco-tourism industry. Studies that have been conducted on waste dispersion modeling in temperate regions offer a promising step forward for the cage culture industry (e.g. Troell and Berg 1998; Chen et al. 2000).

Challenges to Cage Culture in Taiwan

Several unfavorable factors hinder the development of cage culture in Taiwan, including potential environmental impacts, inappropriate laws and regulations, user conflicts, fish diseases, and typhoons.

The recent and continuing expansion of cobia, grouper, and sea bream cage farming in inshore areas and the intention to develop offshore potential has led to questions about the degree of ecological impact that can be expected in the future (Chen 2000a; Su et al. 2000; Chiang 2004; Liao et al. 2004). The high concentrations of nitrogen and carbon discharged from cage aquaculture are a potential threat to the environment in the vicinity of cage farms. Since impacts from intensive cage farming have mainly been studied in temperate areas, there is a need to increase the understanding of environmental effects from intensive cage farming in the tropics (Beveridge and Phillips 1993; Beveridge 1996; Wu et al. 1994, 1999; Chen 2000b). The few studies conducted in the tropics (e.g., Angel et al. 1992; Choo 1994; Troell and Berg 1997; Wu et al. 1999) have indicated fewer negative effects from fish cages on the local environment compared to those from cages in temperate regions. Although these studies may seem to indicate a greater capacity for tropical systems to assimilate aquaculture wastes, the data are insufficient and inconclusive. In fact, severe impacts from fish cage farming have also been documented in the tropics (Wu 1995). In the absence of regulatory control, there is little economic pressure to treat wastes, and comparatively few farms in Taiwan have any form of waste treatment. This is especially the case for cage farms, which normally discharge wastes directly into the immediate environment.

The Fisheries Act was aimed at regulating capture fisheries, but is now also being applied to marine fish farming, and is unfavorable to further development of marine cage culture. In addition, cage farmers face an uphill battle to lobby and negotiate for exclusive use of water that they need for their operations. Taiwan is heavily populated, and rights to water use are long established. In fact, most user conflicts over water started 2-3 years after cage culture commenced. Uneaten feed passing through cages may attract wild fish as well as commercial and recreational fishermen and tourists to the area, which may lead to increased user conflicts. The limited numbers of suitable culture areas add to these challenges.

Wild fish may also bring diseases, such as fish lice (*Benedenia* spp.) and pasteurellosis, increasing mortalities among cultured stocks. Another serious factor is the typhoons that strike every year, which cause major damage to cages, and add to the risks for farmers and investors. Other unfavorable factors challenging cage culture development are a lack of insurance and financial support.

Technical Solutions

To meet environmental impact assessment requirements for the future, it is recommended that investigations of benthic fauna be conducted in the waters around sea cages to identify any significant changes in species ratios of fish (schools of small coral reef fish) and invertebrates (diversity of starfish, crabs, tunicates, bryozoa, hydroids, etc.). To overcome some of the other challenges to developing cage culture, target areas being given high priority include reducing feed loss, use of high quality feed, and avoidance of unsuitable farming sites.

The development of new types of feed processing technology has undoubtedly played a major role in reducing the pollution load from fed aquaculture. For example, the extrusion process reduces the amount of the surface area of the pellet, making extruded feeds far more stable in the water column. Extrusion also fully gelatinizes the starch of the feed and provides a matrix that renders it more digestible. The increased digestibility can reduce the quantity of feces. The material in an extruded pellet is expanded and fused together, unlike material in a compressed pellet, which is simply pressed together. Extruded pellets can be made to float or to sink slowly, which increases the likelihood that the fish will ingest them. Beveridge and Phillips (1993) estimated that the amount of solid waste per MT of fish produced was 320 kg when they were fed compressed pellets, compared to 250 kg with an extruded feed, because of improved ingestion.

Extruded pellets may contain 25-30% fat (and therefore, a higher energy content) than ordinary compressed pellets. Studies have shown improved food conversion ratios (FCRs) for the same growth when the fat level was increased in the diet. High energy diets such as these can reduce the feed requirement per unit of production and use less protein, which is the major source of phosphorous and nitrogen pollution from fish farms.

The most effective way of reducing water pollution from fish farms is to minimize feed loss. One source of feed loss is the dust and small particles not taken up by the fish. Feeds are normally sieved in the feed factory, but rough handling and transport create dust in the packaged product by the time of its arrival on the farm. Extruded feeds have an improved structure compared to compressed pellets, and therefore, less dust.

Adopting good feeding and management practices on the farm can also reduce feed loss. Farmers tend to overfeed the stock, and the excess feed may be uneaten, or ingested by the fish but later regurgitated or pass undigested through the gut. Each culture species can be expected to show different preferences for optimum feeding regimes according to the temperature of the water, growth rates, FCRs, behavior, studies of appetite development, and the passage of feed through the gut. It is possible to immediately reduce feed wastage by presenting feed to the fish when they can use it most efficiently. For example, video camera observations of salmon in net pens have demonstrated that feeding occurs actively in the morning and again in the afternoon. Feed supplied between these periods was largely wasted. It is possible that the feed was digested at night and the appetites of the fish were restored in the morning, and that after feeding in morning, their appetites returned as their stomachs became empty in the afternoon.

It remains a challenge for Taiwan to maintain close relations among fish farmers, fish processors, and researchers to reduce marine pollution.

Protection of Taiwan's Marine Resources

The Taiwan government has taken active steps to protect its marine resources, by establishing 26 fisheries resource conservation zones, 73 zones for artificial reef placement, and 64 reef protection sites along the coast of Taiwan. Measures being taken to maintain the sustainability of coastal fisheries include enhancement of fisheries stocks, the use of orderly fishing activities, promotion of sea ranching, and overall planning of proprietary fisheries. In 2004, the following measures were carried out to protect Taiwan's marine resources:

- Protection of habitat. More than 4,000 artificial reefs were built using recycled materials, and over 5,000 kg of discarded fishing nets were removed from 24 coral and artificial reefs;

- Release of fry from breeding programs, including 10 million finfish fry (e.g., grouper, seabream (*Rhabdosargus sarba*), snapper, *Lutjanus malabaricus*, etc.), 700,000 mollusc spat (e.g., small abalone and hard clams), and 1.65 million crustacean larvae (e.g., horseshoe crab [*Tachyleus tridentatus*] and kuruma shrimp (*Marsupeneus japonicus*), to revive fishing grounds in coastal areas;

- Designation of coastal areas for multi-purpose utilization to balance the needs of different users;

- Reduction in the number of fishing boats. Eighteen vessels were decommissioned, thereby reducing capture fisheries by 590 MT;

- Enforcement of laws regarding illegal fishing vessels; and

- Promotion of marine ranching projects in Penghu and Pingtung. A site in the Chingwan area of Penghu County has been plotted for the development of sea ranching.

Overall planning of proprietary fisheries for the 17 coastal counties under the Central Government will serve as a reference for licensing the proprietorship of designated fisheries, set net fisheries, and sector fisheries. In addition to these strategies, the government is promoting a shift to recreational fishery operations for its fishermen, to reduce the pressure on over-exploited coastal resources (Council of Agriculture 1993).

During the past few years, the Taiwan Offshore Aquaculture Association (TOAA), consisting of about 40 individual members and 20 group members, has enthusiastically supported different projects, primarily assisting the government in managing the natural resources and in preserving the environment. The future objectives of the TOAA are to continually evaluate the use of national offshore water resources and develop the economy of fishing villages.

Literature Cited

Anonymous. 2005. Análisis económico. Las nuevas reglas comerciales, nuestra apuesta a los mercados internationales [in Spanish]. Revista Salmonicutura 7 (65): 6-7.

Angel, D., P. Krost, D. Zuber, N. Mozes, and A. Neori. 1992. The turnover of organic matter in hypertrophic sediments below a floating fish farm in the oligotrophic Gulf of Eilat (Aqaba). Israeli Journal of Aquaculture (Bamidgeh) 44: 143-144.

Beveridge, M.C.M. 1996. Cage Aquaculture, 2nd edition. Fishing News Book, Oxford, UK. 346 pp.

Beveridge, M.C.M. and M.J. Phillips. 1993. Environmental impact of tropical inland aquaculture. Pages 213-236 in R.S.V. Pullin, H. Rosenthal, and J.L. Maclean, editors. Environment and Aquaculture and in Developing Countries. International Center for Living Aquatic Resources Management (ICLARM), Manila, Philippines.

Black, E., R. Gowen, H. Rosenthal, E. Roth, D. Stechy, and F.J.R. Taylor. 1997. The costs of eutrophication from salmon farming: Implications for policy-A comment. Journal of Environmental Management 50: 105-109.

Buschmann, A.H. 2002. Impacto Ambiental de la Salmonicultura en Chile: La Situación en la X región de Los Lagos [in Spanish]. Publicaciones Terram, Santiago, Chile. http://www.terram.cl.

Buschmann, A.H. and A. Fortt. (in press). Desarrollo acuícola y sus externalidades ambientales. Ambiente y Desarrollo.

Buschmann, A.H. and R. Pizarro. 2001. El costo ambiental de la salmonicultura en Chile [in Spanish]. Análisis de Políticas Públicas, Numero 5. Fundación Terram, Santiago, Chile. http://www.terram.cl.

Buschmann, A, D. López, M.L. González, L. Filún, G. Aroca, and M. Cifuentes. 2001a. Sub-proyecto Policultivos [in Spanish]. Pages 58-59 in F.M. Faranda, R. Frache, R. Albertini, and J.A. Correa, editors. Síntesis Histórica y Logros Académicos. Pontificia Universidad Católica de Chile, Santiago, Chile.

Buschmann, A.H., D.A. López, and A. Medina. 1996. A review of the environmental effects and alternative production strategies of marine aquaculture in Chile. Aquacultural Engineering 15: 397-421.

Buschmann, A.H., O. Mora, P. Gómez, M. Botteger, S. Buitano, C. Retamales, P. Vergara and A. Gutierrez. 1994. Gracilaria chilensis outdoor tank cultivation in Chile: Use of land-based salmon culture effluents. Aquacultural Engineering 13: 283-300.

Buschmann, A.H., M. Troell, and N. Kautsky. 2001b. Integrated algal farming: A review. Cahiers de Biologie Marine 42: 83-90.

Cabello, F. 2003. Antibióticos y acuicultura : Un análisis de sus potenciales impactos para el medio ambiente, la salud humana y animal en Chile [in Spanish]. Análisis de Políticas públicas, Numero 17. Publicaciones Terram, Santiago, Chile. http://www.terram.cl.

Cabello, F. 2004. Antibióticos y acuicultura en Chile: Consecuencia para la salud humana y animal [in Spanish]. Revista Medica de Chile 132: 1001-1006.

Chen, Y.S. 2000a. Taiwan's offshore potential. Fish Farming International 27(1): 26-27.

Chen,Y-S. 2000b. Waste outputs and dispersion around marine fish cages and the implications for modeling. Ph.D. thesis. University of Stirling, Stirling, UK. 181 pp.

Chen, Y.S., M.C.M. Beveridge, and T.C. Telfer. 2000. Derived data for more effective modelling of solid wastes from sea cage farms. Pages 157-166 in IC. Liao and C.K. Lin, editors. Cage Aquaculture in Asia: Proceedings of the First International Symposium on Cage Aquaculture in Asia. Asian Fisheries Society, Manila, and World Aquaculture Society, Southeast Asian Chapter, Bangkok, Thailand.

Choo, P.S. 1994. A study of the water quality at a coastal cage-culture site in Penang, Malaysia. Fisheries Bulletin Department of Fisheries (Malaysia) 86. 9 pp.

Chopin, T., A.H. Buschmann, C. Halling, M. Troell, N. Kautsky, A. Neori, G.P. Kraemer, J.A. Zertuche-Gonzalez, C. Yarish, and C. Neefus. 2001. Integrating seaweeds into marine aquaculture systems: A key towards sustainability. Journal of Phycology 37: 975-986.

Cloern, J.E. 2001. Our evolving conceptual model of the coastal eutrophication problem. Marine Ecology Progress Series 210: 223-253.

Council of Agriculture. 1993. Fisheries Development in the Republic of China – Past, Present, and Future [in Chinese]. Council of Agriculture, Executive Yuan, Republic of China, Taipei, Taiwan.

Council of Agriculture. 2005a. Food supply and utilization. Council of Agriculture, Executive Yuan, Republic of China, Taipei, Taiwan. http://bulletin.coa.gov.tw/htmlarea_file/web_articles/6154/3.9.xls.

Council of Agriculture. 2005b. Food Balance Sheet. Council of Agriculture, Executive Yuan, Republic of China, Taipei, Taiwan. http//bulletin,coa.gov.tw/view/php?catid-9908.

Diaz, R.J. and R. Rosenberg. 1995. Marine benthic hypoxia. A review of its ecological effects and the behavioral responses of benthic macrofauna. Oceanography and Marine Biology: An Annual Review 210: 245-303.

Duarte, P., R. Meneses, A.J.S. Hawkins, M. Zhu, J. Fang, and J. Grant. 2003. Mathematical modelling to assess the carrying capacity for multi-species culture within coastal waters. Ecological Modelling 168: 109-143.

Edebo, L., J. Haamer, O. Lindahl, L.-O. Loo, and L. Piriz. 2000. Recycling of macronutrients from sea to land using mussel cultivation. International Journal of Environment and Pollution 13: 190-207.

Ellegård, A. and A. Ungfors. 1999. Conflicts in coastal fishery – A case study from the Swedish west coast. Göteborg University (Human Ecology Report Series, HERS SUCOZOMA Report 1999:2. Göteborg University, Göteborg, Sweden. 43 pp.

Feng,Y.Y., L.C. Hou, N.X. Ping, T.D. Ling, and C.I. Kyo. 2004. Development of mariculture and its impacts in Chinese coastal waters. Reviews in Fish Biology and Fisheries 14: 1-10.

Fisheries Agency. 2005. Fisheries production. Fisheries Year Book. Council of Agriculture, Executive Yuan, Republic of China, Taipei, Taiwan. 5 pp. http://fa.gov.tw/chn/statistics_price/year_book/2004c/93tab8_2.pdf.

Forsterra, G., L. Beuck, V. Haussermann, and A. Freiwald. 2005. Shallow-water Desmophyllum dianthus (Scleretinia) from Chile: Characteristics of the biocoecenoses, the bioeroding community, heterotrophic interactions and (paleo)-bathymetric implications. Pages 937-977 in A. Freiwald and J.M. Roberts, editors. Cold-Water Corals and Ecosystems. Springer-Verlag, Berlin, Germany.

Haamer, J., P.-O. Andersson, O. Lindahl, S. Lange, X.P. Li, and L. Edebo. 1990. Geographic and seasonal variation of Okadaic acid content in farmed mussels, Mytilus edulis Linnaeus, 1758, along the Swedish west coast. Journal of Shellfish Research 9: 103-108.

Hallegraeff, G.M. 1993. A review of harmful algal blooms and their apparent global increase. Phycologia 32: 79-99.

Hites, R.A., J.A. Foran, D.O. Carpenter, M.C. Hamilton, B.A. Knuth, and S.J. Schwager. 2004. Global assessment of organic contaminants in farmed salmon. Science 303 (5655): 226-229.

Hu, S.H. 2000. Aquaculture in Taiwan [in Chinese]. Pages 108-153 in Easy Talk on Fisheries of Taiwan. Fisheries Administration, Council of Agriculture, Executive Yuan, Republic of China, Taipei, Taiwan.

Liao, I C., T.S. Huang, W.S. Tsai, C.M. Hsueh, S.L. Chang, and E.M. Leaño. 2004. Cobia culture in Taiwan: Current status and problems. Aquaculture 237: 155-165.

Lindahl, O., R. Hart, B. Hernroth, S. Kollberg, L.-O. Loo, L. Olrog, A.-S. Rehnstam-Holm, J. Svensson, S. Svensson, and U. Syversen. 2005. Improving marine water quality by mussel farming – A profitable measure for Swedish society. Ambio 34 (2): 131-138.

López, D.A., B.A. López, and M.L. González. (in press). Shellfish culture in Chile. International Journal of Environment and Pollution.

Lutz, R.A., editor. 1980. Mussel Culture and Harvest: A North American Perspective. Elsevier Science, Amsterdam, The Netherlands. 350 pp.

Marmefelt, E., B. Håkansson, A.C. Erichsen, and I. Sehlstedt-Hansen. 2000. Development of an ecological model system for the Kattegat and the Southern Baltic. SMHI Report Oceanography, No. 29. Swedish Meteorological and Hydrological Institute, Norrköping, Sweden. 36 pp.

Miranda, C.D. and R. Zemelman. 2002. Bacterial resistance to oxytetracycline in Chilean salmon farming. Aquaculture 212: 31-47.

Neori, A., T. Chopin, M. Troell, A. Buschmann, G. Kraemer, C. Halling, M. Shpigel, and C. Yarish. 2004. Integrated aquaculture: Rationale, evolution and state of the art emphasizing seaweed biofiltration in modern mariculture. Aquaculture 231: 361-391.

Newell, R.I.E. 2004. Ecosystem influences of natural and cultivated populations of suspension feeding bivalve mollusks: a review. Journal of Shellfish Research 23: 51-61.

OSPAR (Oslo-Paris) Commission. 2004. The Convention for the Protection of the Marine Environment of the North-East Atlantic, 1992. http://www.ospar.org/eng/html/1992-ospar-convention.htm.

Pearce, D.W. and R.K. Turner. 1990. Economics of Natural Resources and the Environment. Johns Hopkins University Press, Baltimore, Maryland, USA. 392 pp.

Rehnstam-Holm, A.-S. and B. Hernroth. 2005. Shellfish and public health: A Swedish perspective. Ambio 34 (2): 139-144.

Ryther, J.H., W.M. Dunstan, K.R. Tenore, and J.E. Huguenin. 1972. Controlled eutrophication - increasing food production from the sea by recycling human wastes. Bioscience 22: 144-152.

Sellner, K.G., G.J. Doucette, and G.J. Kirkpatrick. 2003. Harmful algal blooms: Causes, impacts and detection. Journal of Industrial Microbiology and Biotechnology 30: 383-409.

Smayda, T.J. 1990. Novel and nuisance phytoplankton blooms in the sea: Evidence for a global epidemic. Pages 29-40 in E. Granéli, B. Sundström, L. Edler, and D.M. Anderson, editors. Toxic Marine Phytoplankton: Proceedings of the Fourth International Conference on Toxic Marine Phytoplankton. Lund, Sweden, 26-30 June 1989. Elsevier, Amsterdam, The Netherlands.

SMHI (Swedish Meteorological and Hydrological Institute). 2001. The Skagerrak – Environmental State and Monitoring Prospects. http://www.smhi.se. Swedish Meteorological and Hydrological Institute, Norrköpping, Sweden.

SNP (Servicio Nacional de Pesca). 2004. Anuario Estadístico de Pesca 2004 [in Spanish]. Servicio Nacional de Pesca, Ministerio de Economía, Fomento y Reconstrucción, Santiago, Chile. 160 pp.

Soto, D. and F. Norambuena. 2004. Evaluation of salmon farming effects on marine systems in the inner seas of southern Chile: A large-scale mensurative experiment. Journal of Applied Ichthyology 20: 493-501.

Soto, D., F. Jara, and C. Moreno. 2001. Escaped salmon in the inner seas, southern Chile: Facing ecological and social conflicts. Ecological Applications 11: 1750-1762.

Su, M.S., Y.-H, Chien, and I C. Liao. 2000. Potential of marine cage aquaculture in Taiwan: cobia culture. Pages 97-106 in I C. Liao and C.K. Lin, editors. Cage Aquaculture in Asia: Proceedings of the First International Symposium on Cage Aquaculture in Asia. Asian Fisheries Society, Manila, Philippines, and World Aquaculture Society, Southeast Asian Chapter, Bangkok, Thailand.

Svensson, J. 2002. Validering av en Biogeokemisk 3-dimensionell Modell över Gullmarsfjorden, 1994 (Validation of a 3D biogeochemical model of the Gullmar Fjord, 1994) [in Swedish]. SMHI Rapport No. 16. Swedish Meteorological and Hydrological Institute, Norrköpping, Sweden. 26 pp.

Troell, M. and J. Norberg. 1997. Cage fish farming in the tropical Lake Kariba, Zimbabwe: Impact and biogeochemical changes in sediment. Aquaculture Research 28: 527-544.

Troell, M. and J. Norberg. 1998. Modelling output and retention of suspended solids in an integrated salmon-mussel culture. Ecological Modeling 110: 65-77.

Troell, M., C. Halling, A. Neori, T. Chopin, A.H. Buschmann, N. Kautsky, and C. Yarish. 2003. Integrated mariculture: Asking the right questions. Aquaculture 226: 69-90.

Troell, M., C. Halling, A. Nilsson, A. Buschmann, N. Kautsky and L. Kautsky. 1997. Integrated marine cultivation of Gracilaria chilensis (Gracilariales, Bangiophyceae) and salmon cages for reduced environmental impact and increased economic out put. Aquaculture 156: 45-61.

Underwood, A.J. 1994. On beyond BACI: Sampling designs that might reliably detect environmental disturbances. Ecological Applications 4: 3-15.

Vergara, P. 2001. Efectos ambientales de la salmonicultura: El caso de Bahía Metri, Chile [in Spanish]. Master's thesis, Universidad de Los Lagos, Osorno, Chile. 188 pp.

Vitousek, P.M., H.A. Mooney, J. Lubchenco, and J.M. Melillo. 1997. Human domination of earth's ecosystems. Science 277: 494- 499.

Wu, R.S.S. 1995. The environmental impact of marine fish culture: towards a sustainable future. Marine Pollution Bulletin 31: 159-166.

Wu, R.S.S., K.S. Lam, D.W. MacKay, T.C. Lau, and V. Yam. 1994. Impact of marine fish farming on water quality and bottom sediment: A case study in the sub-tropical environment. Marine Environmental Resources 38: 115-145.

Wu, R.S.S., P.K.S. Shin, D.W. MacKay, M. Mollowney, and D. Johnson. 1999. Management of marine fish farming in the sub-tropical environment: A modelling approach. Aquaculture 174: 279-298.

WORKSHOP OUTCOMES

9 THE ROLE OF AQUACULTURE IN INTEGRATED COASTAL MANAGEMENT: GUIDING PRINCIPLES FOR ECOSYSTEM-BASED APPROACH TO IMPLEMENTATION

Introduction

Purpose

The purpose of this chapter is to provide a framework for each country to consider as they develop or amend their guiding principles for marine aquaculture development. The intent is that these principles address economic, environmental, and societal goals, and are broadly applicable rather than specific to any country or industry sector.

Setting

Increase in global demand for seafood to meet a growing population necessitates a shift from reliance on capture fisheries to alternative seafood production technologies. Recent trends show that aquaculture has enormous economic potential and will play an increasingly important role in meeting the global demand for fisheries products.

Given the current state and projected future direction of ocean management and policy, however, it is clear that for marine aquaculture to succeed in the long term, it must be fully integrated with the collective efforts to implement ecosystem-based management and included in the broader Integrated Coastal Management framework. Therefore, strategies for management of existing operations and new development must embrace not only the social and economic goals associated with seafood production, but also be consistent with broader goals to restore and sustain the health, productivity, and biological diversity of the oceans.

Ecosystem-based management is an integrated approach to management that considers the entire ecosystem, including humans. The goal of ecosystem-based management is to maintain an ecosystem in a healthy, productive, and resilient condition, ensuring diversity and abundance of natural flora and fauna so that it can provide the services humans want and need. Ecosystem-based management differs from current approaches that usually focus on a single species, sector, activity, or concern; it considers the cumulative impacts and interactions of different sectors.

The primary purpose of marine aquaculture is commercial food production. Related purposes include fisheries enhancement, ornamental fish, aquarium supply, and medicinal-biochemical production. It should be recognized that while products of aquaculture are similar to those of capture fisheries, it is a different activity and must be managed accordingly. For

Contributors: Langan, R., D. Keeley, K. Leyden, G. Matlock, and C. Yarish
In J.P. McVey, C.-S. Lee, and P.J. O'Bryen, editors. Aquaculture and Ecosystems: An Integrated Coastal and Ocean Management Approach. The World Aquaculture Society, Baton Rouge, Louisiana, United States.

aquaculture production to be consistent with the concept of ecosystem-based management, it must be undertaken in a way that results in acceptable changes to the local environment, i.e., it must be sustainable. Therefore, to be consistent with this paradigm, long-term sustainability should form the fundamental basis for developing guiding principles for planning and management of marine aquaculture.

Guiding Principles

Sustainable marine aquaculture requires adequate consideration of the interactions among the social, economic, and ecological changes that accompany development. This can be achieved through an integrated approach to planning and management of marine aquaculture within the coastal system. Guiding principles that will help move toward the goal of sustainability include:

Legitimacy

- Acknowledge that marine aquaculture has the potential to produce high quality food and other marine products, contribute to social and economic well being, and that it has a legitimate role in the broader framework of Integrated Coastal Management.

Rights and Responsibilities

- Recognize that there is both common and private property involved in aquaculture, and that intersections between public and private properties entail responsibilities for performance. Property rights and their duration must be explicitly defined and allow for the evolution of the mix of coastal zone uses over time in response to environmental, social, and economic forces. With the allocation and associated rights is attached a responsibility to participate in and comply with environmental management.

Communication

- Provide an opportunity for government and public review and communication of marine aquaculture activities that is culturally and socially relevant.

Science and Technology

- Apply the best available and most appropriate science and technology for all aspects of aquaculture development, including planning, site selection, system design, management, monitoring, and assessment.

- Encourage research and technology development, in the context of existing and evolving mechanisms for industry implementation, to improve the economic and environmental performance.

Allocation of Resources

- Integrate and coordinate aquaculture planning, development, and management within the broader framework of integrated coastal zone management plans, according to local, regional, and national goals for sustainable development and in harmony with international obligations.

- Recognize that aquaculture development must strike a balance between economic opportunity, the quality of the environment, the need to accommodate other legitimate water uses, and the interests of local people, the wider community, and where appropriate, the international community. Integrated resource management must include all levels of public governance (National, Provincial, First Nations, Regional, and Urban) and all agencies in resource allocation decisions.

- Ensure that governance adequately allows for the needs of marine aquaculture and that relevant processes are transparent.

- Employ a risk analysis approach to evaluate development plans that have uncertain implications for the environment, the economy, and society.

- Establish a management framework and social climate that combines both incentives and constraints for minimization of adverse effects.

Assessment

- Establish effective monitoring and assessment programs that demonstrate compliance with environmental standards and signal the onset of environmental change.

- Recognize that effective management may require iteration and adaptation.

- Adhere to established standards for quality and safety of aquaculture products for consumers.

Socioeconomic Considerations

- Ensure that all participants in resource allocation decisions respect all users' interests and aspirations.

- Recognize that market externalities are important in the evaluation of the utility of resource allocation solutions.

- Consider how local, regional, national, and international economic forces and agreements will affect economic optimization.

- Consider economic impacts, employment, and life quality issues at local, regional, and national levels.

10 ECOSYSTEM BASED MANAGEMENT: MODELS AND MARICULTURE

Introduction

Conceptual and numerical models are essential tools in managing and protecting coastal ecosystems. Models may be used in economic, social, and ecosystem simulations for many purposes, including aquaculture design, siting, and operation; ecosystem management and risk assessment; and integration of sustainable mariculture into restoration and management of coastal ecosystems.

At the Ecosystem workshop, particular emphasis was placed on the application of ecosystem models to understand the influence of fed and extractive forms of mariculture and their interactions with the natural environment. Participants recognized the limitations of existing models, i.e., they are typically more useful to assist in the prediction of the possible directions and types of interactions rather than predicting absolute or precise quantitative changes.

Waste products from fed mariculture systems may have a range of effects from nutrient enrichment of the water column and benthos to neutral effects where assimilation by the natural biota is equal to the rate of input. There may even be positive effects, such as food web enhancement of diversity and abundance of benthic organisms in more ideal situations where fish mariculture is sized appropriately and strong currents disperse organic and inorganic wastes.

In less than ideal physical conditions or where nutrient sensitivity is an issue, mariculture of species receiving a food ration (e.g., fish or shrimp) may be coupled with shellfish and/or seaweed capable of extracting nutrients from consumption of enhanced phytoplankton stocks or directly through nutrient removal. This is termed "integrated mariculture" in the literature, or more precisely, "integrated multi-trophic aquaculture," and may be designed to eliminate adverse effects of fed finfish culture. Organic matter and nutrient additions by cultured fish do not have to be perfectly balanced with nutrient removal in space and time as long as the biological communities can assimilate the nutrient loads without adversely changing the composition and character of these communities.

Extractive shellfish and seaweed mariculture offers significant benefits to coastal ecosystems through reduction of excess nutrient loading known as coastal eutrophication.

Contributors: Rensel, J.E.J, A.H. Buschmann, T. Chopin, I.K. Chung, J. Grant, C.E. Helsley, D.A. Kiefer, R. Langan, R.I.E. Newell, M. Rawson, J.W. Sowles, J.P. McVey, and C. Yarish
In J.P. McVey, C.-S. Lee, and P.J. O'Bryen, editors. Aquaculture and Ecosystems: An Integrated Coastal and Ocean Management Approach. The World Aquaculture Society, Baton Rouge, Louisiana, United States.

Worldwide, many coastal seas are suffering from adverse effects of eutrophication which can include oxygen depletion, changes in species composition and in some case harmful algae events. Although not typically defined as such, integrated mariculture could also include directing finfish facilities to areas where companion, extractive crops are not needed due to certain local characteristics.

Some areas with strong tidal current that prevent permanent solids deposition and concurrently that are not nutrient sensitive would not benefit from integrated mariculture to mitigate the effects of fed finfish culture. Algae and nutrients do not limit primary production in high current velocity, deep water, and nutrient insensitive areas (e.g., Cobscook Bay in Northern Maine, USA, and main channels of Puget Sound and the Strait of Juan de Fuca in Washington State that experience light limitation of phytoplankton). Solid wastes from fish mariculture in these areas are periodically resuspended until they are incorporated aerobically into the food web. In general, other areas may be desirable for mariculture if its scale remains within the carrying capacity of the water body so that byproducts enhance, rather than degrade, existing marine resources. In the context of ecosystem-based mariculture, coastal resource managers may achieve protection of sensitive areas while addressing the larger need for food production and coastal economies. Worldwide, only limited coastal areas qualify as physically and chemically optimal for fish mariculture when all siting requirements are considered. In tropical or subtropical areas, especially those near shore, nutrient enrichment may have negative effects, and integrated mariculture would be beneficial in some cases. Initial observations of offshore cages in tropical areas indicate that there may be a food web response to mariculture discharge resulting in increased numbers of invertebrates and fish near the cages. These effects can be positive as long as the enrichment does not flow onto coral reefs and it is aerobically assimilated into the biological community in the surrounding area.

Although mariculture is often believed to have undesirable impacts on coastal ecosystems, the modeling session participants recognized that some forms of mariculture can become part of a solution to coastal problems caused by non-mariculture activities such as point and non-point source nutrient inputs, habitat destruction, and over-fishing. There was consensus among the international participants that models should describe levels and types of effects from mariculture. After some discussion, however, it was agreed that determining "what is acceptable" in terms of end point impacts or benefits is a separate informed political decision made on the basis of each country's local customs, policies, and laws.

Purpose and Use of Models

The purpose and use of models are highly variable and serve the mariculture industry, government planners, scientists, as well as the general public. Some examples of uses include:

- Siting mariculture facilities

- Issuing permits for mariculture operations

- Making decisions and planning the economics of mariculture

- Optimizing mariculture operations

- Assisting in the technical planning and management of mariculture operations

- Identifying opportunities to integrate mariculture activities into solving coastal problems

- Hindcasting "baseline" conditions

- Identifying gaps in knowledge of mariculture activities

- Characterizing and quantifying ecological processes and pathways

- Estimating the effects of human perturbation on the ecosystem

- Educating and communicating with the public

Characteristics and Types of Models

Characteristics of Models

Model characteristics vary widely depending on their purpose, origin, and user. For example, some coastal managers are generally interested in models that are simple, easily understood, completed in a timely fashion with minimal resources, and which have the ability to convey educational messages to the public. On the other hand, researchers engaged in answering complex questions of ecological pathways and fluxes are interested in models that can accommodate more detailed and quantitative biological, chemical, and physical processes. Mariculturists may be interested in the results of modeling by both coastal managers and scientists as well as running their own models on costs and benefit analyses for various husbandry, siting, and operational practices.

There is recognition that complexity is not necessarily a virtue in modeling. Between the extremes of simplicity and complexity, the practicality and "power" of models must be balanced. For example, models with high precision, accuracy, and thoroughness generally need extensive, high-resolution data to allow complete parameterization. Furthermore, such models require advanced computer systems not typically available to coastal managers or mariculturists. Advancing understanding of coastal ecosystem dynamics, complex food webs, and processes, however, will require the use of the more advanced and complex models that rely on extensive databases and computations. As a greater understanding of an ecosystem is developed, complex models may often be simplified as the lesser important variables and components are quantified.

Desirable characteristics of some models include:

- Ease of use and understandability

- Validity that can be established through incorporation of measurable Environmental Quality Objectives

- Ability to assess effects at a scale appropriate to management needs

- Provision to address near and far field effects

- Assumptions, boundaries, and compartments are well defined

- Ability to interface with other models

Several general categories of models exist that can be helpful to the management of Ecosystem Based Mariculture. These include:

- Physical (e.g., hydrodynamic, circulation, wave energy, and plume trajectories)

- Chemical (e.g., sediment diagenesis and chemical transformations)

- Biological (physiological, growth, food web, bioturbation[1], and energetics)

- Resource economics-based (e.g., intrinsic value of shellfish and seaweed for bioremediation services to manage eutrophication)

- Coupled or integrated models – (e.g., integration of any or all the above, typically physicochemical and biological).

The following general comments are made regarding origins, applications, and limitations of models, drawn from a discussion paper the authors prepared prior to the meeting:

- Many estuarine and coastal ocean models were designed for other purposes, e.g., municipal and industrial waste discharge plume characterization or circulation studies.

- No fully functional models yet exist that completely integrate water column and benthic effects of mariculture into a single package[2] or interlinked modules that accurately reproduce benthic-water column coupling.

- Benthic impact models for finfish mariculture are developing but they are still evolving

---

[1] Disturbance of sediment layers by biological activity.

[2] A GIS model known as AquaModel performs these simulations but it is currently being validated and tuned.

to more fully account for various processes including resuspension, saltation (leaping of particles across an uneven surface), bedload[3] transport, and assimilation or bioturbation by differing types of benthic or other fauna and flora. Much remains to be learned about rate constants of aquaculture waste feed and fish feces assimilation in the food web in terms of carbon flux in differing habitats and ecoregions using differing culture techniques, species, and types of feed.

- Several suitable hydrodynamic models are available for water column physical description, but few adequately integrate or link to biological components and processes.

- No existing single model will likely serve all purposes. There is a need for different models with a variety of levels of hydrodynamic sophistication, tuning ability, physiological bases, and eventually, linkage to economic models.

- Different but complementary models may be selected and linked together. For example, water column and benthic models may be linked, but the technical aspects of linking such models so that the various modeled components, such as nutrients or oxygen, are accurately transferred between modeled domains is not a trivial process.

- Lack of species-specific physiological information prevents accurate description of waste products or assimilation (bio-mitigation) processes needed to develop suitable biological models. Some species are well described (salmonids and mussels), but many others are not (various marine fish, some shellfish, crustaceans, and seaweeds).

- Validation of models is often not conducted but is essential. Site-specific calibration is also necessary. Similarly, assumptions and limitation are not always explicit in documentation but they should be.

- Models are not acceptable substitutions for compliance monitoring in North America and are never used for enforcement actions. Predictive impact models are required in some countries for permitting (e.g., large scale finfish mariculture in Scotland).

- Models are currently being developed in the aquaculture therapeutant approval process by the U.S. Food and Drug Administration and the U.S. Environmental Protection Agency.

- Complex models may not be practical for use by public sector managers and regulators or by individual mariculturists or companies. For broad, regional modeling, however, there is a need for complexity to adequately simulate variable and complex hydrographic, physicochemical, and biological conditions and to understand and define boundary conditions of these processes.

---

[3] Sediment moving on or near the streambed of seabed and frequently in contact with it.

- Pragmatic realism is a necessary aspect of modeling, because "All models are wrong. Some models are useful" (DiToro 2001). Not all models are intended to exactly simulate reality. Some models only seek to give insight into key processes, bottlenecks (constrictions) in natural systems, and missing or erroneous components of modeling needing attention.

Types of Models

Following are some examples of models ranging from simple to complex, including several that previously have been used for mariculture applications.

Simple One-Box Models

Box models are one of the most common types of models used by coastal managers, particularly for semi-enclosed bays or waterways. Single box models can be developed using readily available inputs such as surface areas from nautical or topographic charts and volume estimates from published literature or user-performed estimates. Mass balance models are a form of box model that account for principle inputs and outputs of selected properties such as river or seawater, dissolved oxygen, macronutrients (dissolved, particulate, and organic fractions of N and phosphorus, P), particulate carbon, and various types of pollutant measures. Most importantly, these simple and inexpensive models produce results quickly for coastal decision-makers and are easily understood by the general public.

Mass balance nutrient models that seek to quantify inputs and losses of nutrients are among the most useful of these simple models, by providing coastal managers an approximate estimate of the potential effect of nutrient addition or extraction. Very often, however, these types of models fail to take into consideration the assimilative capacity of the surrounding ecosystem, and they equate primary production to phytoplankton production, ignoring the significant nutrient scrubbing function of aquatic macrophytes (submerged aquatic vegetation and seaweeds). Depending on the results, managers may quickly approve or deny a project, or decide that further modeling and/or monitoring is required.

Examples of simple one-box and mass balance models include:

- Tidal prism and salt balance models to estimate flushing rates that are widely used

- Mass balance models that estimate net loss and/or uptake of a constituent by calculating differences between known inputs and removals. At the workshop, John Sowles presented a mass balance model for N in the Gulf of Maine. Other models of this type include those by Gowen et al. (1992) and Sowles and Churchill (2004).

- Combined simple flushing models coupled to biogeochemical/ecological models based on previous studies in a "broad-brush" generic review and comparison of estuaries, as used in Australia (CSIRO 2001). A recent example is that of Grant et al. (2005) in which biodeposition impacts are assessed for mussel culture in eastern Canada.

Index Models

Index models provide a ranking of impacts relative to other water bodies, operations, or technologies. These employ one-box models or empirically derived relationships that have been quantified through measurement, correlation, and other means. Although their absolute accuracy may be variable, these indices are useful to managers and mariculturists responsible for deciding management options including the best location among several options for a certain proposed activity or the degree of impact of existing practices, including aquaculture. Some examples include:

- Index of Suitable Location and Embayment Degree Model used in Japan (Abo and Yokoyama 2005).

- Nitrogen loading model and oxygen depletion indices for Puget Sound, Washington, USA bays and subareas (SAIC 1986; Rensel Associates and PTI 1991; Albertson et al. 2002)

- Benthic oxygen uptake, carbon assimilation, and sulfide content models (several)

- Scottish management indices (e.g., Gillibrand et al. 2002)

Multiple Box Models

Multiple box models are an iteration between one-box models and complex hydrodynamic models with extensive grid representation. In general, the hydrodynamics are collapsed into spatially integrated inter-box exchange coefficients which are used directly in the box model, and are thus decoupled from the hydrodynamic grid. Ecosystem structure may be as detailed as more spatially explicit models, but complexity and computation time are reduced, making them excellent exploratory tools. They have generally been used to examine density-dependent and food-limited growth in bivalve culture, and/or benthic and nutrient impacts of shellfish farming. A recent example is:

- Model of dispersion in Tracadie Bay, Prince Edward Island, Canada where impacts of mussel culture were modeled (Dowd 2005; Grant et al. 2005)

Benthic Impact, Particle Tracking Models

This class of generally well-advanced models is used to predict carbon accumulation on the sea bottom, effects on the benthos, and related topics. Newer benthic models may include a resuspension component to estimate re-distribution of benthic materials by water currents above a critical resuspension threshold. Resuspension components are useful in macrotidal or strong ocean current regimes but they are not necessarily needed in slower, depositional areas. Examples include:

- DEPOMOD (Cromey et al. 2002a, 2002b) is a widely used, personal computer platform, carbon-based benthic model developed for temperate water finfish mariculture with several submodels dealing with consolidation, resuspension, carbon degradation, and bioturbation. A similar model, developed as part of the MERAMED project in 2005 (www.akvaplan.niva.no/meramed/download), has been adapted for use in the Mediterranean Sea, where wild fish actively feed on waste feed from net pens.

- Perez et al. (2002) report a carbon-based model with Global Information Systems (GIS) underpinnings and no resuspension component, validated for depositional sites.

- The Aquaculture Waste Transport Simulator model, AWATS (Panchang et al. 1997; Dudley et al 2000) is a vertically averaged, two-dimensional flow model with particle-tracking waste transport processes. It is among the first models to consider resuspension to simulate the resulting transport of wastes.

Two- or Three-Dimensional Hydrodynamic Models Linked with a Biological Model

These are complex conceptual and computational models that have the capacity to help scientists understand ecological processes, and they may be useful for broad geographic regions (far field) with complex bathymetry and hydrography. Sometimes referred to as coupled physical-biological models, they generated great interest among the workshop participants. These models have several disadvantages, including the requirement for extensive and often expensive database support, major computation power (will not run on personal computers), and require a long development time before output.

Examples of multidimensional models coupled with a biological or water quality model include:

- Finite Volume Community Ocean Model (FVCOM), with a Water Quality Analysis Simulation Program (WASP5) water quality module (Ambrose et al. 1993). This is a powerful and complex model. One example is by Chen et al. (1999).

- Princeton Ocean Model (Blumberg and Mellor 1980; 1987). This model has been widely used and redeveloped over time for ocean plume modeling.

Three-Dimensional Simplified Hydrodynamic Models within GIS Interface

Increasingly useful, especially in the public sector, are the moderate complex scale models that use three-dimensional (3-D) computations with simplified boundaries in a GIS context and a widely understood graphic user interface that operates on personal computers.

Hydrodynamic simulation is simplified to achieve the benefits of easy use by model users and managers. Because of their graphical format, these also have the distinct advantage of being an excellent teaching tool for audiences with diverse backgrounds.

As with several other types of models, 3-D GIS models require species-specific physiological information on metabolic rate, growth, nutrient ingestion, and excretion as well as hydrodynamic data or estimates of current velocity and disrection distribution.

An example presented at the workshop is AquaModel, a finfish mariculture model that runs within a GIS (Environmental Assessment System, EASy). This model concurrently simulates a farm's effects on water quality, including dissolved oxygen, dissolved nitrogen, and plankton dynamics, and it includes a benthic sedimentation and resuspension module. AquaModel traces the flow of carbon, nitrogen, and oxygen in the farm and ecosystem, it runs on a laptop and (data) can be shared in real time on the Internet (Rensel et al. in press).

Direction and Needs

Short Term Plan

The authors propose the development of a one-box index model (Fig. 1) to expedite investigation of ecosystem effects of mariculture activities for situations in which either

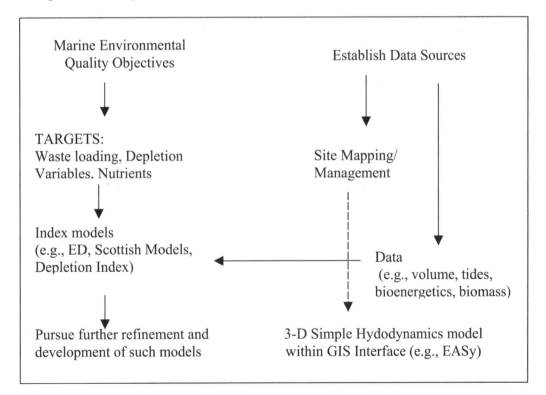

Figure 1. Proposed short-term modeling plan.

environmental data or the resources necessary for advanced modeling are limited. This model will be designed and implemented for several mutually agreed upon international locations, inshore and offshore, with at least one that currently has balanced, multi-species mariculture. This can likely be implemented within a 1- to 3-year time frame with little extra research.

A simple box model or 3-D simple hydrodynamic model within a GIS interface (as described above) can be developed to model the effect of cultured organisms on oxygen demand, N and P content, phytoplankton, opportunistic macroalgal growth, and particulate organic carbon deposition and transport. Such a model requires species-specific physiological information on metabolic and growth rates, nutrient ingestion/assimilation, and excretion, much of which is available for a few key species. Volume of water exchanged within an embayment can be estimated by an appropriate variation of the tidal prism method.

Concurrently, there is a need for better understanding of the temporal variability of effects from mariculture systems from varying feed regimes, physiological and biochemical processes of the cultured species and other factors. The roles and functions of integrated aquaculture practices for improved environmental, economic, and social acceptability should be analyzed within the broader perspective of integrated coastal management initiatives (Troell et al. 2003). Research into these advanced aquaculture technologies should be conducted at scales relevant to commercial implementation to be suitable for modeling, and should address the biology, engineering, operational protocol, and economics of the technology. Studies are needed to elucidate the influences of location- and ecoregion-specific parameters, such as latitude, climate, and local strains/species, on aquaculture performance. One has to ensure that the key functions for an environmentally and socio-economically balanced system are in place. The choice of species for the different functions, however, has to be adapted to the local biological, economic, and social conditions.

Offshore culture systems present a different class of model, especially in terms of physical aspects. Although the impact on the water column (i.e., nutrient enrichment-algal response and dissolved oxygen effects) may be undetectable a short distance downstream, cumulative effects from numerous systems and far-field effects (e.g., plume impingement on coral reefs) must be considered. As in near shore mariculture, local effect on the benthos must also be considered. Models that allow assessment of open water culture systems may be derived from existing benthic deposition models and water column models or new combinations of both (cf. Montoya et al. 2002).

Long Term Plan: Developing More Sophisticated Ecosystem Models (5 Years)

The long term plan (Fig. 2) is international and cooperative development of a "universal" framework for an ecosystem model that can be adapted to local conditions through insertion of modules and the constants that are available for the specific local or regional needs. This framework will:

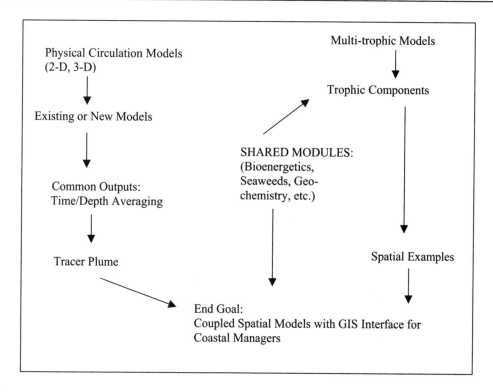

Figure 2. Proposed long-term modeling plan.

- Identify trophic interactions with some degree of certainty, allowing sensitivity analysis and laboratory (physiological submodels) or field studies (combining all submodels) for estimating model accuracy.

- Incorporate a minimal set of properties (e.g., functional components and shared modules) that may have quantifiable influence upon application.

- Use existing 2-dimensional, and in estuarine locations, 3-D hydrodynamic models of water circulation that have often been developed independently by physical oceanographers for regions with mariculture potential (preferably the same locations for which country scenarios were developed.)

- Use emerging integrated aquaculture models presently being developed (e.g., salmon/mussel/kelp project in the Bay of Fundy, on the east coast of Canada).

- Obtain hydrographic predictions formatted in time steps suitable for biological models.

- Use this hydrographic model to predict mariculture plume movement under a range of tidal, riverine discharge to estuaries and oceanic current flows.

- Link to and stimulate development of socio-economic models, including the evaluation of different mariculture practices (e.g., monoculture versus integrated aquaculture) and the quantification of the economic value of the extractive species/crops and the environmental and social value of the services rendered by extractive mariculture (shellfish and seaweeds), as to internalize environmental costs in mariculture operations (Chopin et al. 2001; Yang et al. 2004)

- Provide for GIS interface for use by coastal zone and marine resource managers

The entire interested research community should work toward developing or adapting modules for processes and organisms of interest. Example transferable modules are those that focus on individual components such as sediment diagenesis, particle sedimentation and resuspension, seagrass, macroalgae, microphytobenthos, phytoplankton (including harmful algal blooms), growth/physiology of finfish and suspension feeding molluscs, fouling communities, and so forth. These discrete modules can then be adapted to regional conditions and used as coupled circulation/chemical/biological models. Suitable circulation data and hydrodynamic models will be required, and for many locales, this will necessitate extensive efforts.

Complex and shared community models need to have a central repository that can serve as a clearinghouse for adding new or revised modules. The repository may act as a contact point for groups wishing to implement managed mariculture ecosystem models. Accordingly there is a need to plan for long-term funding for such an entity.

This proposal includes development of a database of aquaculture and ecosystem constants and variables that will be needed for model development and use. Finally, it is emphasized that this approach does not displace or negate ongoing efforts in various countries that are presently using specific models. This proposal is meant as a further enhancement and catalyst. The authors believe this approach will compliment and encourage further development and validation for the models described above, which in turn will contribute significantly to the rational use of coastal and oceanic waters for sustainable mariculture.

Literature Cited

Abo, K. and H. Yokoyama. 2005. Assimilative capacity of fish farm environments as determined by benthic oxygen uptake rate: Studies using a numerical model. Proceedings of 33rd UJNR Aquaculture Panel Symposium. Nagasaki Japan.

Albertson, S.L., K. Erickson, J.A. Newton, G. Pelletier, R.A. Reynolds, and M. Roberts. 2002. South Puget Sound water quality phase 1. Washington State Department of Ecology Publication No. 02-03-021. Environmental Assessment Program, Department of Ecology, Olympia, Washington, USA. 224 pp. http://www.ecy.wa.gov/pubs/0203021. pdf.

Ambrose, R.B. Jr., T.A. Wool, J.L. Martin. 1993. The Water Quality Analysis Simulation Program, WASP5. Part A: Model Documentation. U.S. Environmental Protection Agency, Office of Research and Development, Environmental Research Laboratory, Athens, Georgia, USA. 251 pp. http://www.cee.odu.edu/mbin/wasp/dos/wasp5_ model.pdf.

Blumberg, A.F. and G.L. Mellor. 1980. The Princeton Ocean Model (POM), a three dimensional primitive equation, numerical ocean model. Princeton University, Princeton, New Jersey, USA. http://www.aos.princeton.edu/WWWPUBLIC/htdocs.pom/.

Blumberg, A.F. and G.L. Mellor. 1987. A description of a three-dimensional coastal ocean circulation model. Pages 1-16 in N.S. Heaps, editor. Three-Dimensional Coastal Ocean Models. Coastal and Estuarine Sciences 4. American Geophysical Union, Washington, DC, USA.

Chen, C., R. Ji, L. Zheng, M. Zhu, and M. Rawson. 1999. Influences of physical processes on ecosystem in Jiaozhou Bay: A coupled physical and biological model experiment. Journal of Geophysical Research 104 (C12): 29, 925-929, 949.

Chopin, T., A.H. Buschmann, C. Halling, M. Troell, N. Kautsky, A. Neori, G.P. Kraemer, J.A. Zertuche-Gonzalez, C. Yarish, and C. Neefus. 2001. Integrating seaweeds into marine aquaculture systems: a key toward sustainability. Journal of Phycology 37: 975-986.

Cromey, C.J., T.D. Nickell, and K.D. Black. 2002a. DEPOMOD – modeling the deposition and biological effects of waste solids from marine cage farms. Aquaculture 214: 211-239.

Cromey, C.J., T. D. Nickell, K.D. Black, P.G. Provost, and C.R. Griffiths. 2002b. Validation of fish farm waste resuspension model by use of a particulate tracer discharge from a point source in a coastal environment. Estuaries 25: 916-929.

CSIRO (Commonwealth Scientific and Industrial Research Organisation). 2001. Simple Estuarine Response Model (SERM). National Land and Water Resources Audit. Marine and Atmospheric Research, CSIRO, Canberra, Australian Capital Territory, Australia. http://www.per.marine.csiro.au/serm/index.htm.

DiToro, D.M. 2001: Sediment Flux Modeling. Willey and Sons, New York, New York, USA. 624 pp.

Dowd, M. 2005. A bio-physical coastal ecosystem model for assessing environmental effects of marine bivalve aquaculture. Ecological Modelling 183: 323–346.

Dudley, R.W., V.G. Panchang, and C.R. Newell. 2000. Application of a comprehensive modelling strategy for the management of net–pen aquaculture waste transport. Aquaculture 187: 319–349.

Gillibrand, P.A., M.J. Gubbins, C. Greathead, and I.M. Davies. 2002. Scottish locational guidelines for fish farming: predicted levels of nutrient enhancement and benthic impact. Scottish Fisheries Report 63/2002. Fisheries Research Services, Aberdeen, Scotland, UK. 52 pp.

Gowen, R.J., P. Tett, and K.J. Jones. 1992. Predicting marine eutrophication: the yield of chlorophyll from nitrogen in Scottish coastal waters. Marine Ecology Progress Series 85: 153-161.

Grant, J., P. Cranford, B. Hargrave, M. Carreau, B. Schofield, S. Armsworthy, V. Burdett-Counts, and D. Ibarra. 2005. A model of aquaculture biodeposition for multiple estuaries and field validation at mussel (*Mytilus edulis*) culture sites in Eastern Canada. Can. J. Fish. Aquat. Sci. 62: 1271–1285.

Montoya, R.A., A.L. Lawrence, W.E. Grant, and M. Velasco. 2002. Simulation of inorganic nitrogen dynamics and shrimp survival in an intensive shrimp culture system. Aquaculture Research 33: 81-94.

Panchang, V., G. Cheng, and C.R. Newell. 1997. Modeling hydrodynamics and aquaculture waste transport in coastal Maine. Estuaries 20: 14–41.

Perez, O.M, T.C. Telfer, M.C.M. Beveridge, and L.G. Ross. 2002. Geographical information systems (GIS) as a simple tool to aid modelling of particulate waste distribution at marine fish cage sites. Estuarine, Coastal and Shelf Science 54: 761–768.

Rensel Associates and PTI Environmental Services. 1991. Nutrients and phytoplankton in Puget Sound. U.S. Environmental Protection Agency Report 910/9-91-002. Environmental Protection Agency, Seattle, Washington, USA. 130 pp.

Rensel, J.E., D. Kiefer, J.R.M. Forster, D. Woodruff, and N.R. Evans. In press. Offshore finfish mariculture in the Strait of Juan de Fuca. 2004 U.S. Japan Cooperative Program in Natural Resources 33rd Annual Proceedings. Nagasaki, Japan. http://www.wfga.net/sjdf/reports/publication.pdf.

SAIC (Science Applications International Corporation) 1986. Recommended interim guidelines for the management of salmon net pen culture in Puget Sound. D. Weston for Washington State Departments of Ecology and Natural Resources. Publication 87-5. Department of Ecology, Olympia, Washington, USA. 48 pp.

Sowles, J. 2005. Assessing nitrogen carrying capacity for Blue Hill Bay, Maine - A management case history. In B.T. Hargrave, editor. The Handbook of Environmental Chemistry – Volume 5. Water Pollution: Environmental Effects of Marine Finfish Aquaculture. Springer-Verlag, Heidelberg, Germany.

Sowles, J. and L. Churchill. 2004. Predicted nutrient enrichment by salmon aquaculture and potential for effects in Cobscook Bay, Maine. Northeastern Naturalist 11(Special Issue 2): 87-100.

Troell, M., C. Halling, A. Neori, T. Chopin, A.H. Buschmann, N. Kautsky, and C. Yarish. 2003. Integrated mariculture: asking the right questions. Aquaculture 226: 69-90.

Yang, Y.F., C.H. Li, X.P. Nie, D.L. Tang and I.K. Chung. 2004. Development of mariculture and its impacts in Chinese coastal waters. Reviews in Fish Biology and Fisheries 14: 1-10.

11 CONSIDERATIONS FOR COASTAL MANAGERS

Introduction

This chapter represents a portion of the work completed by one of two workshop subgroups, whose charge was, in part, to create a checklist of considerations for decision-making relative to the placement of aquaculture in coastal ecosystems. Participants in this subgroup also worked together to create a suggested set of universal guiding principles for marine aquaculture (see Chapter 9). The checklist detailed in the following text builds upon those universal principles, adding an additional degree of specificity concerning the actual planning and siting of marine aquaculture in coastal ecosystems.

There were several purposes for conducting this exercise. The primary purpose was to reorient thinking from a current focus on analyzing, permitting, and monitoring aquaculture on an individual site-by-site basis toward consideration of aquaculture in an ecosystem context. In the latter, larger ecosystem context, managers consider and manage the effects of aquaculture on systems, rather than sites, and use aquaculture as a tool to deliver multiple benefits to society such as food production and nutrient recycling. A second purpose of this exercise was to document (for industry, non-governmental organizations and others) the comprehensive list of parameters that decision-makers may consider when planning for aquaculture. This is intended to help others understand what factors managers use to make decisions and to offer a degree of transparency to those considerations. Lastly, the "considerations checklist" was developed with the hope that participating countries (and others) will revise and apply the checklist of considerations within their own jurisdictions.

Audience

Besides industry, non-governmental organizations, and the public, the intended audience for this "considerations checklist" includes two types of coastal practitioners, coastal managers and technical support staff. For the purpose of this chapter, the term "coastal manager" includes those individuals responsible for policy development and resource allocation decisions. In this role, the coastal manager routinely combines technical and/or scientific advice, and traditional knowledge with other policy-related considerations (e.g., socioeconomic, cultural, political, etc.) to make decisions. These managers need a wide array of environmental and socioeconomic information to plan for and respond to aquaculture activities in the context of ecosystem-based management or integrated coastal management. Technical support staff, on the other hand, are directly involved in site assessments (e.g., analyzing physical, biological, and chemical conditions and human uses), site feasibility, and ongoing monitoring.

Contributors: Keeley, D., G. Matlock, and K. Leyden
In J.P. McVey, C.-S. Lee, and P.J. O'Bryen, editors. Aquaculture and Ecosystems: An Integrated Coastal and Ocean Management Approach. The World Aquaculture Society, Baton Rouge, Louisiana, United States.

Ecosystem-Based Management Information Needs[1]

As documented in other parts of the workshop proceedings, it is acknowledged that expansion of aquaculture is necessary to meet society's growing demand for high quality seafood. While expansion of aquaculture is desirable, this goal can only be attained if future aquaculture efforts are fully integrated into coastal ecosystems. That is, facilities are planned for and sited in consideration of a full range of physical, biological, and chemical characteristics of coastal systems, and with full consideration of socioeconomic factors.

Thus, coastal managers need to reorient their thinking beyond consideration of individual aquaculture sites and toward coastal systems. In integrated coastal management, practitioners manage for desired outcomes or results by considering the effects of aquaculture operations on coastal ecosystems (i.e., natural environment and human environment). This includes factors such as:

- Integrated ecosystem effects, i.e., changes in any of the following: ecosystem structure, system productivity, protected habitats or species, biodiversity.

- Disease outbreak potential among aquaculture sites

- Hydrography of embayments, circulation dynamics

- Carrying capacity, assimilative capacity

- Constraints and opportunities for aquaculture siting, optimization of site locations

- Nutrient budgets, uptake needs of polyculture organisms

- Trophic or food chain dynamics

- Social concerns/social carrying capacity/social limiters (e.g., unacceptable displacement of existing uses or public trust uses)

- Impacts of farmed products on human health

Considerations for Aquaculture in Ecosystem Management

The following detailed list of considerations would potentially be used by technical support staff (i.e., advisors to coastal managers), other government authorities, and fish farmers, and would provide information to the public about information used to plan for and site aquaculture.

---

[1] Ecosystem-based management is an integrated approach to management that considers the entire ecosystem, including humans. The goal of ecosystem-based management is to maintain an ecosystem in a healthy, productive, and resilient condition so that it can provide services humans need and want.

The list is divided into three broad categories: environmental, economic, and social considerations. This corresponds to the regulatory scheme used by some workshop participants, where aquaculture is considered in light of environmental, economic, and social feasibility. This list is neither comprehensive, nor mandatory. It should be used in conjunction with the statutory regulatory requirements of each country.

Environmental Considerations

Existing Water Quality

Temperature profile (diurnal and annual variability)
Oxygen profile (diurnal and annual variability)
Primary production
Ambient nutrient profile
Toxic effects - Harmful algal blooms
Pollution (bacterial, chemical, etc.)
Sediment quality
Seawater and freshwater inputs
Drainage area inputs
Exchange rate of water, e.g. turnover
Transparency
Availability of phytoplankton
Assimilative capacity and carrying capacity
Chemical oxygen demand
Acid volatile sulphides
Water column profiles

Potential Exposure to Pollution Events

Shipping and boating
Discharges (including existing aquaculture)
Fecal coliforms and other pollutants associated with stormwater runoff
Vulnerability of water body to pollution

Coastline Characteristics, Bathymetry, and Hydrographic Conditions

Configuration of coastline
Substrate type (hard, soft)
Depth (mean low and high)
Wave height and direction
Currents (direction and velocity)
Storm protection/exposure
Hydraulic retention
Tidal range

Protected or Sensitive Resources

Species (e.g., marine mammals, birds, etc.)
Corals
Habitats (e.g., eelgrass, mangroves, spawning and nursery areas)
Conserved public lands and access
Marine protected areas or ocean sanctuaries
Public trust resources

Biological Communities

Endemic species
Endemic and non-endemic diseases
Exotic and introduced species

Weather

Sea state in storms
Weather tracks in typhoons, hurricanes
Storm exposure
Human Health
Sanitary quality of seafood
Accumulation/residence of chemicals

Nutrient Balance

Net extraction or delivery
Seasonality of flux
Feed type and amount

Chemical Use, Discharge, and Accumulation

Antibiotics, and other therapeutants, pesticides, disinfectants
Antifoulants

Economic Considerations[2]

Aquaculture facility design and operation
Cultured organism(s)
Parasites and pathogens

---

[2] It is acknowledged that a complete analysis of economic considerations associated with aquaculture policy and permitting is beyond the scope of this chapter. In this limited discussion, a short list of features associated with a facility's design and operation that would affect the economic viability of a project is included. This list does not substitute for a complete analysis of economic viability and related business planning for specific facilities.

Genetics
Gear (pens, ropes, nets, bags, etc.)
Configuration (depth, area affected, mooring plan, engineering specifications to withstand local conditions)
Water depth and circulation below system
Entanglement potential
Navigation hazard potential
Deployment (seasonality)

Social and Cultural Considerations

Existing and Potential User Conflicts

Traditional fisheries
Shipping lanes
Navigation
Riparian property owners
Public access and public trust resources
Subsistence activities
Recreation
Impacts to and capacity of landside facilities
Size, use, and ownership of product landing area(s)
Air, land, and sea movement of materials and products

Socioeconomic Effect on Coastal Communities

Local cultural attitudes about using ocean space
Proximity of workforce in site area
Job creation
Effects on existing businesses
Community context (e.g., working waterfront community accustomed to maritime use vs. tourist-oriented community)

Next Steps

To help build capacity for consideration of aquaculture in an ecosystem-based management scheme, the following recommendations are offered for consideration and discussion.

1. Communication strategy – A distribution plan should describe how each country will disseminate this information and provide a mechanism to report on suggested improvements to this information.

2. Country assessments – Over the next 12-18 months, participating countries should prepare informal "country assessments" to determine the degree of alignment of

country practices with these considerations and country-specific strategies to address their desired improvements.

3. Share lessons-learned – The National Oceanic and Atmospheric Administration (NOAA) and/or a program like the Aquaculture Interchange Program (AIP) should continue to document and disseminate effective aquaculture strategies and techniques. Over the next 18-24 months, based on areas of common interest, these agencies should facilitate communication between and among programs to share information and continually refine these "considerations by coastal managers."

APPENDIX A: WORKSHOP PARTICIPANTS

*Indicates Team Leader or Co-leader

Canada

Edward Black*
200 Kent Street, Ottawa, Ontario, K1A 0E6, Canada
Tel: +1-613-990-0272
Fax: +1-613-993-7665
Email: blacke@dfo-mpo.gc.ca
Areas of specialization: Risk-based decision making; Integrated Coastal Zone Management

Thierry Chopin
Professor
Department of Biology, University of New Brunswick, Center for Coastal Studies and Aquaculture, Center for Environmental and Molecular Algal Research, P.O. Box 5050, Saint John, New Brunswick, E2L 4L5, Canada
Tel: +1-506-648-5507/5565
Fax: +1-506-648-5811
Email: tchopin@unbsj.ca
Areas of specialization: Ecophysiology and biochemistry of seaweeds; Integrated multi-trophic aquaculture

Jon Grant
Professor
Department of Oceanography, Dalhousie University
Halifax, Nova Scotia, B3H 4J1, Canada
Tel: +1-902-494-2021
Fax: +1-902-494-3877
Email: jon.grant@dal.ca

Fred Page
Research Scientist
Responsibility Centre Manager, Ocean Sciences Division
Coastal Ocean Sciences Section, Fisheries and Oceans Canada
Biological Station, 531 Brandy Cove Road
St. Andrews, New Brunswick, E5B 2L9, Canada
Tel: +1-506-529-5935
Fax: +1-506-529-5868
Email: pageF@dfo-mpo.gc.ca

Neil Ridler
Professor
Department of Economics, University of New Brunswick, Sir Douglas Hazen Hall, 216,
P.O. Box 5050, Saint John, New Brunswick, E2L 4L5, Canada
Tel: +1-506-648-5760
Fax: +1-506-648-5947
Email: ridler@unbsj.ca
Areas of specialization: Resource economics with a focus on aquaculture

Jamey Smith
Research and Environmental Coordinator
New Brunswick Salmon Growers Association, 227 Lime Kiln Road, Letang, New
Brunswick, E5C 2A2, Canada
Tel: +1-506-454-7170
Fax: +1-504-447-7193
Email: coastal@nbnet.nb.ca

Chile

Alejandro H. Buschmann
Centro de I&D en Recursos y Ambientes Costeros "i-mar", Universidad de Los Lagos,
Camino a Chinquihue km 6, Puerto Montt Región de Los Lagos, Chile
Tel: +56-65-483206 / +56-65-483221
Fax: +56-65-483208
Email: abuschma@ulagos.cl

China

Jianguang Fang
Director
Department of Aquaculture Ecology, Yellow Sea Fisheries Research Institute,
Chinese Academy of Fishery Sciences, 106 Nanjing Road
Qingdao 266071, People's Republic of China
Tel: +86-532-582-2957
Fax: +86-532-1514
Email: fangig@ysfri.ac.cn
Areas of specialization: Mariculture ecology; Carrying capacity of bivalves and seaweed;
Polyculture of bivalves and kelp; Integrated mariculture in coastal zones

Shunan Li
Deputy Director
Fangchenggang Oceanic Bureau, Guangxi Provincial Government; Tianma Tower, Room
602, Yunnan Road, Fangchenggang, Guangxi 538001, People's Republic of China
Tel: +86-770-283-3785
Fax: +86-770-282-0105
Email: sun_moon717@yahoo.com.cn

Wenjun Li
Deputy Division Director
Department of Sea Use Management, State Oceanic Administration,
People's Republic of China
Email: hyc@soa.gov.cn

Qin Lin
Director
Department of Fishery Environment Protection, South China Sea Fishery Research Institute,
Chinese Academy of Fishery Sciences, 231 West Xingang Rd., Guangzhou, 510300,
People's Republic of China
Tel: +86-20-8419-8473
Fax: +86-20-8445-1442
Email: linqinscs@21cn.com

Qingyin Wang*
Professor, Deputy Director
Yellow Sea Fishery Research Institute, Chinese Academy of Fishery Sciences, 106 Nanjing
Road, Qingdao, 266071, People's Republic of China
Tel: +86-532-582-2959
Fax: +86-532-581-1514
Email: qywang@public.qd.sd.cn
Areas of specialization: Shrimp genetics and breeding; Biotechnology; Mariculture

Jianhai Xiang
Director General
Institute of Oceanology, Chinese Academy of Sciences, 7 Nanhai Road, Qingdao 266071,
People's Republic of China
Tel: +86-532-2879338
Fax: +86-532-2870882
Email: jhxiang@ms.qdio.ac.cn

Japan

Katsuyuki Abo
Senior Researcher
Farming System Division, National Research Institute of Aquaculture, Fisheries Research
Agency, 422-1 Nakatsuhama, Mie 516-0193, Japan
Tel: +81-599-66-1830
Fax: +81-599-66-1962
Email: abo@fra.affrc.go.jp
Areas of specialization: Coastal oceanography; Mariculture; Modeling

Junya Higano
Team Leader
Environment and Resources Management Group, Farming Systems Division, National
Research Institute of Aquaculture, Fisheries Research Agency, 422-1 Nakatsuhama, Mie
516-0193, Japan
Tel: +81-599-66-1830
Fax: +81-599-66-1962
Email: higa@fra.affrc.go.jp
Areas of specialization: Bivalve aquaculture; Aquaculture environments; Shrimp-bivalve
polyculture

Kazumasa Ikuta
Director
Farming System Division, National Research Institute of Aquaculture, Fisheries Research
Agency, 422-1 Nakatsuhama, Mie 516-0193, Japan
Tel: +81-599-66-1830
Fax: +81-599-66-1962
Email: ikutak@fra.affrc.go.jp
Areas of specialization: Fish ecology and physiology; Environmental fish biology

Takashi Kamiyama
Chief
Coastal Fisheries Promotion Section, Coastal Fisheries and Aquaculture Division, Tohoku
National Fisheries Research Institute, Fisheries Research Agency, 3-27-5 Shinhama,
Shiogama, Miyagi, 985-0001, Japan
Tel: +81-22-365-1191
Fax: +81-22-367-1250
Email: kamiyama@fra.affrc.go.jp
Areas of specialization: Microzooplankton; Bivalve aquaculture; Harmful algal blooms

Satoru Toda*
Director
Research Planning and Coordination Division, National Research Institute of Aquaculture,
Fisheries Research Agency, 422-1 Nakatsuhama, Mie 516-0193, Japan
Tel: +81-599-66-1830
Fax: +81-599-66-1962
Email: satoru@fra.affrc.go.jp
Areas of specialization: Coastal oceanography; Mariculture

Hisashi Yokoyama
Head
Environment and Resources Management Group, National Research Institute of
Aquaculture, Fisheries Research Agency, 422-1 Nakatsuhama, Mie 516-1913, Japan
Tel: +81-599-66-1830
Fax: +81-599-66-1962
Email: hyoko@fra.affrc.go.jp
Areas of specialization: Mariculture farm environments; Ecology of marine benthos

Malaysia

Jelani Hashim
Perlis State Director
Malaysian Fisheries Development Board (LKIM), Komplks LKIM Perlis Kampung Perak,
02000 Kuala Perlis, Perlis, Malaysia
Tel: +60-4-985-1708
Fax: +60-4-985-1709
Email: sbc1418@yahoo.com.my

Md. Daim Bin Tohiyat*
Perak State Director
Malaysian Fisheries Development Board (LKIM), Kampong Acheh, 32000 Sitiawan, Perak,
Malaysia
Tel: +60-5-691-5420
Fax: +60-5-691-8370
Email: daim8@hotmail.com

South Korea

Ik-Kyo Chung
Professor
Department of Marine Science, Pusan National University, Busan 609-735,
Republic of Korea
Tel: +82-51-510-2279
Fax: +82-51-581-2963
Email: ikchung@pnu.edu
Areas of specialization: Seaweed ecophysiology; Integrated aquaculture

In Kwon Jang
Senior Scientist
Crustacean Research Laboratory, West Sea Fisheries Research Institute, National Fisheries
Research and Development Institute, Ministry of Maritime Affairs and Fisheries,
Ulwang-dong 707, Jung-gu, Incheon 400-420, Republic of Korea
Tel: +82-32-745-0570, ext. 0556
Fax: +82-32-745-0558
Email: jangik@nfrdi.re.kr
Areas of specialization: Shrimp aquaculture; Biotechnology

Yi-Un Kim
Director
Aquaculture Development Division, Ministry of Maritime Affairs and Fisheries, 140-2
Gye-dong, Jongno-gu, Seoul 110-793, Republic of Korea
Tel: +82-2-3674-6961
Fax: +82-33-661-8511
Email: yiunkim@momaf.go.kr

Yoon Kim*
Director
East Sea Fisheries Research Institute, National Fisheries Research and Development
Institute, Ministry of Maritime Affairs and Fisheries, 30-6, Dongduk-ri, Yeongok-myeon,
Kangreong, Kangwon-do, 210-861 Republic of Korea
Tel: +82-33-661-8501
Fax: +82-33-661-8511
Email: yoonkim@nfrdi.re.kr

Jung Uie Lee
Director
Jeju Fisheries Research Institute, National Fisheries Research and Development Institute,
Ministry of Maritime Affairs and Fisheries, 1928 Oedo-2 dong, Jeju-shi, Jeju-do,
Republic of Korea
Tel: +82-64-743-5882
Fax: +82-64-743-5883
Email: justlee@nfrdi.re.kr

Hyun Taik Oh
Research Scientist
Marine Environmental Management, National Fisheries Research and Development
Institute, Ministry of Maritime Affairs and Fisheries, 408-1 Shirang-ri, Gijong-up,
Gijang-gun, Busan 619-902, Republic of Korea
Tel: +82-51-720-2253
Fax: +82-51-720-2515
Email: ohtek@momaf.go.kr
Area of specialization: Physical-biological modeling for ecosystem-based management

Sweden

Odd Lindahl
Associate Professor
The Swedish Royal Academy of Sciences, Kristineberg Marine Research Station, KMF 566,
SE-450 34 Fiskebäckskil, Sweden
Tel: +46-523-18512
Fax: +46-523-18502
Email: odd.lindahl@kmf.gu.se
Areas of specialization: Marine ecology; Eutrophication; Nutrient trading system;
Agro-Aqua recycling of nutrients; Mussel meal production

United States-Team Members

Michael Fogarty
Northeast Fisheries Science Center, National Marine Fisheries Service, National Oceanic
and Atmospheric Administration, 166 Water Street, Woods Hole, Massachusetts 02543, USA
Tel: +1-508-495-2000 ext. 2386
Fax: +1-508-495-2258
Email: Michael.fogarty@noaa.gov

Charles E. Helsley
Researcher Emeritus
Sea Grant College Program, University of Hawaii at Manoa, 2525 Correa Road, HIG 205,
Honolulu, Hawaii 96822, USA
Tel: +1-808-956-2873
Fax: +1-808-956-3014
Email: chuck@soest.hawaii.edu

David Keeley
President
The Keeley Group
710 Augusta Road
Jefferson, Maine 04348, USA
Tel: +1-207-549-3598
Email: david@thekeeleygroup.com
Areas of specialization: Coastal planning, policy, and management

Dale A. Kiefer
Professor
Department of Biological Sciences, University of Southern California, University Park,
Los Angeles, California 90089-0371, USA
Tel: +1-213-740-5814
Fax: +1-213-740-8123
Email: kiefer@physics.usc.edu

Richard Langan*
Director
New England Mariculture and Fisheries Cooperative (CINEMAR), Gregg Hall, Suite 130,
University of New Hampshire, 35 Colovos Road, Durham, New Hampshire 03824-3534,
USA
Tel: +1-603-862-0190
Fax: +1-603-862-2940
Email: rlangan@cisunix.unh.edu

Kathleen Leyden
Director
Maine Coastal Program, Maine Coastal Program/State Planning Office,
38 State House Station, Augusta, Maine 04333-0038, USA
Tel: +1-207-287-3144
Fax: +1-207-287-8059
Email: Kathleen.Leyden@maine.gov
Areas of specialization: Coastal Zone Management; Policy development and planning

Gary Matlock
Director
National Centers for Coastal Ocean Science, National Ocean Service, National Oceanic and Atmospheric Administration, 1305 East-West Highway, Silver Spring, Maryland 20910, USA
Tel: +1-301-713-3020 x 183
Fax: +1-301-713-4044
Email: gary.c.matlock@noaa.gov
Areas of specialization: Fisheries management; Population dynamics; Aquaculture and invasive species; Aquaculture of fishes and shellfish for stock enhancement purposes

Roger I.E. Newell*
Professor
Horn Point Laboratory, University of Maryland, Center for Environmental Science, P.O. Box 775, Cambridge, Maryland 21613, USA
Tel: +1-410-221-8410
Fax: +1-410-221-8490
Email: newell@hpl.umces.edu

J.E. Jack Rensel
Consultant
Rensel Associates Aquatic Science Consultants, 4209 234th Street NE, Arlington, Washington 98223, USA
Tel: +1-360-435-3285
Fax: +1-360-435-7409
Email: jackrensel@att.net
Areas of specialization: Physical circulation and biological studies for mariculture siting; Food web characterization studies in marine and freshwaters; Harmful algae-physiological effects on vertebrates, bloom management and mitigation

John W. Sowles
Director
Ecology Division, Maine State Department of Marine Resources, P.O. Box 8, West Boothbay Harbor, Maine 04875, USA
Tel: +1-207-633-9518
Fax: +1-207-633-9579
Email: John.Sowles@maine.gov
Areas of specialization: Coastal ecology; Eutrophication; Toxic contaminants; Ecological risk assessment and remediation; Coastal policy and management

Charles Yarish
Professor
Department of Ecology and Evolutionary Biology, University of Connecticut,
1 University Place, Stamford, Connecticut 06901, USA
Tel: +1-203-251-8432
Fax: +1-203-251-8592
Email: charles.yarish@uconn.edu
Areas of specialization: Seaweed aquaculture; Bioremediation; Environmentally friendly
aquaculture; Marine algae; Eutrophication

United States-Other Participants

Bruce S. Anderson
President
Oceanic Institute, 41-202 Kalanianaole Hwy., Waimanalo, Hawaii 96734, USA
Tel: +1-808-259-3102
Fax: +1-808-259-5971
Email: banderson@oceanicinstitute.org
Areas of specialization: Fish poisoning; U.S. regulations relevant to aquaculture
development; Communications

John Corbin
Program Manager
Aquaculture Development Program, Hawaii State Department of Agriculture,
1177 Alakea Street, Room 400, Honolulu, Hawaii 96813, USA
Tel: +1-808-587-0030
Fax: +1-808-587-0033
Email: jcorbin@hawaiiaquaculture.org
Areas of specialization: Aquaculture planning, development, and resource management

John Curtis
Director
Bridgeport Regional Vocational Aquaculture School, 60 Saint Stephens Road, Bridgeport,
Connecticut 06605, USA
Tel: 1+203-576-7608
Fax: 1+203-576-7064
Email: jcurtis@bridgeportedu.net

René Eppi
Director
Office of International Activities, Office of Oceanic and Atmospheric Research, National
Oceanic and Atmospheric Administration, 1315 East-West Highway, R/IA, Silver Spring,
Maryland 20910, USA
Tel: +1-301-713-2469, ext. 132
Fax: +1-301-713-1459
Email: Rene.Eppi@noaa.gov

Langley Gace
Aquaculture Manager
Net Systems/Ocean Spar Technologies, 7910 N.E. Day Road West, Bainbridge Island,
Washington 98110, USA
Tel: +1-206-780 0992 ext149
Fax: +1-206-842 6832
Email: engineering@oceanspar.com

Dosoo Jang
Asia Program Manager
International Activities Office, Office of Oceanic and Atmospheric Research,
National Oceanic and Atmospheric Administration, 1315 East-West Highway,
R/IA, Silver Spring, Maryland 20910, USA
Tel: +1-301-713-2469, ext. 195
Fax: +1-301-713-1459
Email: Dosoo.Jang@noaa.gov

Jonathan Justi
International Program Office, National Ocean Service, National Oceanic and Atmospheric
Administration, 1315 East-West Hwy., SSMC-3, 5th Floor, Silver Spring, Maryland 20910,
USA
Tel.: +1-301-713-3078, ext. 219
Fax: +1-301-713-4263
Email: Jonathan.Justi@noaa.gov

Cheng-Sheng Lee
Director
Aquaculture Interchange Program, Oceanic Institute, 41-202 Kalanianaole Hwy.,
Waimanalo, Hawaii 96795, USA
Tel: +1-808-259-3107
Fax: +1-808-259-8395
Email: cslee@oceanicinstitute.org

James P. McVey
Aquaculture Program Director
National Sea Grant College Program, Office of Oceanic and Atmospheric Research,
National Oceanic and Atmospheric Administration, 1315 East-West Highway, R/SG,
Silver Spring, Maryland 20910, USA
Tel: +1-301-713-2451, ext. 160
Fax: +1-301-713-0799
Email: Jim.Mcvey@noaa.gov
Areas of specialization: General aquaculture; Marine ecology; Grant administration

Patricia O'Bryen
Project Manager
Aquaculture Interchange Program, Oceanic Institute, 41-202 Kalanianaole Hwy.,
Waimanalo, Hawaii 96795, USA
Phone: +1-808-259-3176
Fax: +1-808-259-8395
Email: pobryen@oceanicinstitute.org

Mac Rawson
Director
Georgia Sea Grant College Program, School of Marine Programs, University of Georgia,
Athens, Georgia 30602, USA
Tel: +1-706-542-5954
Fax: +1-706-542-3652
Email: mrawson@arches.uga.edu

William L. Rickards
Director
Virginia Sea Grant College Program, University of Virginia, Madison House,
170 Rugby Road, Charlottesville, Virginia 22903, USA
Tel: +1-434-924-5965
Fax: +1-434-982-3694
Email: rickards@virginia.edu
Areas of specialization: Fish ecology; Shellfish and finfish aquaculture;
Research program administration

Michael Rust
Program Manager
Marine Aquaculture and Enhancement Research Program,
Northwest Fisheries Science Center, National Marine Fisheries Service,
2725 Montlake Blvd. East, Seattle, Washington 98112, USA
Tel.: +1-206-860-3382
Fax: +1-206-860-3467
Areas of specialization: Marine aquaculture; Hatchery technology;
Marine stock enhancement

Gina L. Shamshak
Knauss Sea Grant Fellow
Office of Constituent Services, National Oceanic and Atmospheric Administration Fisheries,
SSMC 3, Room 9535, 1315 East-West Highway, Silver Spring, Maryland 20910, USA
Tel: 1+301-713-2379,ext. 172
Fax: +1-301-713-2384
Email: Gina.Shamshak@noaa.gov

Viet Nam

Hien Thi Thu Bui
Marine and Coastal Programme Coordinator
The World Conservation Union (IUCN) Viet Nam, 44/4 Van Bao, Ba Dinh,
Ha Noi, Viet Nam
Tel: +84-4-7261575
Fax: +84-4-7261561
Email: hien@iucn.org.vn
Area of specialization: Marine ecology

Chi Vien Le
Director
Danida Support for Marine Aquaculture (SUMA), 10 Nguyen Cong Hoan, Ha Noi,
Viet Nam
Tel: +84-4-7716516
Fax: +84-4-7716517
E-mail: lvchi.suma@fsps.com.vn
Area of specialization: Marine aquaculture

Nguyen Chu Hoi*
Professor, Director
Vietnam Institute of Fisheries Economics and Planning (VIFEP), Ministry of Fisheries
(MoFi), 10 Nguyen Cong Hoan Street, Ba Dinh, Ha Noi, Viet Nam
Tel: +84-4-7718451
Fax: +84-4-8345674
E-mail: chuhoi.ifep@mofi.gov.vn
Areas of specialization: Marine environments; Coastal geo-ecology

Ly Xuan Nguyen
Professor, Director
Science and Technology Department, Ministry of Fisheries (MoFi),
10 Nguyen Cong Hoan Street, Ba Dinh, Ha Noi, Viet Nam
Tel: +84-4-7716711
Fax: +84-4-7716702
E-mail: nguyenxuanly@mofi.gov.vn
Area of specialization: Marine biology

Thanh Van Nguyen
Vice-Chairman
Provincial People's Committee of Hai Phong City, 18 Hoang Dieu Street,
Hai Phong City, Viet Nam
Tel: +84-4-08031234
Fax: +84-4-31842368
Areas of specialization: Natural resources and the environment

Thanh Van Nguyen
Acting Director
Department of Aquaculture, Ministry of Fisheries (MoFi), 10 Nguyen Cong Hoan,
Ha Noi, Viet Nam
Tel: +84-4-8351663
Fax: +84-4-7716702
E-mail: nguyenvanthanh@mofi.gov.vn
Area of specialization: Aquaculture management

Thong Minh Nguyen
Country Representative
The World Conservation Union (IUCN) Viet Nam, 44/4 Van Bao, Ba Dinh,
Ha Noi, Viet Nam
Tel: +84-4-7261575
Fax: +84-4-7261561
Email: thong@iucn.org.vn
Area of specialization: Nature conservation policy

Quynh Van Tran
Director
National Centre for Fisheries Extension, Ministry of Fisheries (MoFi),
10 Nguyen Cong Hoan, Ha Noi, Viet Nam
Tel: +84-4-8354515
Fax: +84-4-7716881
Area of specialization: Marine aquaculture modeling

International Organizations and Other Participants

Yung-Song Chen
Assistant Professor
Department of Animal Science, National I-Lan University, 1 Shen-Lung Road, I-Lan 260,
Taiwan
Tel: +886-3-935-7400 x 813
Fax: +886-3-935-4794
Email: yschen@niu.edu.tw

Chen-Yu Hsu
Secretary-General
Taiwan Offshore Aquaculture Association, 4F, 410-2-20, Ming Tsu East Road, Taipei 104,
Taiwan
Tel: +886-2-2518-4747
Fax: +886-2-2518-3720
Email: ocean.care@msa.hinet.net

Hyun-Soo Kim
JK Enterprise, Inc., 7349 Suva Street, Suite #7003, Downey, California 90240, USA
Tel: +1-562-927-5810
Fax: +1-562-927-4644
Email: jjkmagic@aol.com

Yoon-Kil Lee
President
Noah Offshore Farm Co., Ltd., Namjeju-Kun, Jejudo, Republic of Korea
Tel: +82-764-4436
Fax: +82-64-764-4084
Email: yk11225@hotmail.com

Dong Hyun Sim
Liaison Officer
Ministry of Maritime Affairs and Fisheries-Korea, National Ocean Service,
National Oceanic and Atmospheric Administration, 1315 East-West Highway, SSMC-3,
5th Floor, Silver Spring, MD 20910, USA
Tel: +1-301-713-3078, ext. 130
Fax: +1-301-713-4263
Email: donghyun.Sim@noaa.gov
Areas of specialization: Coastal management; Ocean policy